The Successful
Engineer-Manager

The Successful Engineer-Manager

**a practical guide to management
skills for engineers and scientists**

Edited by

ROBERT C. HAAVIND

Editor-in-Chief, *Computer Decisions*

and

RICHARD L. TURMAIL

Management Editor, *Electronic Design*

HAYDEN BOOK COMPANY, INC., NEW YORK

1	2	3	4	5	6	7	8	9	PRINTING
71	72	73	74	75	76	77	78		YEAR

Preface

The statement that engineers are far more adept at engineering than they are at managing is perhaps both axiomatic and ironic. Ironic because the statement will no doubt be irksome to those of the trade who realize that the gap separating an engineering decision from a management decision is often no wider than a closed slide rule. Axiomatic because, traditionally, many engineers have found that the jump from the drawing board on the way to the executive board is a longer one than they had bargained for.

The jump to better management, whether it be one of position or career, is long not because engineers are incapable of good management, but because they have not been oriented to the educational and social climate in which the seed of good management grows. Most engineers are capable enough managers when they are engineering *things*. However, when it comes to engineering *people*, and even their own *careers*, they are at a distinct disadvantage. They realize, often late in their career, that the answers to the problems in these areas can not be found by the use of a mathematical equation.

Specifically, why does the gap between people and things exist for the engineer? One answer lies in their specialized education. Engineering educators attempt to train their students to opt for optimum efficiency; the fledgling engineers are expected to be exacting in an inexact world. Thus, they are often unprepared to deal with circumstances and with people that are far from being well defined. Engineers in training are rarely confronted by courses that require interpretation, like one might find in such courses in English Literature and even business administration. Engineering instructors will tell you that most engineering students spend their precious few electives on economics or other courses similarly restrictive to the interpretative juices.

The career payoff for a limited education, then, comes when the engineering graduate does well in the lab of a large electronics firm and suddenly finds himself in a management position that he is totally unprepared to handle. He knows how to design a circuit, and he may even know how to make some of the right decisions, but he's unfamiliar with the methods he must use to motivate his subordinates, finance a project, communicate his proposals, and all the other responsibilities that come with the managerial territory. And if he doesn't learn quickly, his administrative tenure will be brief.

To those engineers and engineering managers who would appreciate an assist in managing their careers, others, a project, and even a company, the editors dedicate this book. For the reader's convenience, the book is divided into six distinct phases of engineering management, including career, decisions, people, projects, finances, and communications.

Written by experts in the field, the book is a veritable variety-pack of data that is composed of a large collection of *Electronic Design* management articles that are specifically designed to help the engineer better manage his future.

Contents

purpose and
conclusions at
beginning; indentify
problems as well as
pros.

active listening
ideas; observe as well
minimize interruptions
and contradiction.

the budget
represents
yesterday's
thinking;
enumeration of
std. objections.

what is
management
really concerned
about?

"yes" approach

The Successful
Engineer-Manager

1 MANAGING YOUR CAREER

How to investigate a company
Try designing your career
That 'dream' job might be a nightmare
Call your shots when you change jobs
Think sales engineering is your thing?
So you want to start a company . . .

There is no law that says an engineer, in order to progress, must become a manager. There are fine engineers who choose to remain engineers. But most every engineer has to do a certain amount of managing. Even managing a secretary, a technician, or a freshly minted engineer takes some skill. And if the developing engineer does his job well, handling the tasks that come along with finesse, he may be surprised at how quickly he moves up the ladder into management or into higher engineering ranks.

As an engineer embarks on his course, he should consider the possibilities for the future. If he wants to keep out of the management ranks, and stick with engineering jobs, he should set his course differently from that of his management-bound colleague.

In whatever direction the engineer chooses to go, it is possible, within limits, to plan his career rather than be unprepared when opportunity comes along. "Try designing your career" describes the steps involved in planning an engineering career.

Sometimes the engineer's career is tied to some employer whose credentials are indiscernible. One way to investigate such a company before accepting its job offer, is to analyze its annual financial reports, preferably those of the last five years; "How to investigate a company," tells you how. "That dream job might be a nightmare!" lists other ways the job hunter can size up a prospective employer so that he will know the company at least as well as the company knows him. One article offers the best way for the engineer to present himself to the company of his choice, as it advises him to "Call your shots when you change jobs."

Should your head be turned by talk of money and position in the sales game, read "Think sales engineering is your thing?" to discover if sales is the career you thought it would be.

One way to avoid the apprenticeship in management necessary in an established company where the engineer moves up the ladder gradually, is to start your own company. Most engineers at one time or another have the urge to cast out on their own to exploit some marketable product that they are capable of designing. In "So you want to start a company?", an engineer who did just that cautions others against plunging too precipitously into such a venture. If you're not an entrepreneur, don't do it at all, he advises. But if you must, he gives some sound advice on how to proceed.

How to investigate a company

Or what every engineer and his manager should know about an annual financial report.

You're an engineer and you have a problem to solve:

- You're about to be offered a job but you don't have a clue as to whether your prospective employer's administrative policies belong in the space age or the ice age, whether he's financially solvent or on the brink of bankruptcy.
- You want to invest in the stock market, but inexperience is making you a "Milquetoast." You can entrust your money to a stockbroker, but you'd feel more secure if you knew something about the art of investing.
- You'd like to supplement your vocabulary with terms like "liquidity ratio" so that the next time the office conversation turns to the stock market, you can make an intelligent contribution.

Where can you find the information you need to size up your employer, speculate on the stock market, and translate the language of investing? As Sherlock Holmes was given to say, "The answer is elementary, my dear Watson." For the solution to your problems is in knowing how to analyze a financial report.

Security analysts are able to determine the strengths and weaknesses of a company by analyzing its "balance sheet" and "income statement." But before you can subject a company to analysis, you must discover the "what," "why," and "how" of a financial report.

What is a financial report?

An abbreviated version of a balance sheet is shown at top right. It represents the financial picture of a company as it appeared on one particular day of operation. The complete report, including the income statement which shows how much business the company does, portrays a corporation's financial progress growing out of the soundness of its operations.

Why a report?

During the days when a town's business was the chief topic of conversation, there was little justification for detailed financial reports. The annual meeting was attended by all of the shareholders, who lived conveniently near their investment. But as corporations expanded, capital needs increased, and the number of share owners grew beyond the boundaries of a particular region, the expense or trouble of attending an annual meeting hardly seemed worthwhile. As a result, an age of greater financial disclosure was launched.

At the turn of the century, the Stock Exchange persuaded the first industrial company to publish an annual statement. One after the other, companies wanting to qualify for listing on the Exchange brought out their annual reports. Today, according to the New York Stock Exchange, more than 1200 leading corporations distribute an estimated 40 million copies of these reports to the press, company employes, schools of business administration, investment firms, other financial organizations, and—most important—to those people who own shares in American business.

The trading floor of the New York Stock Exchange, where speculators bid for securities on the premise of a favorable company analysis.

Typical Electronics Corporation, Inc.
(Abbreviated Balance Sheet)

Assets	1967	1966	Liabilities	1967	1966
Total Current Assets	$ 48.4	$ 44.2	Total Current Liabilities	$ 21.6	$ 18.6
Total Other Assets	5.5	4.6	Reserves	3.6	2.5
Total Fixed Assets	105.2	93.4	Long-Term Debt	26.0	20.0
Less Accumulated Depreciation	−27.6	−25.0	Total Stockholders' Investment	80.3	76.1
Adjusted Total Fixed Assets	77.6	68.4			
Total Assets	$131.5	$117.2	Total Liabilities and Stockholders Investment	$131.5	$117.2

How to read a report

When analysts scrutinize a financial report, they actually read between the lines in order to make value judgments. Before this is feasible, however, one must discover what the lines themselves mean. Like all other professions, accounting has a specialized vocabulary. The following list defines the terms used in a financial report.

Clues to Investing Terms

Terms   **Definitions**

Assets

Current Assets . . . . that which may readily be turned into cash

Cash . . . . in the till, on deposit in the bank

Marketable Securities . . . . investment of excess cash in securities that may be sold quickly when cash is needed

Accounts Receivable . . . . amounts owed the company by its customers and others

Inventories . . . . raw materials, goods in process of manufacture, finished goods

Prepayments . . . . unexpended insurance, unused rentals

Good will, Patents, Trademarks . . . . intangibles: the value varies considerably from one company to the next

Fixed Assets . . . . that which is not intended for sale, and is used over and over again, such as land, buildings, machinery and equipment

Liabilities

Current Liabilities . . . . all debts that fall due within the coming year

Accounts Payable . . . . money owed to regular business creditors

Notes Payable . . . . money owed to a bank

Accrued Expenses Payable . . . . unpaid amounts of wages, interest on funds borrowed, fees to attorneys, insurance premiums, pensions, etc.

Long-Term Liabilities . . . . debts due after one year from the date of the report

Stockholders' Equity

Capital Stock . . . . shares in the proprietary interest in the company

Preferred Stock (cumulative) . . . . shares having preference over other shares as regards dividends or in distribution of assets in case of liquidation or both. . ."cumulative" means that, if the dividend is not paid, it accumulates in favor of the shareholder

Common Stock . . . . shares on the books at a par or stated value (market value is determined by sellers and buyers)

Capital Surplus . . . . contributed assets, premium received from sales of stock over the par value

Earned Surplus . . . . past retained earnings not paid in dividends

Statement of Income

Depreciation and Depletion . . . . provision from income for the reduction of the service life of machinery and buildings and the use of minerals in mines

Operating Profit . . . . the remainder after deducting expenses from sales, but before interest charges and taxes

Interest Charges . . . . amount required for interest on borrowed funds

How to analyze a report

There are no pat findings from the analysis of a financial report. A divergence of opinion exists even among the experts. For example: It was reported in an issue of *Management Review* that some analysts believe that when a company is comprised of a number of firms, a single financial report has little significance. Others were reported to believe that the facts of a company's growth provide a better foundation for analysis than the data gathered from the company "satellites."

More light was shed on the area of disagreement by this analyst's comment: "A majority of companies should be analyzed apart from their industries . . . [for example] Drugs are considered a growth industry, yet 50% of the drug companies aren't growing."

Another analyst was quoted as saying, "An electronics corporation cannot succeed if its research and development program lags behind its competitors'. In the computer business, entire computer systems are outdated within a year or two as a result of R&D."

Because the operations and policies of companies differ, analysts are forced to devise "slide rules" to make meaningful appraisals.

You cannot expect to analyze a company as well as the man who earns his living at it. But you can get more out of a financial statement by applying ratios that focus attention on significant relationships in the statement of income and the balance sheet.

The New York Stock Exchange published an approach to this method of analysis. It is called "The 7 Keys to Value," and these are the keys:

1. Pre-tax Profit Margin

This is the ratio of profit, before interest and taxes, to sales. It is expressed as a percentage of sales and is found by dividing the operating profit by sales. It is usually assumed that an increase in sales will help widen the profit margin.

2. Current (or working capital)Ratio

This is the ratio of current assets to current liabilities. A 2-for-1 ratio is the standard, meaning that for each $1 of current liabilities, there are $2 in current assets to back it up. A gradual increase in the current ratio usually is a healthy sign of improved financial strength. But a ratio of more than 4 or 5 to 1 is regarded as unnecessary, and may be the result of an insufficient volume of business to produce a desirable level of earnings. The ability of a company to meet its obligations, expand its volume, and take advantage of opportunities is often determined by its working capital.

3. Liquidity Ratio

This is the ratio of cash and equivalent (marketable securities) to total current liabilities. It is also expressed as a percentage figure, and it results from dividing cash and equivalent by total current liabilities. This ratio is important as a supplement to the current ratio because the immediate ability of a company to meet current obligations or pay larger dividends may be impaired despite a higher current ratio. A decline in the liquidity ratio often takes place during a period of expansion and rising prices because of heavier capital expenditures and larger accounts payable. If the decline persists, the company may have to raise additional capital.

4. Capitalization Ratios

These are the percentages of the total company investment allotted to each type of investment. Specifically, the capitalization is made up of long-term debt, preferred stock, common stock, and surplus. Usually, the higher the ratio of surplus to common stock, the more assured is the position of the common stock, since there are fewer prior claims on corporate income in the form of debt securities or preferred stock. Companies in stable industries, such as electric light and power, may with safety have a higher proportion of debt financing than most industrial companies.

5. Sales to Fixed Assets

This ratio is computed by dividing the annual sales by the value before depreciation and amortization of plant, equipment and land at the end of the year. It is important because it helps determine whether or not the funds used to enlarge productive facilities are being spent wisely. A sizable expansion in facilities should lead to larger sales volume.

6. Sales to Inventories

This ratio is computed by dividing the year's sales by the year-end inventories. The so-called "inventory turnover" is important as a check on whether or not the enterprise is investing too heavily in inventories. Because inventories are a larger part of the assets of a merchandising enterprise than of most manufacturing companies, this ratio is especially worthy of note in the analysis of a retail business. A high ratio denotes a good quality of merchandise and correct pricing policies. A definite downtrend may be a warning signal of poor merchandising policy, poor location, or "stale" merchandise.

7. Net Income to Net Worth

This ratio is derived from dividing net income by the total of preferred stock, common stock and surplus accounts. It supplies the answer to the vital question: "How much is the company earning on the stockholders' investment?" A large or increasing ratio is favorable. In a competitive society an extraordinarily high ratio may invite more intense competition. An increase due to "inventory profits" may be short-lived because of rapid changes in commodity prices.

Ready for Analysis

Now that you have adopted an investment vocabulary, and understand the "keys to value," you have a working knowledge of how to "investigate" a company. If you are ready to test your powers of detection, apply what you have learned to the complete financial report of Typical Electronics Co., Inc., by answering the questions at the right.

Typical Electronics Corporation, Inc., and Consolidated Subsidiaries
Balance Sheet — December 31, 19___

Assets	1967	1966
Current Assets		
Cash	$ 9.0	$ 6.2
Marketable Securities, at Cost (Market Value)	–	2.0
Accounts Receivable	12.4	11.4
Inventories	27.0	24.6
Total Current Assets	$ 48.4	$ 44.2
Other Assets		
Surrender Value of Insurance	$ .2	$ .2
Investments in Subsidiaries	4.7	3.9
Prepayments	.6	.5
Goodwill, Patents, Trademarks	–	–
Total Other Assets	$ 5.5	$ 4.6
Fixed Assets		
Buildings, Machinery & Equipment (at cost)	$104.3	$ 92.7
Less Accumulated Depreciation	−27.6	−25.0
	$ 76.7	$ 67.7
Land	.9	.7
Total Fixed Assets	$ 77.6	$ 68.4
Total Assets	$131.5	$117.2

Liabilities	1967	1966
Current Liabilities		
Accounts Payable	$ 6.1	$ 5.0
Notes Payable	1.0	.8
Accrued Expenses Payable	3.6	3.3
Federal Income Tax Payable	9.6	8.4
Dividends Payable	1.3	1.1
Total Current Liabilities	$ 21.6	$ 18.6
Reserves	3.6	2.5
Long Term Liabilities		
First Mortgage Bonds, 5% Interest Due 1975	26.0	20.0
Stockholders' Equity		
Capital Stock		
Preferred Stock, 5% Cumulative, $100 Par Value Each: 6,000 Shares	$ 6.0	$ 6.0
Common Stock, $5 Par Value Each, 300,000	18.3	18.3
Capital Surplus	9.6	9.6
Earned Surplus	46.4	42.2
Total Stockholders' Equity	$ 80.3	$ 76.1
Total Liabilities and Stockholders' Investment	$131.5	$117.2

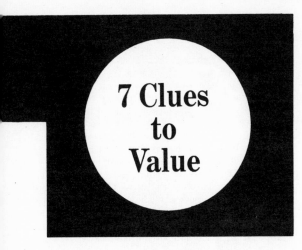

7 Clues to Value

1. Which year had a pre-tax profit margin of 19.5%? Evaluate.

2. The 1967 current ratio was 2.24 to 1. What was the ratio for the previous year? Evaluate both years.

3. What per cent was the liquidity ratio for 1967? Evaluate.

4. What were the capitalization ratios for 1966? Evaluate.

5. Which year has a higher ratio of sales to fixed assets? Evaluate.

6. Which year had a sales-to-inventories ratio of 4.3? Evaluate.

7. What was the net income-to-net worth ratio for each year? Evaluate.

	1967	1966
Statement of Income		
Sales	$115.8	$110.0
(less) Costs and Expenses:		
Cost of Goods Sold	74.8	73.2
Selling, General, Administrative Expenses	14.2	13.0
Depreciation and Depletion	4.2	3.5
	$ 93.2	$ 89.7
Operating Profit	22.6	20.3
Interest Charges	−1.3	−1.0
Earnings before Income Taxes	$ 21.3	$ 19.3
Provision for Taxes on Income	−11.4	−9.8
Net Income for the Year	9.9	9.5
Dividend on Preferred Stock	−.3	−.3
Balance of Income Available for Common Stock	9.6	9.2
Statement of Earned Surplus		
Balance at Beginning of Year	$ 42.2	$ 37.6
Add − Net Income for the Year	+9.9	+9.5
	$ 52.1	$ 47.1
Less Dividends Paid on		
Preferred Stock	.3	.3
Common Stock	5.4	4.6
Balance at End of Year	$ 46.4	$ 42.2

Only the Beginning

While interpreting the facts and figures of a financial report helps you determine the soundness of a company's operation and the attractiveness of its securities, it has been suggested by stock brokers Merrill Lynch, Pierce, Fenner and Smith, Inc., that selecting common stocks for investment requires careful study of factors other than those you can learn from financial statements. The economics of the country and the particular industry must be considered, the management of the company must be studied and its plans for the future assessed. These facts must be gleaned from the press or the financial services, or supplied by a research organization.

If you want to become a serious student of investing, knowing how to read and analyze a financial report is only the beginning. What you have uncovered here, however, may help you to determine what kind of company you may be getting into, what a financial statement can tell you, and, of course, to speak intelligently on such keys to value as "liquidity ratio." ■■

Answers to questions on report analysis.

1. 1967. Good. Profit margin widened. It is usually assumed that material increase in sales will help widen the profit margin. Certain costs are fixed, i.e., they do not rise or fall in the same proportion as changes in volume. Such costs are interest, rent and real property taxes. Ordinarily, because of their fixed costs, profits tend to increase and decline more rapidly percentagewise than sales.

2. 2.38 to 1. Fair. The company did not improve its position in this regard because it used substantial funds to increase its plant and equipment. The ratio could have been better if the company had spent less for additions to its productive facilities, or had raised more funds for this purpose through the sale of securities, or paid less in dividends. This particular case illustrates why the entire annual report and financial statement must be examined.

3. 41.7%. Fair. A decline in the liquidity ratio often takes place during a period of expansion and rising prices because of heavier capital expenditures and larger accounts payable. If the decline persists, it may mean that the company will have to raise additional capital.

4. Long-term debts 20.8%
   Preferred stock 6.3%
   Common stock and surplus 72.9%

Unchanged. The common-stock ratio was somewhat smaller than in the previous year, because of the issuance of additional debentures during the year. Since the surplus was also larger, due to reinvested earnings, the change was slight and the common-stock equity remained high.

5. 1966. Bad. In 1967 the company's ratio of sales to fixed assets amounted to approximately 1.1 to 1 compared with 1.2 to 1 in the previous year. Fixed assets are shown both as a gross figure and as a net figure, i.e., before and after accumulated depreciation. Sometimes the details appear in a footnote to the balance sheet which sets forth the costs of the buildings, machinery, equipment and land. For our computation we have used the gross figure for all fixed assets, $105.2 million in 1967 and $93.4 million in 1966. The ratio is low, which is not good for an electronics company that ordinarily has a larger sales volume in relation to plant investment.

6. 1967. Fair to bad. The company's sales-to-inventories ratio in 1967 was approximately 4.3 to 1 compared with 4.5 to 1 in 1966. This decline would have resulted from purchases of raw materials in anticipation of an increase in prices of a falling off in sales toward the end of the year.

7. 1966, 12.5%; 1967, 12.3%. Unchanged. According to general surveys of all manufacturing corporations in the United States, a return of over 10% appears to be better than average. Although the later year shows a 0.2% deficit from the preceding year, it is not as significant as the return on the stockholder's investment.

Company evaluation? Since the answer to that question would depend on what you plan to do with the information, we'll do the honorable thing and leave the decision to you.

References:

1. "Understanding Financial Statements — 7 Keys to Value", New York Stock Exchange, September, 1968.
2. F. V. Huber, "How Security Analysts Size Up a Company's Strength", *Management Review*, February, 1969, pp. 32-37.
3. "How to Read a Financial Report", Merrill Lynch, Pierce, Fenner and Smith, Inc., February, 1968.

Try designing your career

You can get to the top without a plan, but it's unlikely. Here are some ideas to help smooth your way.

Ed J. Hegarty, Consultant, Mansfield, Ohio.

Last month the fellow in the seat next to me on a plane from Chicago to Cleveland told me of a plan he had laid out for his career. He would stay just so long on his present job, then he would move to a better job, spend so much time on that, then to the next step up and stay so long there. Eventually he expected to land in the top echelons of his company. This was no company training plan, his company had no such plan. This was a plan he had worked out for himself.

"You're assuming a lot in that plan, aren't you?" I asked.

"Certainly I am," he agreed, "but it's better than drifting, don't you think?"

I did think it was better than drifting, but, I said, "You'll get mixed up in company politics."

"I know that, but I'd be in politics no matter what I did, wouldn't I? So why not use the company's political set up to help me get ahead?"

You may say, "Why should this interest me, our company has no politics?" I have been told that hundreds of times, but each time I explain that I am not speaking of the dirty, sticking a knife in your back stuff, the man agrees that politics do figure in the promotions in his company.

Just ask yourself, "Why was my boss given his job?" Then, "Weren't some other men considered for the job? Why weren't they chosen?" When you have answered those questions, you will know what I mean by company politics. It's all those human factors that influence decisions affecting people and projects in your company. If you know what these factors are, you can put company politics to work for you. Your gain is that you will be considered for promotions when you should be considered.

How much career planning have you done? You may say, "I'm doing it every day by my ideas, my designs, my work." That's fine, but are you doing the other things that can help you advance in your company? A career can and should be planned step by step with the same care you use on any of your project designs. Thousands of engineers have done it, and they have found it much more profitable than drifting.

Your plan for advancement.

In planning any advancement within your company, here are the points you should consider:

1. **There are politics in all companies,** some good and some bad. Most are part of normal competition and good management.

2. **Analyze how far you want to go** in your company and what jobs ahead are possible for you. Analyze your own capabilities. Then decide what you want and go after it.

3. **Start training yourself** for the job ahead, since you advance one job at a time.

4. **Do a good job where you are,** an outstanding one if possible. Any advancement will come from what you do on the job you now hold.

5. **Know your competition**—the men who are capable of being advanced to the job you want. Respect this competition, cooperate with it and associate with it.

6. **Find the people who control promotions** in your company. Try to impress them.

7. **Be loyal to the boss,** the department and the company. Instead of complaining about rules, work regulations or management decisions, try to figure out why they are justified.

8. **Make the best possible first impression.** In all your contacts, present an image of competence.

9. **Make friends of everybody**—those above you, those at your level and those among the supporting troops.

10. **Reconcile yourself to the tradeoffs.** Each time you move up, you'll find the bigger job more demanding. Face the fact that you have to trade some freedom for the extra pay the job brings.

Do you have what it takes?

Do you think you have what it takes to be promoted? You may say: "I have seniority. I have as much education and experience as anyone."

Both of these may be good qualifications, but in your company are these the qualifications that push a man ahead? It might be smart to check on what has counted in past promotions in your company.

Usually, you'll find that the man who got promoted was doing a good job where he was. I ask men how the boss feels they are doing on the job. They say, "I must be doing all right, he never says anything." I'd suggest you ask him. You may think you are doing all right, but the boss may see a number of ways in which you can improve. If he does and tells you so, you can act accordingly.

Next, how do you stand on education? Do you have the training needed for the jobs ahead? The training of an executive is a continuous process. You should be learning more every day, and this learning should not be confined to what you learn on the job. Ask your boss what training he suggests for you. By asking how you are doing, he sees that you want to do better and that you want to get ahead. But to hold any higher job, you have to prove that you can handle the one you are doing. On any higher job, you can assume you will need more education and training. One trainer put it this way, "On the basis of the job you are doing, would you promote you?"

What are the jobs ahead?

You advance one job at a time. This is the rule in most companies. Why not make a list of the jobs to which you might advance. Then take a look at the next step up. Suppose that you'd have to supervise the work of several men. (This is probably the toughest task for a man who has had only his own job to worry about and now is asked to supervise the work of others.) What do you know about supervision? Every year hundreds of helpful books are written on supervision. Have you read any of them? Such books are full of ideas to help you hold your next job—the one in which you may have to direct several men. If you are successful with them, management may give you a job that calls for managing more men.

How far do you want to go?

Every man has or should have a goal to shoot for in his company. What's yours? Is it the top job? This is the first question to ask in any career planning. Do you need to get to the top job to be happy? Some men do and some don't. Is your goal to be the vice president in charge of engineering in your company? Perhaps you don't want to shoot that high. In selecting, aim at a job that's possible for you. You may never make out in that

top spot, but you might be excellent in a number of jobs one step below the top. Perhaps you are already satisfied and want to stay where you are. This too calls for planning. Your company may consider the job you have now as a training job, and it may want to move another man into it so he

can get the experience you are now getting. In maneuvering to stay on your present job, you may give the impression that you do not have the ability to advance to a better job.

Who is your competition?

As you move up in your company, you will have competition. Others might want that top job too. Make a list of these fellows and analyze them. Try

to rate them, not on your likes or dislikes, but on their ability to get ahead. These are the men who will also be considered for the jobs you get as you move up the ladder. What have they got that you haven't? You will probably be able to cross off some men because they lack the ambition or desire to advance. This will leave you with a smaller list. These men are your competition.

It's good company politics to know these men, to work with them and to cooperate with and speak well of them. When one man read this in my book, he wrote me, "That's sure good advice, some day one of these jokers may be your boss." Today they are competition. By working cooperatively with them, you impress management with your ability to get along with others.

Who does it pay to impress?

The key to any advancement is the list of men above you. If your company has the right men, it can go on to greater success. Without them, it has to struggle to stay alive. Thus, every company wants men who are ambitious and who will train themselves to handle top jobs. But to move up to a more important job, you have to impress someone that you are one of those ambitious men.

Who is this someone—or is it more than one person? Someone above you has the power to recommend you for a better job, and it will pay you to know who that is. Then you can go out of your way to impress that man or group.

What counts in promotions?

Performance, achievement and ability—are these the only factors that count in promotions, or are other factors also involved, subtle and personal factors never overtly mentioned but nevertheless important in determining who will progress and who will not? Is there any friendship or clannishness involved—school ties, loyalty, family or other such factors that help determine who is promoted? All of these factors are important in some companies. What is important in yours? It pays to find out and include these factors in your career plan.

Your image is important.

In moving about in your company, you are broadcasting two images: the image of first impression and the image of competence.

Keep in mind that first impressions are very important. You look at me and form an opinion. I look at you and form another. Of course, further acquaintance can change that first impression, but why not make that first impression as good as possible? Little things like shined shoes, a hair cut, neat or sloppy dress can mean a lot the first time you meet the man who has the power to promote you. There are things you can't change

about your looks: whether you're tall, short, thin, fat, etc. But you can try to make the most of what you have. You might ask, "What has my appearance to do with my ability as an engineer?" Nothing, maybe. But it has a lot to do with what a stranger thinks of you.

Check the executives in your company as to looks and dress. Why not try to make an impression on them by dressing appropriately. One executive told me of an engineer he sent back to the office to get a coat, a shirt and a tie. "Here we were going before the operating committee to get approval of our year's budget," he explained, "and this joker shows up in a sport shirt." The executive did not want that sport shirt to make the wrong impression on the committee. You can't look like an expert in a sport shirt.

Remember that as you move about in your office, in the cafeteria and through the halls or aisles of the office and factory, people see you and form this first impression. Some of these eyes belong to the men who have some say about your promotion. You may say, "I hate this conformity." Okay, hate it, but go along with it, if you want to advance toward the top.

You also advance your personal stock by broadcasting an image of competence. You build this image by your performance on the job, by appearing willing and anxious to learn, by listening to suggestions and by stating your ideas clearly so that the other fellow understands them. Building this image among those who count takes time and constant effort. Without it you are lost in the competition. So why not ask yourself now, "What is my image of competence today, and what can I do to make it better?" One fellow might improve his image of competence by keeping his big mouth shut and listening more. Another might improve his if he stopped critizing others and their work.

The ability to make decisions, to bring to the boss problems with suggested solutions instead of just problems, to present ideas so they can be understood are all factors in building this image of competence.

Choose your friends wisely.

Pal around with the "comers." In making up your list of competitors for promotion, you checked off some you felt destined to be executives of the future. Make these men your friends, the ones with whom you go to lunch, play golf and discuss ideas. You are judged by the company you keep, so keep company with the group on the way up.

What does the bigger job cost?

On every job you move up to, you have to give up a little of something you have now. As you get into the upper echelons you have to give up more and more. You'll have less free time, you'll see less of the wife and kids. More of your time will be demanded by that big job.

The other evening, a wife of a big executive told me, "I seldom see him any more, he's got that company for a wife." She has her own car, she belongs to the country club, her children are in better schools. Most of these advantages come because of his job and the money it brings in. If you aim for one of these top jobs, it may save trouble later if you explain all this to the wife and get her on your side. For if you are to go up to the bigger job, you have to forfeit some of the freedom you have now.

You don't have to play.

You don't have to accept any of these ideas, but they are the "rules of the game." You won't advance in your company if you refuse to play according to the rules. You may make some small advancement, but you'll never get up near the top. In deciding what to do, you are the key man, your wants and desires come first. Follow these suggestions, and your road to the top will be easier. Buck them and you may get nowhere. ▪ ▪

That 'dream' job might be a nightmare!

To ensure against employment disappointment, get to know your prospective employer as well as he knows you.

Anthony W. Whitworth, Marketing Coordinator, Communications, Sangamo Electric Co., Springfield, Ill.

Are you in the market for a new job? If so, or if you plan to be, consider how elated you perhaps felt when you were offered your present position. Perhaps you later experienced a vague, dull disappointment when you discovered that the employment package so handsomely wrapped for you proved to be something other than a present. The message should be clear: Before you leave your present position, take a long and thorough look before you leap into a new one.

Even if you are reasonably satisfied in your current position, there is an obvious career advantage in keeping aware of the operations of competitive companies.

Evening the odds

When you hand your resume to a personnel recruiter, the odds are that he has virtually unlimited resources to check it out. And he knows that, if he makes a mistake in hiring you, the mistake is rather easily rectified.

However, if you make a mistake in your evaluation of the position or the company, you can be stuck with your decision, at least temporarily. And the odds are against you, because you probably have a limited knowledge of the company interviewing you. In fact, if you are seeking a position in one of the new growth areas—such as computer peripherals—you may not have even heard of the company that replies to you.

But to make the hiring game a better gamble for you, there are certain sources of information that can help you to learn almost as much about your potential employer as he learns about you.

There are two phases to the investigation you should undertake:

▪ Determining where the company is going and how fast; what the chances of success are.

▪ Determining whether or not a particular company has a future for you, personally; if it is the kind of place where you want to work.

The annual report

Much information about a company's operations is a matter of public record. However, corporate policies, internal procedures, management attitudes, and real working conditions are not published information. Investigation and interpretation are required on your part.

The best place to start finding out about a company is its *annual report,* which will be available if the company's stock is publicly traded. A stockbroker will be able to show you a copy, or a businesslike letter from you to a company officer will usually produce a copy, if you state that you are a potential investor.

A professional financial analyst can read as much information between the lines of an annual report as he can from the published details of operations. Although you can't expect to do as good a job as a professional analyst, your observations will give you a pretty good idea about long range company plans.

Securing one of these comprehensive reports requires a good contact, such as your banker, and you may be required to pay for the service. However, if you contemplate going to work for a small, new company, organized and managed by people you do not know, consider the fee a good investment.

Would you want to work there?

Having determined whether or not the prospective company is what you are looking for in terms of your career needs, you should then determine what life with that company would be like for you. Besides your own personal questioning of both recruiting and technical people during a company interview, information about the internal policies and operations of a company may be gathered from the following sources:

Professional Colleagues. You probably belong to a professional society. One or more of your colleagues probably has some knowledge about any given company. If possible, also, ask the company's vendors, customers, and competitors how they rate your prospective employer. An even better source is a man who currently works for the company. It's true that a satisfied employee is a company's best recruiting ad.

The Community. Today many electronics companies are located in small towns and suburban areas. When you travel there for an interview, talk to as many non-company people as you can. This includes airport personnel, cab drivers, service-station attendants. If a company has been around for a while, and has a mature, community-minded management, most local people will have a positive opinion about it. Also check the local paper. (You'll need to pick up a copy anyway, to check housing and food prices, and local recreation facilities.) See if the paper carries any mention of the company personnel and their involvement in the community. If the company is expanding it might be running local ads for recruiting factory personnel. If so, observe what they promise in benefits. Also, contact the local chamber of commerce for literature. This material will tend to tell you how much influence the company has in local affairs and plans.

Your Prospective employer. Some questions are best answered on the spot by the recruiting interviewer (concerning company policy) and by the technical administrators (about working conditions). But that does not always ensure you against receiving incomplete answers. Some recruiters are not very candid. Always keep in mind, however, that you are entitled to ask any pertinent questions.

Exercise your right to inquire

Support Personnel—What is the approximate ratio of nontechnical to technical personnel? A high ratio means that you'll probably have to spend less time on non-engineering work. In other words, count the technicians.

Professional Societies—Does the company encourage participation in professional societies? Do they pay dues and expenses? What is company policy in regard to trade-show attendance? What are travel policies? Is publication of papers and articles encouraged? How many members of engineering management are active in local professional-society leadership? Too many negative answers could mean that the company is not concerned about individual requirements.

Reference Material—Is the company library well organized? Is there a full-time librarian? Are there microfilming and duplicating facilities?

Management Training—Does the company have any, formal programs for management training or personnel development?

Continuing Education—What are the policies for continuing education? Time off for classes? Full or partial tuition reimbursement? How many company employees teach at the local college or university?

Internal Communications—What employee communications are available? Are publications designed to keep all employees well informed of the company's over-all goals and accomplishments? Is there an internal engineering newsletter for dissemination of design information?

Physical Conditions—Are normal working conditions better than what you have now? Well lighted? With relatively quiet separate offices, or a large "bullpen"?

Job Potential—It's important to find out how high one can go within a particular company

and still practice engineering. In some situations, a man must switch from engineering to management if he desires to advance beyond a certain point. In other companies, line responsibility for engineering extends into top management. Some companies permit older, competent engineers without desire for management duties to fill specially created "assistant to the chief engineer" or "consultant" positions.

These positions are usually more predominant in companies heavily engaged in R & D activities, and such positions are obviously limited in number. Their presence indicates, however, that the company has recognized design competence enough to reward it. It is also interesting to note the percentage of sales management and top management team members who started with the company as design engineers. Although your planned career path may not include sales or corporate management, it is worthwhile to discover if such career paths exist.

Replacement Policies—Companies in some "cyclical" industries, such as the aerospace industry, cooperate in placement programs when massive layoffs result from contract cancellations. For instance, if an aerospace company loses a large contract (as happens when Congress cancels a defense hardware program) the company is faced with the prospect of laying off a large number of professional, technical, and skilled employees. It then contacts all logical prospective employers for these people and offers assistance in their recruiting. It will set up offices for interviewing within its plant, and will supply employment records and references to meet stated requirements of the recruiting companies.

At first glance, this seems a strange way for competitors to operate; however, in the aerospace industry it seems to work out well. Companies get a chance to hire professional people easily and at reasonable cost; the personnel that are laid off get an opportunity for continuous employment; and the company, of course, assumes that when fortune smiles upon them again, they will be able to rehire the same employees in the same manner.

Switch, don't fight

Today a properly designed engineering career includes an infrequent, but calculated, job change. In the computer industry, engineers with 16 to 20 years experience reported having an average of over five positions per career. It's important to prepare yourself psychologically for changing jobs. Other engineers are making changes, too.

And remember—when you decide that your objectives demand a change, consider any job offer you receive as a special evaluation for a most important client: You. ■■

Call your shots when you change jobs

Set your career on course with a resume that shows where you're going, not only where you've been.

Harold K. Mintz, Editor-in-Chief, Publications Section,
RCA Aerospace Systems Div., Burlington, Mass.

What do you want in your next job? Put it in writing, and you'll be a lot more likely to get it.

You can eliminate half the waste motion and discouragement that often typify an engineer's job-hunting effort when you (1) set down your job objectives at the beginning of your resume, (2) show how your educational and occupational experiences support your objectives, and (3) see that your resume goes to those places where those stated job objectives can be fulfilled.

Job hunting is very much a fact of life with electronics people. One survey of chief engineers made this time last year showed the average chief engineer had worked in four companies over a 15-year period in his rise to top management.

The first thing an engineer contemplating a job change usually does—and sometimes it's the most critical thing—is to prepare a resume. Yet an informal poll of managers who review resumes in electronic companies indicates that most resumes they receive are weak or barely adequate for the selling job they're meant to do. Only a few are outstanding.

Give top billing to your wants

According to the conventional definition, a resume is an inventory of your education, experience and other qualifications, together with personal data. But a good resume is also a written sales presentation designed for a specific task— to help you get an interview for the job you want.

And what you want, unless you're changing out of sheer desperation, is not just any old job your experience may enable you to fill—but a job with *your kind* of responsibilities, work parameters and specializations. *Build the capabilities into your resume that will enable it to guide you into that job.*

Set up your resume so it will focus the attention of those who will read it onto your job or career objectives at the outset. Outline them. Set them under a capitalized or underlined "Job Objectives" or "Career Objectives" heading. And place them on your resume second only to your identifying information (name, address, telephone number, date of resume).

A statement of job objectives, often omitted from resumes, aids prospective employers in evaluating you in the proper context. It directs the employer's consideration of you toward work with the characteristics you are after and away from work you're not interested in. Without this statement, the resume can be routed to the wrong party, and thus to a dead end.

A little thought and note-taking on what you want out of the move you're planning, made prior to the actual composition of your "Job Objectives" paragraph, can greatly strengthen it and the organization of supporting information in your resume as well. What do you want from a job change—in type of industry, size of company, in work parameters, travel, freedom of action, social environment, other job factors? Do any of these factors possibly loom over-large as a result of recent negative work experiences? Be sure you know yourself; for once established, your job objectives become the theme of your whole resume.

Turn experiences into accomplishments

Educational and working experience is a must in any engineer's resume, but the way you describe it can result in a resume that's an effective selling tool, on the one hand, or a dull listing, on the other. When you set down your qualifications under "Education" and "Experience," keep in mind that employers reading your resume will be on the lookout for potential advantages to them. So point up those potential advantages that are uniquely yours.

When you're listing your experience indicate as well the accomplishments such experiences have enabled you to make. "Leader, digital design group" tells a lot more when you can add, "Supervised four-man team that developed first missile-borne digital subsystem." Similarly, "B.S. in electrical engineering, Ampere University, 1959" assumes a more positive look when you can add, "Ranked in top fifth of class." The additions give your resume reader something actively visible and something tangible with which he can justify selecting you.

Which should come first, education or experience? The answer is whichever will make the stronger first impression. Many managers in the electronic field prefer education first because to them, more than to nontechnicals, your degree, the year you received it, your specialty, and your college is especially important. Another reason for detailing education first is that it can usually be wrapped up in eight lines or less. Your experience, on the other hand, may well occupy most of the rest of the page and may even spill over onto another page.

Incidentally, besides your college, degree, graduation year and major study, there are several other items you should mention under "Education," whether you are an old or a new graduate. Among them: scholarships and awards won, minor study if it is of professional value, accredited summer, evening, or correspondence courses, on-the-job training in the military or with previous employers, and class standing if in the upper third. Call attention to aspects of your education that tie in with and lend substance to your stated job objectives.

Of course, any master's degree or PhD merits attention. If you're currently progressing toward an advanced degree, you should indicate how much of the program you've completed as well as the type and probable date of the degree.

Boost your signal-to-noise ratio

Without question, for all engineers except recent graduates, the section under "Experience" is the most critical and therefore should occupy the lion's share of space. While you should not include a tiresome list of, say, inappropriate summer student jobs, a fairly complete work history is called for. A test for inclusion or exclusion of peripheral data in the resume: If it strengthens your resume—makes your stated job objectives more realistic—use it; otherwise, don't.

The "Experience" section gives you your big chance to stress that you're a responsible individual, a self-starting, cost-conscious engineer who can get things done. A statement that these qualities would probably contribute toward solving some of the prospect company's problems would catch more than one executive's eye.

In listing experience, start with your current position and work backward chronologically. Indicate in the order given the years of each job, its title, the department you worked in, and the company's name, address (city and state) and chief product or service. Briefly explain your responsibilities, range of activities, accomplishments, number and type of people supervised, promotions earned, and major decisions taken.

Start sentences with strong, active verbs like designed, created, directed, specialized in, coordinated, developed, planned, etc.

If your military service carries civilian transfer value, devote a few words to that topic; and if you must use military nomenclature, translate it into civilian English.

Don't 'sell yourself by the pound'

A minimum of personal data should be included in the resume, but don't make the mistake of selling yourself by the pound, as many do—giving prime selling space at the beginning of the resume to your weight, height, age and other minor facts. Marital status, citizenship, draft status, level of security clearance and willingness to travel, appearing after "Job Objective," "Education" and "Experience," are usually enough. This information can be presented in double-column form and should not be more than an inch and a half deep. The interview and the company application form which come later, will take care of any details an employer wants.

Topics covered so far are basic to a good resume. There are, of course, many other topics (professional activities, references, patents, copyrights, language ability, licenses acquired, etc.) that may be covered if they pass the "Does it strengthen your resume?" test. You can easily tell whether they do.

Professional activities: Papers published and patents acquired reveal an active, thinking, creative mind—a rare asset that all companies want. If you've had one or two papers published in a reputable magazine, give the title of the paper, the name of the magazine, and its date of issue. If you've had a string of papers published, merely state the number of papers, the field of interest, and the names of the more prominent publications involved. With one or two patents, merely list their titles and numbers. If you have many patents, handle them the same as you would many papers. Other mentionable topics are memberships in professional organizations, offices held, and talks given at meetings and symposia.

References: There are two kinds of references —personal and professional. In a resume you should be more concerned with the second. Before listing them, (usually three), you should contact them to make sure that use of their names is acceptable to them. Then include their full names, titles, company affiliations and addresses.

Languages: If the prospective employer does business overseas, the ability to speak, read or write a foreign language is a definite asset. If you happen to have a specialty, say business French or legal Spanish or scientific German, mention it—as long as the skill is pertinent. Indicate your level of proficiency.

Military service: This block of text, if you believe it is pertinent to your career, should include branch of service, dates of entry and dis-

Two resumes describing the same man --

RESUME

Allison Record
007 Electron Avenue
Wilmington, Mass.

Tel. 685-0000

Height - 5 feet 11
Weight - 170
Age   - 32
Health - good

Education --

Was graduated from Ampere University with a B.S. in electrical engineering, 1959.
(Course completed in six years, result of illness in family.) Graduated Ohmsville High School, Ohmsville, N.J., in 1953 and Ohmsville Junior High School in
1950. Extracurricular activities: Member of both high school bands, member
Hi-Y (high school) and Tau Beta Phi (college).

Experience --

December 1966 to present -- Arming and Fusing Technology Department, Alma Corp.,
1120 Junction Road, Wilmington, Mass. 01888. Digital Design Group Leader.
   Work includes design and development of digital subsystems and supervision
   of personnel. Filled vacancy created when Ramirez (see below) left the
   company. Immediate superior: George William Richman, subsystems supervisor.

May 1965 to December 1966 -- Arming and Fusing Technology Department, Alma Corp.,
Wilmington, Mass. Senior Design Engineer.
   Worked on systems and development of digital subsystems. These subsystems
   provide accurate timing, remotely controlled setting or verification or real-
   time trajectory computational functions. Immediate superior: Sean Ramirez,
   group leader.

August 1961 to May 1965 -- DEF, Inc., 22 Hoboken Avenue, Newark, N.J. 12004.
Design Engineer.
   Assisted on circuit design of a toll ticketing system for an endependent
   telephone company in New Jersey. Designed several telemetry systems for
   the National Areonautics and Space Administration. Worked on the design
   of a high-speed multiplexer, synchro-to-digital converter system and a
   telemetry digital channel synchronizer. Immediate superior: A.G. Bell,
   design coordinator.

July 1959 to July 1961 -- Military service. U.S. Air Force, Chanute Air Force
Base. Private first class.
   Was company supply clerk for nine months and a member of the Air Base band
   for 15 months. Honorably discharged.

Prior -- During the two-year interim in my schooling (1953-1959) I worked at
Burke & Hare, electronic and TV parts distributors, Ohmsville, N.J., as an
order clerk.

Personal information --

Native American
Married, three children
Home owner
Own car

But which one gets him the interview?

Manager, Digital Subsystems Design and Development

ALLISON RECORD   October 1968
007 Electron Avenue   Tel. (617) 658-0000
Wilmington, Mass. 01883

JOB OBJECTIVE

A managerial position enabling me to utilize my education and experience
more fully in designing and developing digital subsystems. The position
should offer challenging military and industrial assignments and the
opportunity to coordinate work in same.

EDUCATION

B.S. in electrical engineering, Ampere University, 1959. Ranked in top
fifth of class and was elected to Tau Beta Phi, national honorary engineering society. Post-graduate courses in Practice of Value Engineering and in
Motivational Techniques, 1967-68, Gantt Institute.

EXPERIENCE

December 1966 to present -- Leader, Digital Design Group, Arming and Fusing
Technology Department, Alma Corporation (aerospace and ground support R&D),
Wilmington, Mass. Responsibilities include hiring, training, long-range
planning, project management, supervision of three engineers and four aides
as well as the design and development of missile-borne digital subsystems,
among them a digital data set for the Mark 17 Minuteman missile. This was
a promotion from my former position of --

May 1965 to December 1966 -- Senior Design Engineer, with the same group.
Was responsible for designing and developing digital subsystems, and for
developing relevant specs through coordination with other contractors.
These subsystems incorporate the latest in high-reliability integrated
circuitry, magnetic core memories and circuitry hardened to nuclear effects.

August 1961 to May 1965 -- Design Engineer, DEF, Inc., Newark, N.J. Worked
in data collection and PCM telemetry, collaborating on design of a data collection center for an environmental test facility, a universal PCM ground
station and a PAM/PDM/PCM decommutation system, all for NASA. Had complete design and implementation responsibilities for the first high-speed
solid-state airborne multiplexer and syncro-to-digital converter systems,
and for a completely digital channel synchronizer for a telemetry system.

PERSONAL INFORMATION

American citizen   Height - 5 feet 11
Married, three children   Weight - 170
Military service - U.S.A.F., July '59 - July '61   Age   - 32
Draft status - 3A   Health - good
Security clearance - secret
Am willing to relocate and travel one week each month.

charge, highest rank held, responsibilities and duties, skills acquired, schools attended, medals earned, reserve status, present classification, and type of discharge.

Among tidbits of information almost certain to flunk the "Does it strengthen your resume?" test are names of supervisors, reasons for leaving, shortcomings of present or past employers, and personal problems.

A cover letter presenting additional details whose appropriateness varies with the circumstances may accompany your resume. In it you may bring up acceptable salary, expand on specific accomplishments thought to be of special interest to the employer, and make a point of your availability. It can also serve for minor updating of a quantity-run resume; but in any case the resume should be revised each year. A caution on the letter: keep it short.

Neat format wraps it up

Of two resumes detailing equal qualifications, the resume with the neater, more balanced format will attract first attention and probably more favorable attention. Simply because format is not a crucial factor does not justify your downgrading it.

Managers prefer brief resumes; so limit yours to one or two pages. Be sure your name is at the top of page two, and staple the pages in the upper-left corner.

White space greatly improves format; so use all-around margins of an inch or inch and a quarter. Single-space the text, double-space between paragraphs, and consider triple-spacing between major headings. Avoid having four or five depths of indentation at the left.

For a limited number of copies get a skilled typist using good bond paper and carbon-paper ribbon (this ribbon produces sharper typefaces than a cloth ribbon). For a big run, submit a clean original to a competent printer for offset reproduction (sometimes called Multilith).

All dressed up—now where to go?

An in-depth study of 50 engineers' job-seeking habits sponsored by Deutsch and Shea, Inc., technical manpower communications consultants, re-

---

Resume hoax shows:

It pays managers to 'read between the lines'

Engineers and electronic specialists are seldom trained writers, and the "gold" that's in their real-life qualifications often fails to glitter through their typed pages. Managers must search it out "between the lines" of resumes that can underplay, bury or even omit desirable applicant qualifications.

To illustrate the potential danger in taking resumes at face value, *Careers in Technology*, an annual publication for graduating seniors, presented "hoax resumes" to a panel of hiring officials representing 18 top technical employers.

Each resume, prepared by science writers in on the gag, sought a professional position for an actual person from the past or present. "Applicants" included famous frauds and failures as well as the greatest scientists of all time. Code numbers concealed actual identities.

Among the resumes that were factual, but written so they failed to convey strengths and potential: that of the late Norbert Weiner, founder of cybernetics and developer of basic electronic equations relating to computers and communications. His resume elicited not one single request for an interview.

Among resumes that pulled well (14 out of 18 wanted to interview him): that of Rube Goldberg, cartoonist noted for his comic drawings of overly-complex, obviously impossible mechanicisms. Hiring men were attracted by his heavy experience in "design and depiction of systems taking into account the role of the human being in the use of machines to meet an end functional objective."

Two separate resumes on Marcellus Merrill, a Colorado engineer who invented, and now manufactures, an electronic automobile wheel alignment machine, showed what emphasis on career objectives in a resume can do. One dwelt exclusively on Merrill's extensive technical background and accomplishments. It brought him 13 interview requests. The other brought out, in addition, a goal orientation and his management experience. It drew interview requests from all 18 employers on the panel.

The few extra minutes a manager spends on resume evaluation may help him make more right decisions about whom to interview. Does a pattern show in a writer's elective studies that indicates a knowledge of and direction toward a field not indicated in his work experience or job objective? Are the areas of his technical activity likely to have generated additional experience in a specific area, even though such experience is not mentioned? Is the job experience extensive enough to suggest a certain amount (unmentioned) of supervisory experience?

The added effort may keep a manager from bypassing "Norbert Weiners" and "Marcellus Merrills" because of what their resumes don't say.

veals that the engineer selecting his future employer behaves much like a housewife on an impulse shopping spree.

The clinical psychologists conducting the survey found that secondhand reports by colleagues, rumors about administrative and employee practices, the finesse of company advertising and promotional materials, and hearsay all figure importantly in steering engineers' resumes to certain companies.

Unanalyzed preconceptions build unrealistic company images that heavily weight engineers' decisions as to which companies to contact when they're planning a move—often to their subsequent regret.

Want to leave a company that's dragging its heels and latch onto a comer? Check the prospective employer's sales and total staff over the past few years. Look through trade news for companies with projects of sufficient technical challenge, duration, size and diversity to fill your needs.

Looking for an operating climate where you can shed non-professional detail work, make more decisions? Seek information on a prospect company's ratio of non-engineers to engineers on its technical staff; a high ratio could mean less dissipation of your time on non-professional work. And you needn't necessarily seek out a small company in order to boost your decision-making status. Locating in a large company, which your investigations have revealed to have a decentralized management, can bring about the same effect.

No matter how strong and effective your resume, if it reaches the wrong target it's in line for oblivion. The company you send it to may be too small to support the specialty you want—or too specialized to want the man seeking to broaden his experience. Even in a "right" company, your resume, in the wrong hands, may be tossed out. Ascertain the individual to whom it should be addressed.

Battle-scarred job hunters with experience in targeting potential employers and stirring up their interest recommend dispatching the resume to the manager or supervisor most directly concerned with the position you want. But try to find out the man's name and title first. Should you lack that information, there are a number of directories available in company and public libraries that may give it to you. There you can also find particulars on component manufacturers and major subcontractors and listings of top brass down to the chief engineer.

Keep your 'cool' after mailing

Be prepared for a bleak "form letter" answer, if any, after your resume is sent in answer to an ad. In a test mailing of 100 resumes answering urgently-phrased "electronic engineers wanted" ads, most of the replies which came back were signed by personnel people.

Although the ads answered had stressed the high level of professional contact in store for the applicant, only three of the 85 replies to resumes received within the first month came from engineering departments.

One out of five replies were mechanically reproduced form letters, and most of the hand-typed balance were as unexciting and impersonal as the original ads were provocative and promising.

Accept a tardy, colorless answer for what it is —the coarse-screening output of a somewhat uncoordinated recruiting mechanism. ▪▪

Think sales engineering is your thing?

What if it isn't? This may help you to answer two key questions:
Are you the type? What do you want to be doing in five years?

Frank J. Burge, Vice President Marketing, Data Technology Corp., Palo Alto, Calif.

Although nearly a quarter of a million persons in the U. S. have invested time and tuition to become electronics engineers, thousands of them desert their profession every year to go into sales. For some, the step represents rewards, both in terms of earnings and personal satisfaction; to others, it is the beginning of a frustrating career with a limited future.

If you've been considering such a giant step, you should know that a sales career, like an iceberg, is never what it appears. Most of the details are below the surface.

Before making a decision in favor of selling, find out what you're getting into:

- Why some engineers go into sales.
- What a professional salesman is.
- What paths successful sales engineers have taken.
- What company officials look for in a salesman and the chief reasons many engineers fail as sales professionals.

Why engineers forsake engineering

What makes selling such an attractive career to some engineers?

Some of them are attracted to the money. These engineers hear about the guy that used to work in the lab with them: he now makes $34,000—and he wasn't even a good engineer.

Others switch to sales because they feel they can't keep up with the changes in technology.

Still others make the change because they want to be their own boss, and a salesman is pretty much on his own most of the time.

And, of course, excessive layoffs help convince some engineers to consider other careers—sales among them.

In any case, many engineers go into selling for the wrong reasons. Perhaps the biggest mistake they make is in not understanding what is expected of them as a salesman and objectively appraising their own talents. Sales aspirants certainly wouldn't apply for a job in chemistry unless they had an understanding of what a chemist is, but they apply for a selling job without any knowledge of what a professional salesman is. So what is he?

Profile of a professional salesman

The professional salesman is in the business of communicating with people. To get the job done, he is going to need:

Technical Skills: He must have the basic technical skills, either through formal education or experience, to learn enough about the product to sell it. A basic knowledge of accounting, for example, might be required to sell business machines. Most engineers have the qualified skills.

Empathy: Can he put himself in the customer's shoes? This is empathy, and a salesman without it never knows if he is convincing or alienating his client. All too often engineers lack empathy; they are too logical and count on their technical knowledge to win the order.

When I was a sales manager I made several calls with a bright engineer turned salesman. On the surface he had all the apparent skills needed to be a successful salesman, but he was consistently the man with the poorest sales record.

On one call, it was obvious to me that the prospect actually preferred a competitor. But our engineer turned salesman didn't even sense he was about to lose an order nor why. He lacked empathy.

It is almost impossible to develop empathy. Do you have it?

Winner's Attitude: The Mets found it, Vince Lombardi almost invented it, and you've seen it in every sales pro. It's the ego drive that refuses to accept defeat. The professional uses his empathy to identify and clarify objections. His winner's attitude drives him to do what is necessary to overcome the objections and close the order. It may mean that he has to persuade the factory to give him extra support, or that he has to spend long hours rewriting his proposal. Whatever it is he does it because he has confidence in his own ability to close the sale.

This pro feeds on his success and gets stronger after every order. He is driven even harder by his failures. The engineer turned salesman without the winner's attitude is usually shattered by a loss; several losses in a row can destroy him.

Do you have a winner's attitude?

Engineering a road to sales

Because some engineers have the technical skills, and the intangibles empathy and winner's attitude, they make good in sales. Let's take a look at a few actual success stories.

Frank Kelliher; age 34; vice president, Scientific Devices Northeast; BSEE—Rensselaer Polytechnic Institute.

After a tour of duty in the Navy, Kelliher worked as a test-equipment design engineer for a major semiconductor manufacturer. He was eventually put in charge of the test-equipment department, with responsibility for the design and selection of all production test equipment.

Then he was offered the opportunity to go into sales with a manufacturer of test equipment for semiconductors as their East Coast sales engineer supporting reps from North Carolina to Canada.

Before he accepted the job, he checked his aptitude by taking a series of vocational evaluation tests at the University of New Hampshire (where he was working on his engineering master's degree). The results indicated that he was suited for sales. Kelliher admitted that at first he had to swallow his pride since the thought of the transition from professional engineer to "peddler" was a difficult emotional step to take. Now he considers himself a sales professional.

In looking back, Kelliher says that the biggest benefit from his early days in selling was that, because he was on his own, he had to learn to manage himself. He made his own schedule, set his own objectives, and had to measure his own performance on a daily basis. That was a big step, and Kelliher feels that it's the best lesson to be learned when making the transition from the lab to the field.

Frank J. Burge; age 35; vice president marketing; Data Components Group, Data Technology Corp.; BSEE—University of Notre Dame.

After graduation, Burge went into a computer training program with one of the large East Coast computer companies. After a tour of duty in the Coast Guard, he joined a midwest communications company and worked on the Air Force 465L computer-controlled communications system. In 1960, he moved to California and, at age 25, started his career in sales because he felt he could make more money with his "people" skills than with his technical skills. He sold high-speed data-acquisition and telemetry systems. In 1963, he was the top salesman for the company.

According to Burge, he had wanted to be a salesman as early as 1958, but when he tried to transfer into sales with the computer company, he flunked the aptitude tests. "They asked me if I wanted to be a professional golfer, a butcher, or a policeman. I said, 'Why not? I guess I could be happy doing those things if I had to.' Instead I should have said, 'No, I want to be a salesman.' Anyway, I didn't make it into sales in '58."

Burge felt the greatest thrill came when he was given accounts that no one had ever been able to sell before. It was intended as a good training ground, but Burge brought in about $2.1 million from these accounts in the next 18 months.

"It was like a game. All I did was listen, frankly admit when I didn't know the answer, and try to figure out what this guy really wanted to own. In every case, the prospect had different reasons for wanting to own our equipment. My competitors were selling data-acquisition systems, while I was selling accuracy or ease of maintenance or whatever benefit that was most important to the customer."

Ron Johnson, age 25; sales engineer; Electronic Marketing Specialists; BSEE—Healds Engineering College.

Johnson joined Data Technology as a junior engineer working in the Digital Data Group, and within two years he was project engineer on special logic systems. He decided to make sales a career because he was getting bored in engineering, and it seemed as if the sales and marketing people were having all the fun. When Data Technology went to a direct sales force in California for its line of logic cards and computer-aided design and packaging services, Ron went into sales. When the company went back to reps, he became a salesman for a rep firm.

Ron recalls that in his first sales call he was scared to death. To make matters worse, he hardly had introduced himself when he was given the brush-off: "Sorry, I don't need any of that stuff."

He lost a great deal of confidence but went out and tried again. After five calls that day, he found two prospects that would at least listen to his presentation. Before long more prospects were listening, and some were even turning into customers. Although Ron has been in sales less than a year he advises, "If you are thinking of a career in selling, I would recommend a sales training course before you start. Without an understanding of the fundamentals, a tough job is almost impossible. It is important to be able to recognize objections and overcome them—in fact, that is what selling is all about."

George Shukov; age 31; director, European marketing, Electroglas; BSEE—Fenn College.

After completing graduate studies in computer

systems at MIT, Shukov spent four years in the aerospace business as a systems engineer assigned to the design of ground-support equipment for checkout of missile systems. In 1966, he decided on a career in sales, mostly because he was shooting for a tour of duty in Europe and felt that sales was the easiest way to get there. George was born in Europe and speaks fluent German, French, Russian, and Hungarian.

His first assignment was in Los Angeles, working for a systems house selling to the aerospace companies in Los Angeles and San Diego. His first year in sales was a successful one. Shukov says of his technical abilities: "I understood not only the product line I was selling, but also the customer's application. I could show him how he could solve his problem."

After a year in Los Angeles, the company decided to open up an office in Chicago, and Shukov claims he was selected because he was a bachelor. "A bachelor wouldn't mind spending his life on an airplane, and that is what I did for 18 months. (His bride of one year is an ex-stewardess). At the end of 18 months, he increased sales by $1,300,000 and developed the company's largest single account.

Looking back, Shukov says his biggest step came when he called on the top management of one of the major computer companies to negotiate a corporate agreement that included this company's plants throughout the world.

"Until then I had been selling primarily to technical people, but here was the top dog who didn't know or even care about test speed and accuracy. This was an entirely different sell, and quite frankly at first I was scared. After that experience, I felt equally at home with a project engineer or the president of a large company. In fact, I think some engineers turned salesmen spend too much time with the technical types and not enough time with the management people who are making the policy."

What the sales bosses say

Any description of what it takes to succeed in sales engineering is not complete, of course, unless it includes comments from representative members of sales management. What, then, do the men who do the hiring and firing of salesmen have to say about the ingredients needed to succeed?

Bernie Marren, director U. S. sales at Fairchild Semiconductor says: "As products become more technical we dip into the engineering ranks for our salesmen. After all, a customer really wants a problem solved. Our biggest hiring problem relates to our inability to measure *drive*. We can test and interview for intelligence, technical skills, personality and, to some extent, empathy,

but we have been unable to find a way to positively identify if the guy is a self-starter. To be a sales professional, drive is essential.

Marren went on: "We have started a program trying to identify what it is that makes salesmen successful. We are testing the top performers, the average performers, and the marginal performers with the hope that it will permit us to do a better job of selection. We have had cases of outstanding performers in product marketing who have been sent into sales and were failures. When we brought them back to marketing, they were again top performers. We do know that the supertechnical guys sometime lack empathy and end up selling down to the customer. The customer wants a problem solver, not a dictator.

"There is another type of salesman," he said, "who usually ends up doing a mediocre or poor job, and that is the guy who decided he has to put in two years in sales as part of his career plan. This chap is much like the draftee who goes through the motions for his tour of duty. It all gets back to motivation, or drive—and for the short-timer the motivation doesn't seem to be there."

David Pivan, president of Pivan Engineering (manufacturer's representatives) says: "We specialize in application selling, (i.e. a minicomputer system in a process control environment). This type of selling requires the sales engineer to have expertise in the utilization of the product. Potential sales candidates are engineers with three to five years in engineering and, of course, men that can develop the other essential sales skills.

"We look for men," says Pivan "who are inquisitive, have imagination, broad interests, and want a lot of things. We have found that the guy that wants an airplane or a boat usually has the drive it takes to earn them. The fellows that are satisfied with what they have usually don't have the drive.

"We have seen a number of engineers fail when they go into sales because they really don't like people the way they thought they did. It's one thing to be friendly, but still another to spend every hour of every day selling people, and, in some cases, working with people who are not enthusiastically supporting you. Selling involves people, and unless you are genuinely comfortable in a constant environment with people you are probably making a mistake by getting into sales."

Peary Nelson, vice president/marketing, of Semiconductor Specialist (distributor), says: "Although we are a distributor, we hire engineers and senior technicians for our outside sales force. We give every candidate an intelligence test and look for three things in our interviews."

These qualities are, he explained:

1. *Sales Personality:* How well does the applicant sell himself? More importantly, has he already sold himself to himself? In the interview, we do a pretty thorough job of asking questions, and some of them are tough to answer. How well does he stand up under this sort of inquisition?

2. *Technical Skills:* We evaluate a candidate's college grades and technical proficiency during his work history. We also test all candidates to verify their technical competence.

3. *Diligence:* This is a tough quality to identify, but we need people who are willing to work hard. A good insight comes from chatting with former associates and employees.

"In our experience," said Nelson, "some engineers fail to make it in sales simply because they didn't understand the role of the salesman when they started. Some never learn to qualify an account to find the real decision makers or identify the dominant buying motives. Others never learn to manage their time or assign priorities. They spend too much time on the unimportant things and completely neglect the job that means the most to their success. Usually they spend too much time calling on friends and not enough time with the guy that gives them a bad time but represents a lot of business."

Is selling really your thing?

A sales career can be interesting, even exciting, but it can also be frustrating. Before you jump into selling, take the time to learn more about the profession. Talk to the salesmen and sales managers and find out what will be expected of you. Try to determine if you've really got the drive needed to carry through. Be sure to evaluate your own abilities—not only your technical skills, but your "people" skills. Remember that a good salesman likes people.

But keep in mind that the worst mistake of your engineering career would be for you to leave the profession you've trained so hard and long for, only to discover too late that the world of the salesman, is for you, uninhabitable. ■■

So you want to start a company . . .

So don't, unless you're an entrepreneur, says this company founder who began as a successful engineer.

You're employed by a large electronics company. Your job isn't too exciting, and you often disagree with company policy. One day at work you get an idea for a new electronics product. You believe that the product idea is good enough to start your own company to produce it in quantity. But you need advice, assistance and capital.

So you approach two co-workers and tell them about your idea and your plan to start a company. They are, of course, honored that you sought them out. Secretly they have wanted to start their own company, too. They eagerly agree with your plan, and with their help, and the help of a few others, you're your own boss within six months. Within another six months, you're bankrupt.

Why? How could such a good plan for starting

a company fail? Nicholas DeWolf, engineer and co-founder and president of Teradyne, a Boston electronics corporation specializing in test equipment, answered that question and many others with the following comments:

Potshots

First, I'll offer some opinions of a general nature:

■ A good product idea is probably the worst reason of all for starting a company. There are about 750,000 new product ideas from engineers each year, but only 0.01 per cent of them are worth justifying production.

■ You must be an entrepreneur to succeed at starting a company, and entrepreneurs are born, or at least made or broken, by the age of 16. If you're an entrepreneur, the chances of your operating a successful company before you're 35 are good.

■ Managers usually do not make good company founders because they're too cautious. They do not want to break eggs. They do not work well in shirtsleeves.

■ The inventor and the researcher know the product, but they tend to overestimate the imagination of customers and investors.

If you're still determined to start a company, DeWolf offers four broad suggestions that should help the fledgling founder:

■ Help someone else start a company. Since the mortality rate is high, he may fail, but you can learn from his mistakes.

■ Work for a large company. They're the ones that innovate, and they have unlimited services.

■ You must be able to explain your proposals and have the ability to influence others.

■ University engineering instructors should get a job in the industry before attempting to become their own boss. The practical training will be worth the effort.

Now let's get to some specifics.

What drives you?

You must decide what you really want in life, what your real motives are for starting a company, because you're about to risk everything, including your reputation. What drives you varies widely, but the standard motives are:

1. The need to be fashionable.
2. The desire to be rich.
3. The fatherhood instinct.
4. The fact that you can't get along with other people.
5. A good idea.
6. The need for a sex substitute.

Be honest with yourself. Is your motive on the list? Do you have the right temperament for the job? The thing to think out is: what would happen if you failed? Could you take it if you lost a large amount of money, or if you had to let your employes go?

Seek an opposite partner

A partner is a necessity for me in owning a company because he shares the load of responsibility, and he is experienced in areas I am not. Make real sacrifices to get a partner of comparable status. In our company I am "engineering" and take care of tomorrow, my partner is "marketing" and takes care of today. Least desirable as a partner is someone you are now working with; you need someone who is a pole apart from you in experience and temperament.

A good partner must be adjustable. He must be able to negotiate finances at the bankers' club and negotiate equipment in his shirt sleeves later the same day.

An electronics business is considered to be a highly speculative investment. Such businesses succeed or fail widely. However, most investment portfolios include a small percentage of electronics stock for the excitement of speculation. As a result, there is more money available for electronics investment than there is demand.

It is, however, difficult to raise funds for a new enterprise on favorable terms. Banks and private investors usually demand 25 to 33 per cent of the controlling interest in the company. Therefore it is necessary to employ a good lawyer. There is a great deal of imagination on the part of the financiers on how they propose to invest. But fear not, common sense still prevails.

The first money you raise will go quickly, because expenses always run higher than anticipated. Most important are the terms under which you raise the second money. If second money is necessary, it's usually a sign that you didn't do your homework pertaining to your initial financial needs. If you're not careful, you could lose your company in the attempt to raise the funds. Often you must auction company stock in the public market. Rather than go bankrupt, you are sometimes forced to auction away the controlling interest in the company. Usually the second financing comes at a time when company morale is at its lowest ebb. You haven't made a profit yet, and you're tired and depressed. That's a bad time to negotiate terms.

To obtain the best possible second-financing terms, try to anticipate when you will need the money, so that you can be prepared to make terms of your own. Also, stay friends with your stockholders. Don't promise them too much the first time around.

Hire a 'war' staff

The most valuable job any new company undertakes is that of recruitment, for people are more important than any product. What makes a company go are the people who are willing to "go to war," if necessary, to push ideas across.

Too often you'll hire people with whom you've worked successfully. An amazing percentage of them will not work out, because you are involved in an entirely different environment than before. Sooner or later you and your employes will become disenchanted with the situation, and if they don't quit, you'll have to let them go.

A new company should hire the people who are receptive to new ideas and who can adjust to a variety of situations. Hire also the people whose work background is at variance with your own.

De-emphasize the new-product idea

A new product fulfills either a need or a demand.

The engineer who devises a novel service or object is speculating that it will fulfill a need. This type of product, from the company viewpoint, promises a wide range of success or failure —and it is extremely risky.

It's more traditional and safer to build a new product for which there already is a demand. It's easier to sell, even though profit margins are slimmer because there is more competition.

The most common invention in electronics is the "new twist" in a measurement instrument, because these tools are the favorite playthings of electronic engineers. Such ideas are cheap.

Almost all engineers underestimate the difficulties of selling a new product. The number of units sold in the first three years is rarely greater than one-third of the estimate. To make ends meet, a company must overcharge. And to overcharge, the company will have to oversell, which is far more difficult than the work on the product.

The key to marketing success is to get a good product into production and turn it out as fast as possible. Don't stop to listen to the applause of those who admire technical innovations—that doesn't pay your bills.

Three points to remember about new-product ideas:

1. If the product is easy to make and exciting, the market for it is overcrowded.

2. The fundamental idea for a new product must be explainable in three sentences and understood by a 16-year-old.

3. A new product may fail because of superior competition. Therefore the market that first new product created is often more unusual than the product itself.

Why engineers start companies

I feel strongly that large companies invest a great amount of money hoping to stumble onto something worthwhile. When they do, their own inertia frustrates the people involved in a project, and as a result, those people want to start their own company. Sometimes the project workers will stumble onto something very promising, while the company has been backing a loser.

Unfortunately, most companies are reluctant to change and are afraid of novelty. Almost any exciting new product that emerges from the lab produces a frustrated would-be entrepreneur. I've never heard of a committee being emotionally excited over change.

I believe that due to a number of mergers, the number of small companies is dwindling. If good times continue, "risk" capital will be available for investment in the electronics industry, but there will be a shortage of entrepreneurs to organize the forces necessary for company founding.

The country is now weathering the silent generation of the 50's. They are not a generation of entrepreneurs. Until the "hip generation" comes of age and takes charge, I believe there will be many more failures than usual in the attempts to start companies in the electronics industry. If you're not an entrepreneur, your new company will most probably be one of those failures. ■■

2 MANAGING DECISIONS

Play your way to better decisions
Elude the traps to sound decisions
How sinful is engineering management?
Committee meetings waste time
Test your engineering management skill

It has been said that all decisions are easy to make, until you have to make one. One of the most important aspects of good decision-making can be summed up in a comment that comes from an unexpected source, a professional football defensive lineman, who once said that if he didn't control events, he would be at the mercy of them.

How does one control the events around him in order to make the proper decision? The best way is to know how to separate fact from fiction so that a decision will be as correct and as objective as possible. The skill required to do this must be nursed slowly through a combination of experience and maturity.

One way to hasten the process of becoming a good decision-maker is to learn by example. When the engineer reads "How sinful is engineering management?" he may want to determine if he is the victim or the perpetrator of the half dozen management sins that are described.

Like Congress, many U.S. companies are "governed" by committee. The basic trouble with committee rule is that since it is necessary to reach a consensus of opinion on any given issue, few meetings have ever produced an imaginative, creative decision. "Committee meetings waste time," tells what's wrong and what's right with such meetings.

The engineer should be prepared to shed some common biases when he reads "Elude the traps to sound decisions." This potpourri of management snares reminds the reader how he can tell the difference between a problem and a task.

Why decision-making requires group practice and why making the proper choice is considered to be an art instead of a science is illustrated in "Play your way to better decisions." A complete game is included to test the reader's skill.

Six problems are listed in "Test your engineering management skill." Here's a chance for the engineer to pit his knowledge against the managers on the spot.

Play your way to better decisions

Better decisions with management training games. Right 'choicemanship' is an art which requires group practice.

Erwin Rausch, Vice President, Wing Manufacturing Co., Linden, N.J.

When you play a game, you play to win by making the best possible score. When you play the game of decision-making, you play to win by making the best possible decision.

To play a game, you must know the rules; to make a decision, you must know the facts. And beyond the facts are countless behind-the-scenes influences—such as the unpredictability of changing conditions and the expectations of people involved. Although these influences make decision-making more exciting and challenging than any other game played, they also make the worthwhile decisions more difficult.

Practice is the name of the game

If you're wondering how you can learn to make better decisions, you can practice the techniques by participating in discussions, role-playing, "in-out basket training," case studies and simulations. The way that combines all methods, is "game-playing."

The Didactic Game Co., a division of R. B. Enterprises, Westbury, N.Y., has devised what it calls Didactic Games. By projecting trainees into a simulated environment, these games can be used as management-training laboratories.

Typical games involve collective-bargaining, inventory control, or a purchasing department program. The background of each situation is explained in advance, and within this context the trainee is asked to make decisions. Trainees may compete as individuals or as part of a team competing with other teams. In the latter case a trainee is frequently asked to discuss his decisions with his team-mates.

Before you compete, let's look at the steps involved in making effective decisions. You must:

■ Sift relevant criteria from the less relevant and see which parts of the relevant factors are quantifiable (tangibles), and which are not (intangibles).

■ Employ a logical process for selecting and evaluating data to find which alternative is best.

■ Have a knowledge of group dynamics. This leads to competent conference leadership, sensitivity to the attitudes and opinions of group members, and the ability to convince others to accept your point of view.

A list of decided thoroughness

Consciously or intuitively, you follow a decision-making process like this every time you make a decision. But when you do it intuitively, you often are not as thorough as the decision may require. That doesn't mean that you should— or could afford to—do a thorough analysis every time you make a choice. But for the more important decisions, you should review these steps:

1. Clarify or define the problem. Tackle the problem's cause, not a symptom or a reflection.

2. Propose alternatives from which to choose.

3. Collect pertinent facts so you can evaluate the alternatives.

4. Evaluate each alternative on the basis of quantifiable data.

5. Balance tangible and intangible factors, side by side.

6. Make the decision.

To get the most out of the following "training experience," assemble at least two associates before you read on.

In this exercise you will assume that you are the supervisor of a small department of engineers and that you regularly meet with friends who are in similar positions to discuss common problems. If several such groups play the game at the same time, you are in competition with them. You also compete with associates within your group to achieve the best performance.

NEVER TURN THE PAGE UNTIL THE INSTRUCTIONS TELL YOU TO DO SO. Once your team has turned the page, you may not change the previous decisions.

Problem: Salary Administration

You supervise a department of several engineers. You have just hired two engineers for your department, one at a slightly higher pay rate and the other at the same rate as three engineers who have been with you between three and four years and who joined the company directly after graduation from college. The two new men are in the same age group as the three men on your staff. One of them has had specialized experience at another company in a field where your staff is weak. The other has exceptional promotion potential—he is very intelligent, enthusiastic, has a master's degree in engineering that he earned in night school and is now studying management.

The three employes already on the job are unhappy because the two newcomers will be getting the same or higher salary. They feel they should receive additional compensation for their longer service with the company. The performances of the three were reviewed three months ago, and two received merit increases. The third man's performance was not considered good enough to warrant an increase, and he was told so. Job performance reviews are held annually in the company, and increases are usually given shortly thereafter. Rarely does the management grant merit increases at any other time.

The three dissatisfied men come to you and explain their complaint. What should you do? Review the alternatives below and, WITHOUT DISCUSSION with the other members of your team, select the one you like best. Indicate your choice with a check-mark in the "P" column for personal choice. As soon as all members of your team have made personal choices, DISCUSS them and agree on a group selection. Indicate this choice in the "G" column.

Possible Solutions:

(a) Listen to their story, explain the company's position and then tell them that there is nothing that you can do because company policy prevents you from giving them an increase—and stick by that even if it appears one or two will quit.   **P** ☐ **G** ☐

(b) Listen to their story and then try to convince them that the pay rates are equitable in the light of the qualifications and the company's needs. Stick by that even if it appears one or more will quit.   **P** ☐ **G** ☐

(c) Listen to their story and, after explaining the justification for the existing pay scale, promise to review the situation. (If you take this choice, assume that the review leads you to refuse any adjustment at this time and you so inform the men. You stick by that decision, even if it appears one or two will quit).   **P** ☐ **G** ☐

(d) Listen to their story, explain the company's position and promise to take the matter up with your boss and to follow his suggestion, whatever it may be. (Assume that you expect him to lean toward not making any adjustment for the three unless you clearly recommend it.)   **P** ☐ **G** ☐

(e) Listen to their story, explain the company's position and then promise to try to get all three modest salary adjustments immediately. (Assume that your recommendation will be honored by your superiors.)   **P** ☐ **G** ☐

(f) Listen to their story, explain the company's position and then—in individual interviews with each man—promise to try to get the two better men modest increases immediately and the third man a raise as soon as he shows improvement. (Assume that your recommendations will be honored by your superiors.)   **P** ☐ **G** ☐

(g) Listen to their story, explain the company's position, tell them that you can do nothing now but will see to it that they get somewhat greater increases at the next salary review—in approximately nine months.   **P** ☐ **G** ☐

If you would prefer a different approach from those listed, write it on line "h." If you decide on one added by a team member on line "h," it must be accepted exactly as written.

(h) _____

Now, turn the page, NOT BEFORE.

Solution Values:

Score the personal and group choices as follows:
(a) Saying that "company policy" prevents your reviewing the situation in more detail will not ring true to the dissatisfied employes. It is likely to prompt at least one to quit and to leave the others disgruntled on the job. *Allow 0 points for choice "a."*

(b) Making a serious effort to convince them that the pay rates are equitable is better than speaking in generalities, but still you are not likely to satisfy them without at least some recognition of their position. You will probably lose at least one employe. *Allow 2 points for "b."*

(c) A promise to review the situation shows that you have some empathy with their position. The fact that your review will not produce results satisfactory to them, however, is likely to leave them quite dissatisfied, and one or two may quit, though the chances for this are a bit less than in "a" or "b." *Allow 4 points for "c."*

(d) Passing the buck to your boss is not a wise thing to do, from your point of view. He is likely to feel, at the least, that you should come up with a recommendation and will probably ask you for one in any event. If you refuse to make one, he will probably assume that you don't feel strongly enough about it and will decline to make any salary adjustment, since he can always give one at a later time on your recommendation. Your men will be dissatisfied, you will probably lose one or two, and you will have lost a small amount of your superior's respect.
Allow 0 points for this choice.

(e) Making an effort to obtain a small salary adjustment immediately isn't a bad choice. If newly hired men with similar qualifications are indeed worth the same amount or possibly more, you should be able to pay a little better to capable employes already on the job. A small amount of additional pay for longer service with the company should be recognized as equitable. *Allow 10 points for choice "e."*

(f) Giving only the better men some modest increases now is an even better choice than "e." It has all the advantages of "e" and adds some additional incentive to the third man to improve. *Allow 15 points for "f."*

(g) Promising greater pay increases at the next periodic review is neither a particularly bad choice nor a good one. It will leave the men somewhat dissatisfied for a long time, and there will always be doubts in their minds about your sincerity in recognizing a valid grievance. *Allow 6 points for "g."*

(h) If your group has accepted an alternative solution written by one of you, the "manager" who made the suggestion gets 15 points in his personal score, and the group also scores 15 points. Though there is no written standard for this decision, the assumption is that any suggestion that is agreed upon by the group must be a better one than any of the existing alternatives. If an individual solution is not accepted by the group, no points are awarded to the individual.

Minimize "snap-judgments"

In a complete didactic game, there are many situations like the one you have just played and all have a teaching objective. If you actually play this sample game with a few associates, you will notice their deep involvement. You will also notice how many different approaches to the problem are possible besides the ones that you thought of immediately.

The same is true of the day-to-day decisions we make in our professions, and therein lies the real value of these games. They help explore alternatives to everyday problems and they show that careful analysis, preferably in conjunction with a colleague, will often bring about better results than those brought about via "snap-judgments."

Elude the traps to sound decisions

You're on your way to successful managing with sound decisions.
But be prepared to shed some common biases first.

Don Fuller, Director, Engineering Div., Industrial Education Institute, New York.

Important decisions are harder to make than less important decisions.

Or are they?

Many people believe that they are, but in fact there is no direct correlation between magnitude and difficulty. The man making major decisions may have more going for him: in addition to his own qualifications that have put him where he is, he has greater access to information and the skills of others to help him make the "right" decision.

All decision-making leans on the same foundation—fact plus theory. All decision-makers face similar fundamental traps to success.

Decisions are choices made by interpreting things observed (fact) in the light of things believed (theory).

As a decision-maker, you start first with facts —the incontrovertible, irrefutable and unarguable. But keep in mind that not all facts are immutable. With progress and change, today's fact may be out of date tomorrow.

In the absence of fact, you must fall back on the best available information, which is often well laced with opinion. This is not necessarily bad, if your sources of information are reliable and if the opinions are well founded. But in accumulating data, all successful decision-makers must learn to avoid the traps for the unwary. These may involve the information itself or the way it is collected.

Trap 1: Misdirection

Your real problem here is to ask the right questions. The questions must pinpoint the problem and properly focus the attention of the expert on it. The expert must know clearly what information is wanted from him. One of the easiest ways to misdirect him is to try to find out something from him without revealing anything significant to him. This will certainly be a case of the blind leading the blind. Solution: Explain the problem to him clearly.

Trap 2: Amateur sampling

Sampling is a legitimate and useful research tool—but only when it is handled by a qualified person. In sampling, you hope to learn about the thinking of the many by questioning the few. You can be successful if you ask the right questions of the right people.

Since a sample generally is kept as small as possible for economic reasons, the difficulty is in securing a sample that is both adequate and representative. There are usually so many human factors involved that it is extremely difficult to find individuals who can faithfully mirror the thinking of thousands. Thus you—the amateur poll taker—should be dissuaded from placing too firm a reliance on your own inexpert collection of data. A sample that is adequate in the hands of an expert may be woefully inadequate in the hands of an amateur. An error of 10 per cent may be disastrous to your findings.

Trap 3: The ubiquitous average

The word average has several legitimate meanings, which may vary widely when applied to a particular item. If the number of units involved is small, the mean average may be far from the median or the mode.

Suppose you had to estimate the engineering manpower needs for a project, based on the figures for the year as shown in the table on p. 31. It would be misleading to use the median and to conclude that if the work load remains the same, you would need 75 engineers each month. In this illustration, 300 government engineers might have been on special assignment in the plant for the month of October to work on one phase of the project. The mode or mean (both 50) would be a more accurate guideline for your usual monthly engineering needs.

Averages bury extremes. A man can drown in a river that is on the average two inches deep if he falls into the one spot that happens to be 50 feet deep.

Trap 4: Selecting only the favorable

If you hope to reach the right decisions, you must learn to recognize and curb your personal biases. Otherwise, in evaluating the facts, you may reject the unfavorable ones and accept only the favorable. Guard against selectivity by getting all the facts, including the figures swept under the rug.

Another case of selectivity is to correlate the general with the particular. If a general study of children indicates that the average age at which a child sits up is x months, don't necessarily conclude that your child is retarded if he falls short of the average. Before you make a frantic call to the child expert, find out how many children did not sit up after x months but still managed to win a Nobel Prize or sit on the Supreme Court.

Nor must you correlate the frequent with the normal and then quickly conclude, "What is normal must be right and therefore good." Cannibalism is frequent among cannibals. Anthropologists can tell you this is normal; theologians or lawmakers can say if it is right; whether it is good will depend on whether you are the eater or the eaten.

Trap 5: Interpreting it my way

The same set of data may be open to several interpretations. Unless you have special qualifications, you would be rash to dispute the interpretations of qualified experts. Remember that in accepting their interpretations and weaving them into your decision, they become your interpretations when they go up to your superior.

Thus be wary of the interpretation that distorts the data. The distortion is not always deliberate; one man's distortion may be another's straightforward presentation. Your interpretation may be distorted only because you were misled. If your R&D budget has risen from 3 per cent to 6 per cent of the company's total budget, should you say it has gone up 3 per cent or 100 per cent? It may be best to avoid a percentage altogether and say it has doubled.

Table. Monthly manpower needs

Month	Number of engineers
January	50
February	48
March	46
April	50
May	52
June	54
July	50
August	50
September	50
October	350
November	48
December	52

The mere physical layout of a graph, chart or table may distort. For example, if you are accustomed to thinking of something in terms of months, the reporting may be distorted by graphing it in weeks to slow down the movement of the curves, or in quarters to accelerate it (see figure on p. 32).

Trap 6: Biased connotation

This bias is the implied emotional content you add to an explicit literal meaning. While it is natural to draw out all the meaning there is in a remark, don't draw out meanings that aren't there. Your boss says, "If it doesn't work as you expect, we'll have to make some changes." This may mean nothing more than a change of approach to the secure engineer, but it may imply a change of personnel to the insecure one.

Trap 7: The jumped-at-conclusion

This is a trap you set up and fall into all by yourself.

Consider these two premises:

Premise 1: More plane accidents occur during clear weather than during foggy weather.

What you can conclude from this information is simply that more plane accidents occur during clear weather than during foggy weather.

What you *cannot* conclude from this information is that it is safer to fly in foggy weather.

Premise 2: More plane accidents occur during clear weather than during foggy weather; however, the mortality rate is higher for flights made in foggy weather.

What you can conclude from this information is that it is safer to fly in clear weather.

Consider and interpret all the factors before making a decision. Don't take mere words and statistics at face value.

Trap 8: The meaningless difference

The meaningless difference and its twin, the meaningless similarity, are cases where a lot is hoped to be done with practically nothing. You cannot create a difference where none exists nor make the insignificant seem significant.

Don't inflate minor differences to increase their importance or the validity of your decision.

Trap 9: The status syndrome

The status barrier between superior and subordinate limits communication in either direction, because of fear of disapproval on the one hand and of a loss of prestige on the other.

The boss may fear to ask a question. To do so, he thinks, may suggest that he does not know his business. So he acts as though he already knew the answer.

The subordinate may fear to ask the boss a

question. "Maybe I should know the answer," he thinks, "and if he finds out I don't, I may be in trouble." ·

Trap 10: Ignoring failures

It's human nature to want to forget about past failures, but they do have a great value—as a warning. Assume that these failures occurred when intelligent men made the wrong decisions. If not reminded or warned, equally intelligent men in like circumstances might go astray again. Profit from past mistakes. Find out how and why past failures—whose initial circumstances resemble your present problem—came to pass.

Guidelines for decision-makers

Good decisions—which mean good programs—accomplish five things:

- Solve problems.
- Develop people.
- Improve the company's position.
- Encourage progress, in thinking as well as acting.
- Create opportunities.

The solving of problems is the first goal of decision-making and planning, but the degree to which the four other points are included distinguishes the pedestrian manager from the superior one.

The better you can answer the following questions, the better your final decision will probably be and the better it will accomplish the five points in good managerial decisions.

Who?

Who *should* make the decision? Who *will* make the decision? Hopefully the answers are the same. If not, adjustments should be made.

Who should advise on the decision? Identify the specialized areas and consult the proper specialists.

Who should participate in the decision? Determine what other activities will be involved or affected.

Who should be informed of the decision? Never allow yourself to be accused of failing to keep people informed.

Who should implement the decision? In other words, once a decision has been made, how does it "get into the works?"

Who will be responsible for results? Responsibility must be fixed early, so that the man made responsible can be in on all phases of planning and performance.

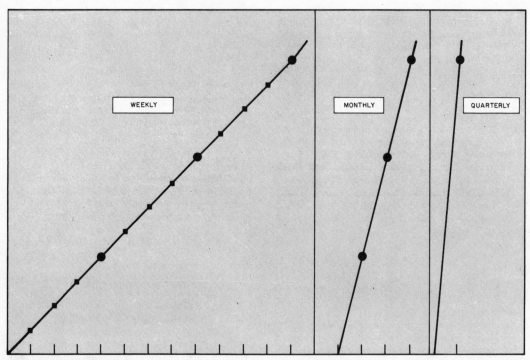

Distorting the interpretation: If your data are usually plotted monthly (center), the graph may be distorted by plotting it weekly (left) to slow down the movement, or in quarters (right) to accelerate it.

What?

What *should* be decided? What *must* be decided? What *can* be decided? "Should" is a maximum, the most you can wish for; "must" is a minimum, the least acceptable; "can" is what is currently possible, with the hope of expanding toward the maximum.

What information is needed? What facts are now available? What information is lacking?

What orders and requests are necessary? Will normal procedures take care of them? If not, what steps must be taken?

What benefits will result from the decision? What disadvantages, if any must be considered?

What possible risks are involved?

What are the limitations of your action?

Where?

Where are the personnel to come from? This is often a key question in implementing a decision. If you cannot get certain people, your whole approach may have to be revised.

Where will you go for the facts, both those available and those missing?

Where will your decision lead? Where will it lead you? The wise decision-maker looks ahead and does not let himself get into blind alleys or untenable positions.

When?

When *can* the decision be made? When *should* the decision be made? When *must* the decision be made?

When *can* the decision be announced? When *should* the decision be announced? When *must* the decision be announced?

When *can* the decision be followed up? When *should* the decision be followed up? When *must* the decision be followed up?

In all three groups of questions, the key point is: Timing can be vital; make time work for you; try not to be too late, but at the same time be aware of the hazards of being premature.

How?

How can you get the facts?

How can you get the participation?

How can you get the support?

How can you get the personnel?

How would you implement the decision? A good decision-maker makes decisions as if he personally will have to implement them. In other words, he has a plan and at least a general idea of the methods by which the desired results can be achieved.

Some managers think they are doing their planning job when they no more than meet and solve day-to-day problems as they arise. These men manage to achieve a "passing grade"—but just barely. They make their superiors nervous by being just within the acceptable limits of performance.

Superiors are made uneasy by the thin margin by which success is achieved and worry that the next job will fail by an equally thin margin. Such "just make-it" managers are fond of saying, "But I've never let you down yet, have I?" What they do not realize is that they are like men who leap onto a train just as it is pulling out of the station, after you have finally given them up. The "just-make-it" manager can easily trip and not just make the train the next time.

Finally, the good decision-maker distinguishes between a *problem* and a *task*. You are faced with a problem when an answer must be found. When the answer has been found, then you are faced with a task. ■■

How sinful is engineering management?

There are times when the engineer has a legitimate gripe; one concerned designer comments on six of them.

Bernard Daien, Project Engineer, E.M.P. Electronics,
Tempe, Arizona.

No engineer wants to be accused of being a "chronic complainer." Occasionally, however, he will have a legitimate gripe about his job, his supervisor and/or company policy. To help him air his complaint, I have, as a design engineer, commented on some of the more common sins of engineering management. They are: :

1. Inconsiderate administration
2. The art of indecision
3. The paper tiger
4. Appearance of performance
5. Two speeds—fast and faster
6. Technician's work at EE's wages

It is time the engineering fraternity was heard from in the mutual interest of greater corporate profits and better engineering jobs.

The characters and situations in this article will seem familiar to you. They are all real.

Inconsiderate administration

Bill, a project engineer who works on expensive hardware, puts in long hours on the job. He feels he's neglecting his family and worries about it, so he finds it hard to concentrate on his work. The personal tasks he is unable to do in the evenings he crams in on an extended lunch hour.

The company makes pointed comments if Bill arrives a few minutes late in the morning, despite the fact that he regularly works late. And to keep him more tense, the company promptly notifies him whenever his project appears to be slipping into the red. But if the project turns out to be a real profitmaker, the profit figures became classified information that he cannot obtain.

Early in the program, Bill foresaw the problems that keep him at work late, but his recommendations were given scant consideration by the company. Now that these problems have materialized, the administration is concerned mainly with pushing Bill, emphasizing that no hours are too long, no efforts too great. (Bill's hours and efforts, that is.)

Bill figures he has a list of grievances: he is convinced that the company has no consideration for his family; that his advice is disregarded by management; and that when the going is tough, the company will unhesitatingly sacrifice his well-being to expediency. He has been made to feel that he is expendable.

Bill must make a decision. He can stay on the job and possibly develop an ulcer, or he can quit and look for another company that recognizes its employes' efforts and shows consideration for them.

If Bill stays where he is, he will soon ask for higher wages and gradually diminish his extra-hour efforts.

But Bill would rather finish the project he started. He would prefer to have his administrator say, at 8 a.m., "Good morning, Bill. Work late last night? How can I help you with your problems?" Under that kind of administration, Bill would probably wait until regular review time for his raise, finish his project, and remain totally oblivious to the union talk floating around the plant.

The art of indecision

Joe is a senior engineer, handling several modest but "hot" projects simultaneously. His manager, the vice president of engineering, feels that when one project is delayed for parts procurement, another project can be worked on. "It's a good way to get efficiency out of the engineering staff," the V.P. says. "This sort of piece work might succeed except that the deadlines for several of these jobs fall at about the same time.

Joe has discussed the situation with the V.P. and pointed out that no matter which job is worked on, one or more of the other jobs will be delayed. Joe has asked for a "priority list" indicating which project should be expedited and which can be deferred. The V.P. has nodded and replied, "We must have the Jones job out first, but don't hold up the others to do it."

Joe then insisted that a job preference sheet be issued. The next day to his amazement, he received the following priority list:

Jones 1.1
Harris 1.2
Dynamo 1.3

Noting that all projects were listed in varying degrees of "first," Joe suddenly realized that his superior had neatly avoided making a difficult decision and was passing the buck to a subordinate engineer. One of the projects would have to be last, and late and Joe would be responsible.

If delivery was late, the V.P. could state, "Joe let me down. If he had got the Dynamo job out before the Jones job we would have been O.K. Too bad we lost the Dynamo account." Of course the V.P. did the "right thing" by Joe. He added, "But Joe is a good engineer. And we're shorthanded right now. We can't afford to lose a man."

And so Joe will remain on the payroll—as long as he doesn't discuss the issue. Joe will understand that he remains on his job at the pleasure of the V.P. because, after all, Joe didn't get the Dynamo job completed on time, did he? And the V.P. will keep Joe on the job until Joe retires because he can "depend on Joe," can't he?

The company will pay for an uninspired senior engineer, and a politician who masquerades as an engineering administrator, and wonder why the competition always seems to lead the way with new ideas, better designs, and lower bids.

The paper tiger

Much of Len's time is spent filling out numerous charts, forms, and reports, which are generated because the controller and the president of the company believe that engineering problems should be solved on a written timetable, "the way we have to pay our bills on the first of the month."

Len had estimated four months to solve a knotty problem, but management insisted on ten weeks. Yielding to heavy pressure, Len carefully stated, "I will do the best I can to meet this schedule, but it's cutting time too close."

To insure that the schedule was met management insisted upon extra paper work in order to "maintain controls over the project." Because of the reports and numerous meetings called by management, Len's engineering time was cut in half, and the ten weeks became five actual work weeks. Len finished the job in close to the four actual *work months* he had originially estimated. But because of management policy the project took eight *calendar months.*

Top brass was furious over the way "those engineers have no idea of time and money." Len was disgusted because his chance for promotion had been seriously affected, and the customer received the product months after the promised delivery date.

But the cause of the fiasco will be conveniently forgotten as management marches forward to repeat the same mistake.

Appearance of performance

Walter is a competent engineer who spends time in thinking, planning, and scheduling before he acts. He anticipates problems in parts deliveries, machine shop work, and production. As a result, his work is performed with deceptive ease, with very little need for overtime.

Other engineers in the department are seen continually rushing about at a frantic pace, berating the purchasing agent for failing to get parts on 24-hour notice, cajoling the machine shop foreman to push their job ahead of turn, and working overtime. They find it necessary to rework designs, and this keeps the drafting department unduly busy. Management beams benevolently upon them because they look like hard workers. And they are hard workers. They make even the simplest assignment seem like hard work.

But what about Walter? Well, it's true that Walter is dependable but he never seems to have that sense of urgency. You never see him rushing about. And it's true that his work is good—you have to expect quality when a man can't be hurried. But Walter is definitely not management material, for you can't promote a man to be a "pusher" if he never seems to push himself or anyone else.

Management must be capable of evaluating technical performance in a thorough and objective manner. Anything less is incompetence, and is dereliction of duty to the company. Unfortunately, management's performance is seldom reviewed by the stockholders, and the situation forced the competent engineer to leave the company.

Hired by a competitor with more astute management, Walter became a formidable threat to his old company, which began losing accounts to him. His old supervisor has gone through three engineers in the last 18 months and has complained that he can't understand why it is so hard to find a replacement for Walter.

Two speeds—fast and faster

Barney was hired by the company because it felt a new engineer would bring a fresh viewpoint, and know-how into the department. Barney was able to solve many long-standing problems and management told him they felt he was very productive. Encouraged, Barney worked at full throttle.

A wise administrator would have understood that Barney could not continue indefinitely to transfer new knowledge; he would eventually be "drained." In addition, most men cannot work at full speed all of the time.

It came as something of a shock to Barney when one day he was told, "We have a crash program coming up. We'll all have to work harder." Barney was confused. A short time before he had been praised for his production. He knew he had been doing the work of two engineers. Was he expected to do the work of three?

The "crash program" was required because an important order had lain on an administrator's desk for three weeks while he was away on a combined "business and pleasure trip." To solve the problem of delay, the administrator submitted the engineering staff to a little more pressure.

Barney now keeps a big jar of stomach pills on his desk and eats them like peanuts. "I keep getting this heartburn," he says. He has received several raises, and a very generous major medical insurance policy from the company.

Technician's work at EE's wages

Some engineers, instead of technicians, can be found at the bench doing their own assembly, wiring, soldering, and testing, as well as running technical errands. Three reasons for an engineer doing a technician's work are:

- Many technicians eventually become engineers.

- The draft takes many young technicians into the armed forces.

- Management is reluctant to pay the wage a good technician merits today.

The project budget is drained by engineers doing technicians' work at engineers' wages. All too frequently, management takes the short view, concluding it has saved a tech's salary.

But to do this, the engineer has to put engineering chores aside. When production begins, essential data proves to be missing. The engineer must deliver a working model and the only thing he can defer is the paper work. The resulting inefficiency is blamed on production, engineering, or both, depending on which department has the greatest influence with management. When the confusion ebbs, corridors echo with the old saw, "Engineers never follow through."

Any administrator who doesn't understand that a productive engineer can keep several technicians busy, should get off the golf course and spend a few weeks in the engineering lab with his eyes and ears open and his golf bag shut.

Committee meetings waste time

Unless strict standards are enforced, committee meetings waste time. Check these guidelines on how to make them useful.

W. D. Rowe, Consultant, Sudbury, Mass.

As an engineer or manager, how much of your time do you spend at committee meetings? These meetings may be within your company, in professional societies, or in your everyday life. Most people spend more time this way than they would like to. Much of it is wasted time. What can you do about it?

Committee meetings can't be eliminated entirely; some are useful. But their number should be slashed drastically. Here's why:

One man working alone gets things done. Two working together may have an argument. But three or more make up a committee, and committees don't get things done; they should be used only for coordination and communication.

Here are some of the reasons why committee meetings are held, even though they shouldn't be. How many of them do you recognize?

1. To delay action or postpone decisions.

A manager may establish a committee to reconsider an idea. The objective, which may be hidden from the committee members, is to delay action or postpone the decision until a later date. But the pros and cons can be weighed only so many times. A decision must be made eventually. Why not now? The very nature of committees makes them slow and inept when speed is important.

2. To avoid or spread responsibility.

Instead of making a clear-cut decision, a person may establish a committee to make the decision for him. If the decision is wrong, nobody can pin the blame on any one person, especially if the committee members are all on the same level.

3. To mask individual incompetence.

A person assigned to a task, and lacking the

ability to do it, often calls a committee meeting under the guise of seeking advice. He is really attempting to have the people on the committee do his job for him.

4. To provide an audience for the boss.

Many mangers like to have their egos bolstered by calling a meeting. With the spotlight on them, they then begin a monologue that is designed to prove they are managers.

5. To get together for a bull session.

Committee meetings that are scheduled on a regular basis can end up as bull sessions if the meetings are called simply to fulfill the schedule. Often there really is nothing to discuss.

6. To make unimportant decisions.

Committees sometimes meet to decide matters that are not worth a group decision in the first place. Like: decisions relating to the execution of different tasks, orders or plans.

7. To provide a "rubber stamp."

A committee meeting may be held to approve a decision after it has already been made and it is too late to do anything else about it.

8. To ease the pain of decisions.

Committee meetings offer opportunity for a compromise decision when such a decision is unwarranted. When a clear-cut decision is required, a committee involves a multiplicity of people, a diffusion of ideas and, ultimately, a compromise—which may be considerably less suitable than the decision sought.

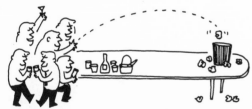

Committee meetings that are scheduled on a regular basis can end up as bull sessions. . . .

Committees can be useful

But let's look at the other side of the coin. Committees are valuable in specific areas, but where their very structure makes them useful. Here are some valid reasons for calling committee meetings:

1. To provide integrated group judgment.

In matters of extreme importance, a committee can provide broad depth of background and experience in evaluating decisions—for example, a properly run design review.

2. To promote coordination of inter-related efforts.

When a project extends beyond the responsibility of two or more people, it often is necessary to call meetings of the people involved to coordinate their efforts and understand the entire problem—for example, coordination among marketing, engineering and production personnel.

3. To obtain cross-fertilization of ideas.

When attempting to find new approaches to a problem, brainstorming can be a useful device. However, it must be used properly—for example, in R&D planning sessions.

4. To enlist cooperation.

To secure action outside of your area of responsibility, it may be necessary to call a number of people together, so that you can explain what you are doing and invite their cooperation—for example, functional management action.

5. To communicate in parallel.

A meeting is useful when information must be imparted to a large number of people at the same time. This is more a seminar or lecture than a committee meeting. Its advantage over written communication is that feedback is instantaneous.

To secure action . . . it may be necessary to call a number of people together, so that you can explain what you are doing and invite their cooperation. . . .

How to hold a good meeting

Since you undoubtedly have to spend some time at commitee meetings, make sure that they are held properly: that they conserve time and manpower and accomplish the objectives in a reasonable manner. Here are essential steps:

▪ **Determine explicitly the purpose and the objectives of the committee meeting.** Are the objectives legitimate? Are they things that can be properly treated in a committee meeting? Or are they best accomplished by individuals working alone?

▪ **Organize the committee properly.** Define the duties and authority of the committee and its participants. Make sure everybody knows these objectives and is properly informed prior to the meeting. Limit the invitations to the meeting to those necessary to reach objectives.

▪ **Staff the committee properly.** Make sure the members are qualified people who give you the representation you require. Be certain they have accompanying decision-making authority. Support the committee with necessary staff assistants.

- **Establish committee procedures.** Set up the procedures in a way that insures bold and effective action. Formal procedures can be used when necessary.
- **Appoint the right chairman.** This is, perhaps, one of the most important considerations, since a good chairman can make a meeting run efficiently, can stir participation by the rest of the committee.
- **Know the participants.** Committees are made up of people with a variety of individual personalities. The action will result from the interplay of these personalities. Desirable traits must be encouraged; negative ones must be suppressed. Know the strong and weak points of the participants and play them accordingly.
- **Indoctrinate the members properly.** Make sure they know the rules (and why not give them a reprint of this article to read prior to getting down to business?).
- **Be prepared for the subject.** Too much committee time is taken up by detailed explanations of the subject. Be sure that all committee members are told in advance both what the subject is and what references are available—for example, memos, specifications or reports. Avoid restless waiting while one man—who has pleaded, "Too busy"—is brought up to date.

Committee personalities

To help you recognize and control the personality types that committee meetings attract, check this list:

1. **The loud one**—Likes to hear himself talk and is most reluctant to quit. A chronic time waster, he should be squelched. It takes either a strong chairman with a formal set of rules, or a gag, to keep this type quiet.

2. **The detached observer**—Is secretly amused by the proceedings and the people participating in them. Since he doesn't really consider himself a participant, he doesn't help. So get rid of him by not inviting him.

3. **The wallflower**—Afraid to open his mouth or commit himself. He may have something to contribute, but nobody ever knows it. An adept committee chairman will encourage him to participate. Once given a little confidence, he may have something important to say.

4. **The take-charge guy**—Has to have his way or else. He's apt to think he'd make a better chairman than the appointed one, regardless of who the chairman is. He aims to dominate the meeting, regardless of the results or the wishes of others. Send him off with the "loud one" to a subcommittee, away from the rest of the members.

5. **The antagonist**—Against any idea, good or bad. He sometimes tries to sell himself as a "dev-

The **detached observer** is secretly amused by the proceedings and the people participating in them, since he doesn't really consider himself a participant. . . .

il's advocate." He thinks he's a necessary adjunct to the committee. Nothing wrong with criticism, but let's make it constructive.

6. **The hedger**—Always wants to back off to some extent. Although no decision can satisfy everybody, this fellow always wants to try to modify it—in case it isn't right. Don't let him wreck the proceedings.

7. **The yes man**—Never disagrees. Since he never stands on his own, don't have him at the meeting, unless you are trying to pack it for a vote.

8. **The mediator or peacemaker**—Often serves a useful purpose when a stalemate is reached, but he may also dilute the impact of any decision that has to be made. He bears watching.

9. **The climber**—Talks to make an impression, even if his offering is worthless and he knows it. He'll usually delay proceedings by asking questions for which he already knows the answers, simply to impress everybody with how much he knows. Insult him by insinuating that he's stupid if he really doesn't know the answer to his question.

10. **The cynic**—Thinks the whole effort is a waste of time anyhow, so why bother? He is negative in the beginning and will be the same at the end; so place him and the "antagonist" in a separate subcommittee, where they can be miserable together—preferably in a remote location.

11. **The salesman**—Tries to sell his idea to the group, to the point of beating it to death. He just doesn't know when to stop. He requires preventative action by the chairman to keep him from defeating his own idea.

12. **The fanatic**—Has established his own doctrines and can't be budged from them, short of mayhem. When dealing with people, it helps to have an open mind. The fellow who doesn't is a real obstacle. The sole purpose of a committee meeting can often be to outvote or bring pressure to bear upon the fanatic.

Whether you're an engineer or manager, these guidelines will help you cut down wasted time. I know, because I've applied them. And now, if you'll excuse me, I'll quit writing. I have to attend a committee meeting, and. . . . . ■ ■

Test your engineering management skill

Suggest solutions for these actual problem situations; then find out what the "men on the spot" really did.

Robert B. MacAskill, Product Manager, The Hallicrafters Co., Chicago.

A growing and dynamic business requires steady change. Each step along the way represents a challenge to management at all levels. One wrong decision can undo a company unless it is recognized soon enough and corrected. At the same time, taking no action at all can be just as destructive. Steps *must* be taken to modify procedures and organization as each department takes on more work, more people join the company, and facilities expand.

These problems are particularly serious in the electronics industry, which has been growing at an annual rate of about 15%. This is three to four times the growth rate of industry in general. A static position in the electronics industry is usually a losing position. Because of the industry's dependence on technology, an engineering department's ability to adapt to each new situation can boost or blight the company's future. Engineering managers cannot afford to bury their heads in design problems. They must be alert to new techniques, the total company situation, and to each impending problem.

Six managers on the firing line

Following are six real situations that have occurred in actual companies. In each case the engineering manager was the one who had to come up with the right answer at the right time. In some cases, proper action was taken and success was the result. In others, the wrong thing was done and the company suffered—in one instance, bankruptcy. In the other instances, the trouble engendered by improper decisions was spotted early enough for corrective action to be taken and the companies recovered.

To give the reader an opportunity to test his own managerial skills against those of the men who actually faced these situations, the problems will first be presented without solutions. Then the actual solution that succeeded, or the one that should have been applied, is given.

Problem No. 1:
The booming-business dilemma

A well-established microwave company was receiving orders faster than the shop could put

them out and slow deliveries were becoming a way of life. The chief engineer found that, however hard his group worked, it never caught up with its schedule. Also, because of the slow deliveries, income was insufficient to keep pace with the need for new parts and supplies. Thus there were periods when the shop was not working at full capacity despite the heavy work backlog. The re-

sult of all this was that production and engineering costs were quite high, and profits were negligible.

The chief engineer went to management and admitted that the production operation, for which he was responsible, was working inefficiently. He asked for permission to hire an industrial engineer to straighten out the scheduling and ordering.

Management agreed that the troubles needed to be cleared up, but thought that hiring another man in the engineering department was no solution. They suggested that, if they borrowed some money, a stock of parts and materials could be accumulated and an extension could be built onto the plant. This would surely cure the trouble, they felt.

Should the chief engineer accept this solution? (Solution, p. 41.)

Problem No. 2:
The overburdened engineering group

A small Midwestern firm that had grown easily for several years found that, no matter what new products or sales efforts it attempted, it could not make more than $1 million annually. The bottleneck appeared to be the engineering department. Hiring more technical people did not help the situation. The engineering department head worked long and hard and was so busy staffing new programs and putting out little fires that he found no time to plan lasting solutions. Business was being stifled by the department's apparent inability to develop profitable products.

Markets, customers and profits were dwindling. No matter how hard the engineers tried, they seemed unable to catch up with the problems of existing product lines or the production difficulties of new lines.

Clearly something had to be done or the company would turn from meager profits to actual losses.

What should the chief engineer do? (Solution, p. 42.)

Problem No. 3:
The perfect products plan

An audio components company was falling behind its sector of the industry. Competitors' technology had outstripped its own, so a new engineering head was hired. He was brought in on the understanding that only top-quality products in each line would be put into the field, so that the firm could reestablish its place in the consumer equipment industry.

The manager agreed to this plan, and immediately set up a system to accomplish management goals. He set up a rigid set of controls for new product development, ranging all through the selection, development and testing cycles. There was to be no room for mistakes.

After six months, the company was coming out with very few new products. Those that were introduced were slow getting into production. Although the products were good, the competition was taking an even larger share of the market and prospects were bleak.

What should the engineering head do? (Solution, p. 42.)

Problem No. 4:
The new plant caper

The engineering department of a small instrument company was becoming overcrowded and inefficient because it was outgrowing its working space. Management agreed to build a plant extension with a large section for the engineering group to move into. The old space would be turned over to production.

The chief engineer estimated the space he would require for the next two years, but then decided that it would be necessary at this time to buy the office furniture, drafting tables, and other equipment needed only for the first year's expansion. Thus the cost of the additional equipment for the second year could be deferred. He decided to divide the floor space allotted to him into two sections: one for the first year, the extra space for storage until it was needed for the additional expansion.

Then he assigned one of his good design engineers, who was momentarily not needed on any design project, to work out the details of the layout. These, of course, would be approved by the chief engineer once the design engineer had completed them.

In the space of a few weeks he was able to inform management that all his planning was completed, and the building program began.

Did the chief engineer handle this job correctly? Do any of his plans seem faulty? If so, how should the situation have been handled? Solution, p. 42.)

Problem No. 5:
The price of glory

A well-known electronics company prospered early in its history by restricting its line and becoming an outstanding manufacturer of its select products. It gained an enviable reputation for sophisticated work and grew to many times its original size. A competent production capability was established, nourished by many product innovations from the engineering department.

After a decade of profitable growth it became apparent that many of its products would be supplanted by equivalent solid-state models. A shift in techniques was obviously necessary if the firm was to maintain its leading position. The shift began, but after several months' concerted effort new product development still had not reached the production stage. Meanwhile, compet-

itors' products were gaining wider acceptance. Obviously the company was in a dangerous technological situation. A consultant was called in to help.

The consultant found that the company's managers were all experienced engineers with years in the business. They were past masters at every phase of the technology involved in the particular type of products being manufactured. But these men were now pretty much removed from detailed product development work. The younger engineers had been trained to take the place of the more experienced men who had trained them and they were floundering.

What should the consultant recommend? (Solution, p. 42.)

Problem No. 6:
Riding herd on rising costs

The product manager of a fast-growing automatic-controls company found that his engineering costs were rising faster than the business warranted. These costs were beginning to endanger the firm's competitive bidding position. Accounting, purchasing and payroll records shed little light on the problem. Only after the manager had followed several contracts from quotation through delivery was the problem apparent.

His analysis indicated that slight variations in the design of the company's products were being introduced into each job.

The solution seemed clear. A product standardization program was instituted. The product manager called all the engineers together to discuss the new policy. They expressed strong doubts about the new approach. "We tried it that way before," they claimed, "but it failed." But the manager insisted that the new policy be followed.

Thereafter he kept an eye on the cost records, and for a time it appeared that the problem had vanished. Meanwhile, a growing number of installations kept the manager on the road working with individual customers for much of the time.

A year later, the manager realized that profits had picked up very little and the cost problem was as grave as ever.

Where did he go wrong, and what should he do now? (Solution, p. 43.)

CAUTION: These situations have of necessity been simplified. Situations in your own company that may bear a superficial similarity could be quite different. Many other factors are involved in every company's business. Each situation must be studied separately and carefully, with full consultation between all departments before acting.

SOLUTIONS

Solution No. 1:
The booming business dilemma

The chief engineer should not accept the solution offered by management. Any department head who cannot keep his costs down and efficiency up soon becomes a drag on a company. When such a situation arises, its causes must be dealt with directly and immediately. The new extension would bring with it serious new problems—installing new equipment, setting up new operations—while existing shortcomings would remain unchanged. The chief engineer himself would be too busy to straighten out the scheduling and ordering problems.

This is a common case in industry. The cost-saving aid appears to management simply as a new expense. Yet a good industrial engineer, especially in a situation like this, can save his salary many times over. The chief engineer should estimate what savings might be achieved so he can present management with a convincing case.

In this particular instance, the chief engineer accepted management's advice without argument. The money was borrowed, the new extension built.

Soon afterwards the company went out of business. It is highly probable that this company would have survived, even without the loan, if they had employed the services of an industrial engineer to attack the immediate cost problem.

Solution No. 2:
The overburdened engineering group

This firm's most valuable resource, engineering talent, was being wasted. Designers were being used to get products out of the door instead of being assigned to develop products that would ensure a successful future.

Fortunately, in this case, the engineering manager paused in his treadmill activities long enough to recognize the problem. He saw his responsibility clearly. He had to reorganize his department to meet company goals better. He consulted with management to assess the financial potential of each program. Top men were assigned to products with the best prospects.

A new criterion was established in the selection of new products. All things being equal, the product with the lowest ratio of engineering to nonengineering time was selected for continuing development. Other products were dropped. Thus engineering resources were freed for other, more profitable new-product programs.

This honest appraisal of the problem and the determination to achieve a solution corrected the company's growth pattern. The company has been successful and the engineering department, now applying its resources properly, is a dynamic force in this growth and progress.

Solution No. 3:
The perfect products plan

In attempting to delegate the responsibility for getting results, management sometimes fails to delegate the right to make mistakes. Both these must be delegated if the company is to be dynamic and grow.

In this situation the fear of making a mistake was stifling initiative and slowing progress. The engineering department had so many restrictions on new-product development that a negative attitude had evolved. Of course, it is bad for an engineering manager to be surrounded by unshakable optimists. But it is equally bad to have a group of engineers who are expert at showing only why any idea will not work. This sort of thinking inflates minor problems and impedes progress.

This engineering head understood the problem and took the correct course. He lifted his rigid restrictions and encouraged ideas for new products. Stringent testing procedures were relaxed. Controls were still applied to major specifications,

but there were more compromises on minor specifications for a particular product. Mistakes were no longer blasted.

This company has gradually recovered. Now its growth rate is better than that of the industry as a whole.

Solution No. 4:
The new plant caper

This chief engineer made serious errors, and his department's morale and efficiency suffered as a result. He started out on the wrong foot. He should have viewed the expansion as an opportunity to save money, increase efficiency and earn better profits. Instead, he handled the whole matter rather casually.

After minimal planning on his own part, the chief engineer assigned laying out the new section to the first available person, regardless of qualifications. The trouble with the plan that was the outcome did not become evident for about a year. Then it was clear that each subdepartment within the group was outgrowing its assigned space. New equipment and furniture was indeed needed, but within each of these smaller units where no room had been left for it! It was obvious that the total space should have been laid out to cope with the full two years' expansion. Now it was necessary to tear down most of the partitions and restructure the entire space once again. Work slowed down, schedules slipped and people groused about the need to shuffle around again only a year after a big move.

The answer here is that qualified advice must be sought when expansion plans are made. These situations can be forecast, and the plant layout adjusted to minimize inconveniences. The engineering business, like any other, must view problems as potential cost centers and treat them from the beginning as opportunities for future savings and profits.

Solution No. 5:
The price of glory

Since past achievements are no assurance of future progress, an engineering firm can be misled by the image it has of its capabilities. That is what happened to this company. Although engineering management had the foresight to realize the need for a change, it did not recognize the technical limitations.

The consultant pointed out that the older engineers, who were responsible for training the younger ones, were experienced in tube design but had had little experience with semiconductors. Since the old products had earned a high reputation, these managers had resisted any major innovations. The younger engineers were kept

busy filling the design gaps left by the older engineers who moved into management, and they were given little encouragement to gain new knowledge. Thus the engineering department was almost obsolete, and a rigorous training program in solid-state techniques was required. It was also obvious that several experienced solid-state design engineers had to be hired.

There would be a time lag between this learning process and effective application of the new knowledge, the consultant pointed out. Therefore, management would have to be prepared to see business suffer unless it was willing to put an intermediate program into effect. Although this program promised to be financially rewarding, it would be an affront to the engineering department's pride.

The course would be to forget about innovation for at least a couple of years, and produce instead variations on solid-state developments that had already gained market acceptance. To be a follower after so many years of leadership was a bitter pill to swallow. But management recognized that this would be transitory, and that during this time all operations of the company—production, marketing, administration—would be fully employed. The total plan was accepted with the result that the company survived and now makes a unique line of solid-state products.

Solution No. 6:
Riding herd on rising costs

The trouble here was lack of follow-through. The product manager's analysis of the problem and his solution were correct, but he evolved no system of control to see that his program was being effected. A plan cannot run by itself. And if the people who are implementing it do not really believe in it, a manager can expect it to run into trouble. This possibility must be recognized in advance, and steps taken to counter it.

In this specific case the weakness was to assume that the engineers would stop their experiments on the standard line without some sort of continuing discipline. Fortunately, the product manager recognized his failure and added a new element to the program. He assigned his most economy-minded and experienced engineers to manage each project, and then periodically reviewed the standardizing situation with them. He approved changes only when the need warranted them. After another year with these controls, standard designs became the backbone of each quotation, putting the company in a solid competitive bidding situation. The engineering time thus conserved permitted the company to widen its range of activity and to progress handsomely. ■ ■

3 MANAGING PEOPLE

Hire the bright engineers
High-powered engineer training
Diary of a leadership trainee
Yes, you can develop your creativity
Managerial sensitivity training works
Do you like your job?
Money is not the only motivator
Don't wait for brainstorms
Stop the revolt in the labs!
Manage creative engineers creatively
How to upgrade job performance
A manager can't do it all himself
Appraisal programs can be effective

Among those truths that are held to be self-evident is the one that a man must know how to manage himself before trying it on others. Before a man is capable of hiring, training, motivating, and delegating work to subordinates, he should be able to prove himself capable in each regard.

It follows, of course, that if a man knows his own weaknesses and strengths, he will have the insight necessary to recognize abilities, behavior, and personalities of those under his authority. The job of manager encompasses much more than just making decisions. If a manager fails to instill confidence in the members of his staff, he will fail to gain their respect. No matter how exceptional a manager's decisions are, if they're not carried out, he'll be an unemployed manager.

The first step in the right direction to properly managing people, is in hiring the proper people. One of the leading figures in the electronics industry, Dr. C. Lester Hogan, offers his hiring philosophy in "Hire the bright engineers."

Training subordinates is the next logical step in managing people, and the techniques used to lead new engineers from classroom theory to business practicality are discussed in the article, "High-powered engineering training."

The next two articles offer separate reports on the action of and the reaction to one variety of sensitivity training. Often the success of an engi-

neer's career depends on his ability to make people see him as he sees himself. One training program designed to tell the attendee how others see him is discussed in the article, "Diary of a leadership trainee." The reaction of the seminar members to the training program is discussed in the article, "Managerial sensitivity training works," with some interesting observations made by a personnel manager who attended.

Five of the articles offer guidelines on how to motivate others by suggesting that although, "Yes, you can develop your creativity", "Don't wait for brainstorms." Engineering managers can pick up a few pointers on how to involve their staff members in their work to "Stop the revolt in the labs!" Also, a good engineering manager and/or engineer should remember that "Money is not the only motivator." One of the most important questions is posed in "Do you like your job?" By learning how "Appraisal programs can be effective", both engineers and managers can discover how well they like their job and how well they're performing it.

And, finally, if delegation of authority is an engineering manager's concern, he should know that "A manager can't do it all himself." What he should know, however, is "How to upgrade performance."

Hire the bright engineers

And let them develop the design on their own, Dr. C. Lester of Fairchild advises.

You're a manager for an imaginative electronics company, and you want to hire the best engineers. What qualities should you look for in applicants?

Men who will be loyal to the company?

Engineers who will check periodically with the boss while doing a job, so they're sure to please him?

Employes who won't hog all the credit for a job well done, but will remember to share it with their superiors?

Not at all, says Dr. C. Lester Hogan, president and chief executive officer and a director to Fairchild Camera and Instrument Corp. Forget the loyalty—what he looks for are bright people. Never mind checking back with the boss—he wants men who can do the job "wholly and completely." And as for sharing the credit with superiors, forget it: "When the job is done and done well, they know—and you know—they deserve the credit."

Hogan, who left Motorola Semiconductor in 1968 to head Fairchild's operation from headquarters in Mountain View, Calif., gives his views on personnel management in answer to the following questions:

What qualities do you look for in prospective employes?

I look for people who are smart, and that's the main thing I ask for. I want bright, alert, aggressive, dynamic, energetic fellows. You want the best you can get. If they leave you and start a business of their own, consider yourself lucky to have had them for a while if they were that damn bright.

How do you maintain staff loyalty?

I don't really look for people I think will be loyal—I couldn't care less. I never will hire Mr. A because I think he's going to be loyal. I'll hire bright Mr. B every time, because he'll get the job done.

If you have people you don't have confidence in, the thing to do is not to direct their effort every day but to fire them and hire people you do have confidence in. That's the way I operate. I think it's a mistake to keep a man around you think is incompetent—someone you're pestering and nit-picking all day long, day in and day out. You don't trust him—not his loyalty, but his competence.

How do you motivate your people?

You get good people and give them the authority to do the job wholly and completely, so they get complete satisfaction out of their performance.

I don't always agree with my people. Half the time they're right, half the time I'm right. But, I have so much faith in the capability of the people I have that if I can't convince them of my point of view, I do it their way. I have always done that. When the job is done and done well, they know—and you know—they deserve the credit. They don't have to share the credit with me. I just provided an atmosphere in which they were able to perform—that's the big thing.

How do you provide that atmosphere?

You have to provide the facilities in which to perform. I have not been noted to be a niggardly spender, but I have been noted for giving a helluva good return on an investment. I don't believe in tip-toeing into this kind of business. I believe in having so much confidence that you jump in with both feet. You either sink or swim. And if you're wrong, it's a big mistake. When I'm wrong you're going to know about it—they'll write textbooks about me.

How do you keep an employe who's been offered the potential of a better reward than he's getting?

I don't want to lose good people. Now that I have the authority of being the chief executive of a corporation, I am using stock options much more freely and at much lower levels than anyone I've known. I'm trying to harness entrepreneurial ability by making employes feel a part of the business—that they have a piece of the action. If they feel that if they do a fine job they will personally profit, you've done a lot toward keeping them. They'll think twice about going with a smaller operation, where the potential rewards can be greater, but the risk is a lot higher. You have to balance the risk with the financial reward. ∎∎

High-powered engineer training

Six managers reveal techniques that lead young designers from theory to practicality.

Sink-or-swim never did gain much of a following among engineering managers as a way to train newly hired college graduates. The cost of the new engineers' services while they were sinking, and of their mistakes when they swam in the wrong direction, proved too high.

So a number of companies developed elaborate, formal orientation programs to introduce the new engineers to company policies and operations. Typically the programs ran a year or more, and they included guest speakers, lectures, field trips, advanced studies and rotation of the newcomers' work, not only throughout the engineering department but throughout the company.

The trend today seems to be to simplify, shorten and integrate orientation of new engineers into their work procedures.

The Central Research Laboratory of Singer Co., Denville, N.J., for example, reports chopping its orientation program from a year to three and a half months. Where a beginning engineer used to spend a month in the field with a field service man, he now spends one day. And in the early days of orientation at Scully-Jones Co., Chicago, the program was replete with forms and paperwork. The program remains. The paperwork doesn't. Supervisors handle it informally.

Easing the move to the unknown

Here are ways in which two companies attack problems created by the abrupt transition of engineers from school desk to industry bench.

Immunize recruits against new-job jitters: "Will I like the work?" . . . "Have I learned the right things for it?" . . . "How will I get along with that unknown quantity, the boss, and will I ever catch onto the ropes here?"—Inner doubts are more typical of the starting engineer's outlook than is the popular concept of a brash "know it all," says Aldo B. Coultas, personnel manager of Singer's Central Research Laboratory. "And," he adds, "they are powerful inhibitors to job performance." Coultas has made it his job to knock out these doubts before new graduates ever go onto the company payroll.

Under a plan he has set up, the graduating engineer pegs down just what kind of work he'll be doing, where he'll be doing it and for whom he'll be doing it before he joins the company. At a pre-employment visit to the laboratory, he meets the various engineering heads, examines the work done under each and picks the jobs that best fit his interests.

"He may choose to work on integrated circuits, solid-state motor controls or any of a number of other areas under development," says Coultas. "And his choice carries major weight in his initial job assignment. But pinpointing his job in advance of our offer is a mutual affair. Among other things, we've found examination of his choice of electives in his studies to give us worthwhile clues in weighing the validity of his choice at this early stage."

Once the new engineer is hired, his orientation further insulates him against functioning amidst unknowns. It consists of three and a half months of field trips to customer installations, company manufacturing operations, sales centers and the like, punctuated with talks by company authorities. He should, at the end of that time, be on his guard against turning out designs that risk customer rejection, call for costly new facilities or court patent problems.

Staff up with seasoned graduates: For over 30 years, while less fortunate companies have been developing, running and evaluating elaborate operations to orient engineers fresh from college, General Radio Co., West Concord, Mass., has been hiring graduates who already know their work and the company in detail. These men are "co-ops," engineering students who alternate periods of undergraduate study with periods of work in the company.

Ivan Easton, senior vice president of engineering and himself a General Radio-Northeastern University co-op (class of '40), tells what's in it for company and engineer under the co-op plan:

General Radio co-ops with Northeastern, the Massachusetts Institute of Technology and, to a lesser degree, with Cornell. A Northeastern co-op goes to school for his first year, alternates quarterly periods between school and the company for four years and enters the job market with a bachelor's degree. An MIT co-op goes to school for two years, alternates for three years and can get a simultaneous BS and MS degree.

For his periods of work within the company, the student at General Radio earns the going pay rate for the work to which he's assigned. Students start in various shop and inspection jobs and work up to engineering aide posts.

"It's co-op income that's enabled thousands of would-be engineeers, who otherwise couldn't, to get their degrees," Easton notes.

Neither the company nor the student engineer enters into an obligation regarding post-graduation employment under a co-op arrangement. As a matter of fact, according to Easton, General Radio now hires permanently less than 50 per cent of its co-ops. But the company picks up quite a few co-ops processed through others.

"We're so used to knowing just what we're getting and just what to do with it when we hire our graduating co-ops that we find it extremely difficult to interview a graduating engineer who's not co-op," Easton complains. "What can we tell in a couple of hours? We're spoiled."

Introducing business realities

A common problem with new engineers is their tendency toward perfection in design without regard to practicability and costs. Various measures to counteract this bent are reported, but one outstanding for its speed and effectiveness is that used at Lear Siegler, Inc., Cleveland:

An overnight reorientation from textbook perfection to "like it is": There's an Army saying that one soldier who's actually been in battle is worth five who haven't. And Robert Hebel, chief engineer of Lear Siegler's Electro-Mechanical Systems, applies this principle to new electronic designers. He sees to it that they learn, "You build what you can, not what you want," by putting them immediately into his company's "battlefield"—the design review meeting—where designs either survive or die.

"Engineers just out of school tend to create designs that are precise and highly functional but—wow—what they do to cost specs!" Hebel notes. "They solve the engineering problem, but not the cost problem.

"When the new man is thrown into design review meetings, he sees designs that overlook the realities of our production and marketing setup get hacked to death. He sees the sweat of a fellow designer when the controller points out that his specified operational amplifier costs $75 as against another that can be had for $30, and when the production control man further points out that it carries a six-month delivery bogey while its $30 alternate may be had off the shelf.

"It's unforgettable; it's instant; and it's far and away more real than all the lectures on interrelated responsibilities we could arrange."

So effective has Hebel found this ready-made teaching tool that he has added attendance at protoype reviews and production reviews to his quickie liberal education for new engineers.

Making work personally meaningful

The art of motivating professionals to new peaks of performance is fast becoming a "science." Two practicing "motivational scientists," both engineering heads in companies heavily involved in electronic design, tell of two completely different, but highly successful, approaches to the motivation of new engineers:

Don't let the new man inherit the department's "KP" duties: A beginning engineer's first-day assignment at the Kodak Park Division, Eastman Kodak Co., Rochester, N.Y., would not meet the company's objectives if it failed to offer him a minimum challenge, wasn't geared to his known capabilities or was not designed to bring the company meaningful result. And the same applies to his assignments on any day thereafter. No drudge work, no "work on whatever's around" and no make-work for the new man at Eastman.

"Our aim is to provide the engineer with an atmosphere conducive to creativity and rewarding innovation," says Harold A. Mosher, director of engineering. "And we make every effort to see to it that our work assignments, physical facilities and engineering supervision all pull together to this end."

The company's engineering supervisors make a point of letting newcomers know that the company values their skill and training. From the start, engineers are encouraged to free themselves for creative work by using mechanical and electronic facilities and technician personnel provided for such tasks as calculations, information retrieval and clerical work.

Spur the beginner's performance with short-interval progress scheduling: "To a new designer or engineer, full professional performance is a discouragingly nebulous and distant goal," says Bernard R. Better, research vice president, Scully-Jones Co. "He is unequipped to gauge its distance; it's easy for him to lose sight of it in the welter of daily work; and, as a result, more often than not it takes him much longer than it should to reach this goal. This situation need not exist. There is something engineering supervision can do about it with substantial benefits to the man and his department."

Better's technique to speed newcomers up the competence scale is application of the principles of short-interval scheduling to their progress.

The principle involves setting up a string of

Some advice for colleges

If engineering managers had their way, what changes would they like to see in college curriculums to help ease the transition of the new engineer from classroom to shop? Here are broad areas that occur to five managers:

Harold A. Mosher, Eastman Kodak Co.: "Some educational organizations have tended to be training institutions—information suppliers—rather than truly universities. A student might come out well informed on, say, conductivity characteristics of a metal, but ignorant on the economics that prevent its use. Students would benefit from guidance and experience in developing creative solutions to real-life problems, even if the problems are far removed from those in our labs."

Robert Hebel, Lear Siegler, Inc. "While engineering institutions turn out surprisingly well-informed graduates, they seem to break down when it comes to balancing engineers' attitudes toward areas of endeavor. Most show an affinity for what I call 'broad brush' work, such as systems design, while at the same time it's hard to interest new engineers in designing practical, everyday hardware such as an amplifier."

Aldo B. Coultas, Singer's Central Research Laboratory: "A shortcoming of engineering institutions is that many don't train students in the use of computers. We've found computers invaluable in speeding up the results of an engineer's work and have one available for that purpose. But more often than not we have to train new men from scratch in computer usage before they can take advantage of it."

Ivan Easton, General Radio Co.: "We're sold on co-op schooling of engineers. And fortunately the number of institutions involving themselves in it is growing. Some institutions not in co-op are reaching for its effect through their summer placement programs. And so far this is a step—but only a step—in the right direction."

Reinhold Vogel, Federal Scientific Corp.: "Unfortunately the trend today in the universities is to lean more to the theoretical aspects of engineering. Laboratory courses are being abandoned. Many new circuit techniques are not being taught. And, to make it tougher on circuit designers, what practical application is being taught is often two or three years behind the state of art. The company must literally complete their education."

short-range intermediate objectives leading to a final goal. When a person has a short-range goal to achieve, his sense of urgency is multiplied. Short-range goals become visibly attainable challenges, and each one reached is measurable as progress toward the long-range goal.

Engineering supervisors in both the test equipment and the diagnostic equipment divisions of Scully-Jones are trained to plot, with each graduate coming into the division, an individualized short-interval schedule. It delineates work experience and supplementary training that the engineer must get to arrive at full competency. It shows "when" as well as "what" for each unit. Both parties subsequently keep a close check on the engineer's job life to make sure it fits into the charted short-range steps leading to his goal.

Starting the climb into management

A far cry from the learning of management theory in school is the way Reinhold Vogel, chief design engineer, Federal Scientific Corp., New York City, describes his company's system of progressively immersing the learning engineer in the nitty-gritty of what a manager does. The rule here is:

Blend training for planning and future supervision in with the nuts and bolts: At Federal Scientific Corp. most transitional training of the new design engineer is accomplished through group leaders, through work on group projects and through attendance at engineering meetings. According to Vogel, new designers typically start out performing tests on designed equipment, so they can learn about the company's test equipment and the limitations imposed on circuits by temperature variations, cable loadings, component placement, voltage variations and the like. They then design some basic circuits used in new equipment. And it is in this phase that they become responsible for the scheduling of their own design effort.

This first move of a designer into scheduling is then coupled with his assumption of financial responsibility for his designs. He learns to review his estimates on tasks assigned against actual costs, and with this background, he moves into program planning.

Throughout these steps of added responsibility, he receives guidance from his group leader and the project engineer. As he develops skills, he is given larger roles in the design effort, which lead to program supervision. ■■

Diary of a leadership trainee

"I fluctuated between gratitude and fear in this constructive self-development, job-centered critique for managers."

How do you impress others? Are you making the impression you want to make? If you're not sure, ask yourself: Would your friends and co-workers describe you as confident or self-conscious? Open-minded or narrow-minded? Honest or deceitful? Intelligent or stupid?

There's a possibility that you aren't aware of how you affect others. You may even be communicating an impression that is the opposite of the one you intend to convey. We don't always know when our motives are misinterpreted, our voice inflections misread and our words misunderstood. Yet such personal behavior strongly influences our effectiveness on the job.

If you're an engineering manager or an engineer on the brink of an advance in your career, you are, or will be, responsible for managing others. Before you can manage others effectively, you must learn to manage yourself. An important part of managing yourself is knowing how you impress your superiors, your peers and your subordinates. How can you find out if you're coming across?

Making an impression—the LDA way

There are workshops designed for the development of the business personality. One session, in particular, that I attended recently is called Leadership Workshop. It's a two-phase program for supervisors, managers and executives designed by Leadership Development Associates (LDA) of Westwood, N. J. The two phases of the program are Self Development and Management Interaction. I participated in the Self Development phase, which LDA describes as "a unit that focuses on the individual—his present job effectiveness and his career potential."

"During this phase," LDA continues, "the individual will be able to secure a constructive appraisal of his leadership skills and the impact his behavior and attitudes have on others. He will be able to take stock of his own strengths and improvement needs, plan his career goals and develop a specific action plan for self-improvement on-the-job and career development."

In some secluded spot

Because more and more electronics companies are sending their managing and prospective managing engineers to programs like this, I decided to investigate the effectiveness of the approach. I enrolled in the LDA course and was assigned to a workshop at the Mount Hope Farm, Williamstown, Mass. Secluded in the Berkshire Mountains as we were, we found there were no distractions through which we could have avoided each other, no plans or tasks to which we could have subordinated each other, and no credentials or titles behind which we could have hidden. We were forced to abandon the accustomed poses we use in dealing with people, and thus we were stripped of our various barriers to communications. As a result, we were receptive to new ideas, new relationships and new experiences.

Thus the stage was set for interaction. I knew that to offer an objective and meaningful report, I had to participate fully in the activities of the next five days. I could pull no behavioral punches. On the eve of the program, I was the personification of anticipation. My reactions and comments follow in diary form.

Putting psychology to work

Kurt Lewin, a German-born psychologist, is generally credited with being the father of sensitivity, or leadership, training. He is said to have been the first to use unstructured, leaderless discussion groups to develop leadership. After his death, in 1947, his colleagues moved to expand his concept as a training device. Led by Leland P. Bradford, a social psychologist, the National Training Laboratory in Group Development, now affiliated with the University of Michigan, organized a series of human relations laboratories. These sessions were held in Bethel, Me., and were subsidized by the Carnegie Corp.

Arise   : 7:30 am

Breakfast: 8 am

Orientation: 9 am

There are 18 of us registered for the program. The two LDA management trainers, who are industrial psychologists, divide us into two groups of nine each. They tell us that we will study ourselves and our own group at work rather than abstract concepts or theories. This appeals to me. It would seem to be a most honest and practical approach, because everyone starts on a par. We are advised that the data used for analysis and improvement planning will be obtained from three sources:

1. The Self-Assessment Form each of us filled out prior to our arrival.
2. Our boss's assessment of us.
3. The appraisal we receive from the members of our group.

One trainer leads our group to an overstuffed, but comfortable, Victorian parlor.

Getting to know me: 10 am

We are asked to introduce ourselves.
Ray, personnel recruiter.
Charles, machine shop foreman.
Frank, research engineer.
Jim, chief engineer.
Lon, packaging engineer.
Sid, accountant.
Arthur, staff systems analyst.
Paul, research physicist.
I tell the group that I have a B.A. degree, that I was an actor and playwright for several years before entering the publishing field as an editor and a writer, that I am married and have no children, and that I am currently renovating a carriage house in Brooklyn, N. Y. I tell them also that my hobbies include playing bridge and participating in competitive sports.

Each man responds with his own data.

Buddy bidding: 11:15 am

Our trainer, whom I nickname "Guru," tells us to bid for a partner. Our partners, he says, will be responsible for revealing their impressions of our behavior to the rest of the group; they will be especially helpful in watching for our blind spots. My "buddy" will study my Self-Assessment Form to get

an idea of who I am and where I'm heading.

To bid for a partner, we have to list our first two choices and our last choice. Guru tells us that our bids should depend on how much help we think our choice can give us.

I jump in quickly and bid for Ray. Ray turns me down and chooses Lon. Frank bids for me. I think that if I can't pair up with my like pole, I'll go with my opposite. I accept. There are no challenges. The other members of the group also choose their opposite poles. The bidding is closed, and we break for lunch.

After lunch we are given a couple of hours to get acquainted with our partners. Frank and I read each other's Self-Assessment Form and interview each other. Frank asks me why I didn't fill out all the questions on the form. I explain to him that those particular questions are not applicable to my job. He insists that they should have been filled out; he also wonders why the answers to the other questions are so brief. I explain to him that I am an editor, that "brevity is the soul of wit," and that my boss's assessment of me will be even more brief. He smiles, but he shakes his head. His own report is filled out in painful detail. A behavior pattern is already beginning to take shape. He impresses me as being abrupt and narrow-minded. As a result, he tends to make snap judgements about people. Heaven knows how I impress him!

The critique: 3:30 pm

The group convenes in the overstuffed parlor to report its findings. We notice that Guru leads the group activities with a minimum of direction. Ray suggests that Guru is obviously trying to get us to take charge of our own group. I suggest we elect a spokesman to keep things going. Since the idea is mine, the group elects me.

Guru gives us an outline to follow for reporting orally on the results of our interviews:
I. How does your partner see himself?
  (a) Major strengths.
  (b) Job effectiveness.
  (c) Career goals.
II. How does he feel about being here? What would he like to get out of the week?

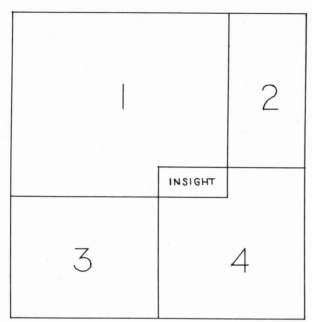

It's called the "Johari Window", but it acts as a mirror because it reflects one's interaction on many levels. Leadership Development Associates says the ultimate goal of each participant in its workshops should be to enlarge the first pane of the Johari Window. When the first pane intersects any other pane, insight results.

III. How do you see him?

IV. How do you feel you can help him this week?

V. On a 1-to-9 scale, how well do you feel you know him?

VI. Other impressions.

For the next two hours, we give our reports in polite fashion. No one is offended. We break for supper at 6:30 pm.

After dining, we are given an outline to follow for evaluating our partner's critique of us:

I. How would you describe and rate your partner's skill and effectiveness in:

(a) Establishing a climate that encouraged you to open up?

(b) Digging below the surface to secure deeper understanding?

(c) Organizing and directing the interview so objectives are met?

(d) Listening actively?

II. What did he do that helped during the interview?

III. What did he do that blocked or slowed down or diverted progress of the interview?

IV. How do you feel about the report he gave you?

V. What changes would you like to make?

VI. Other observations?

A stream of analyses follow—again, without animosity—and the hours slip by.

The 'longest day' ends: midnight

The evaluations are finished. It is midnight. I know now that Frank's negative impression of me is that I am evasive. I feel we all know each other perhaps a little better than even some of our friends at home know us. Getting to know each other is, I believe, the LDA objective this first day. In the process, I have spent one of the longest days of my life; I am drained, physically and mentally.

Except for one member of the group who seems to be losing interest, and another who complains that he is not interested in having his head shrunk by a bunch of amateurs, everyone appears to be interested in the program. But the group seems to lack direction; still we do have a feeling of wanting to get on with it. To what, no one knows.

Tuesday, May 20

Arise   : 7:15 am

Breakfast: 8 am

Observation posts: 10 am

Guru tells us that for 20 minutes we are going to watch the other group in action. We are to focus on the process of the interactions, not the content of the conversations. We are to determine what conversation patterns emerge, which members of the group attempt to monopolize the conversation and who does not participate at all. Then, we are told, the group will watch us.

In our critique of the other group, we say that two or three of the members are vying for leadership; that there is a "chimer-in"; that there are a couple of guys who don't participate very much; that the group as a whole is loud and overly animate, and that although there is give and take around the table, there is also a good deal of "bull" thrown.

In their critique of our group, they say that we are boring and nauseatingly polite, that if they had been assigned to our group, they would have walked out, and that there seems to be a battle for leadership developing between Ray and me.

We are generally stunned by their assessment (especially the part about being boring), and Ray feels it is necessary to defend us. We counterattack as a group by contending that the other group did not abide by the ground rule—that of commenting on process rather than content.

The groups break, and we are led by our trainer to our parlor. We are, as a group, a bit shaken and quite a bit angry.

First impressions: 11:30 am

Abruptly, Guru tells us to list each group member's name on a piece of paper. Next to each name, he says, write three adjectives that describe our impressions of him. My impressions of the members are:

Ray:	quick - direct - friendly.
Charles:	quiet - calm - inexpressive.
Lon:	honest - friendly - searching.
Jim:	direct - courteous - friendly.
Paul:	direct - factual - logical.
Frank:	questioning - logical - open.
Arthur:	friendly - confused - unhappy.
Sid:	frustrated - frank - unhappy.

The group tells me I impress them as being friendly, dramatic, positive, helpful, refreshing, interesting, articulate and perceptive. I am overwhelmed with gratitude.

Each of us gives his reasons for his choice of adjectives. Each person is given a chance to dispute the adjectives assigned to him. Everyone is kind, not wanting to criticize.

The group also tells me I am evasive of personal revelation. There it is again, "evasive." Hmmm.

We have supper at 6:30 pm.

After supper Guru asks us to complete a written questionnaire.

On the basis of present behavior in the group, he asks, who do you predict will:

- Assume prominent leadership functions in the group?
- Be inclined to sit back and not participate in discussions?
- Be a source of annoyance to you?
- Be interested and helpful to you and others in the group?
- Be a lot of fun in the group and in social activities?
- Be the kind of person you would like to work for?
- Be the kind of person you would like to work with?

I score high in "leadership" and in being "helpful." But the barriers to constructive criticism have indeed been lowered. I shall concentrate on the most provocative item on the list, the source of annoyance.

I list Frank as a source of annoyance to me. His reaction: shock! He does not understand. I explain to him in front of the group that he annoys me because, after telling him that I left some of the questions blank on the form because they do not apply, he promptly tells the group that I did not finish the form and what I did finish was too brief for him to bother with.

Frank thinks about my accusation. He says that he was not aware of the impression he was creating. He says he understands now why he annoys me. It is a breakthrough!

Suddenly we call for reactions to the workshop. The scale for scoring ranges from "want to leave the group" (1) to "very enthusiastic" (9). The group averages 7.5.

It is 10 pm. We call it quits for the night. Tomorrow, we might even get enthusiastic about the program.

Arise   : 7:45 am

Breakfast: 8:30 am

Boss's assessment: 9:30 am

Guru gives our boss's assessment to our partners for evaluation. It is based on a rating scale of 1 to 9. It contains:

A. What you think your boss's assessment of you will be.

B. Your own assessment of yourself.

C. The boss's assessment

Although there are 12 performance areas on the regular profile, there are only seven areas that apply to my job. The other performance areas are: Conducting Performance Reviews; Training Subordinates; Making Subordinates Promotable; Organizing and Delegating Work; Controlling Costs.

In two areas, my own assessment and my boss's are the same. In one his assessment of me is lower than my own. In the remaining four areas, his assessment of me is higher than my own. All in all, my boss's assessment of me gives my ego a boost. Unfortunately the same kind of boost is not forthcoming for some of the other group members. Sometimes a difference of three or four points on the scale separate a self rating and a boss's rating.

During the ensuing discussion, we attempt to ascertain if there are any similarities between some of our behavioral shortcomings that have been spotted at the LDA workshop and the shortcomings that could have caused the boss's negative assessment. We arrive at three basic conclusions:

1. There's a lack of communication between some group members and their bosses.
2. Some bosses would benefit if their subordinates could assess them.
3. It is impossible to standardize the rating scale. Personal values vary. Some bosses obviously believe that no one rates an 8 on the scale much less a 9. We cannot agree, however, on a better rating system.

The discussion has not helped everyone. Two members of our group are still shaken by their boss's assessment of them.

It has been another long day but these first three days have really sped by. We have been looking for tomorrow ever since we started. It is the day we assess each other.

Now, at 4 pm, we take the rest of the day off.

Wednesday, May 21

GENERAL DUTIES	PERFORMANCE AREAS	KEY		RATING SCALE								
				1	2	3	4	5	6	7	8	9
COMMUNICATIONS	STAFF MEETING PARTICIPATION	A	GUESS							X		
		B	SELF							X		
		C	BOSS							X		
	KEEPING BOSS INFORMED	A	GUESS							X		
		B	SELF							X		
		C	BOSS							X		
	KEEPING SUBORDINATES INFORMED	A	GUESS								X	
		B	SELF								X	
		C	BOSS							X		
TASK LEADERSHIP	DECISION MAKING	A	GUESS							X		
		B	SELF				X					
		C	BOSS							X		
	MAINTAINING PRODUCTIVITY	A	GUESS							X		
		B	SELF				X					
		C	BOSS								X	
	MAINTAINING MORALE	A	GUESS									X
		B	SELF								X	
		C	BOSS									X
	CARRYING OUT INSTRUCTIONS	A	GUESS								X	
		B	SELF						X			
		C	BOSS								X	

Arise : 8   am

Breakfast: 8:30 am

A dip in the "fishbowl": 9:30 am

Guru picks five members of the group and instructs them to sit facing each other in a circle in the middle of the room. They are given a simulated problem to solve: Should we or should we not change partners for the rest of the week? While the discussion takes place, four of us watch and listen.

Frank, my partner, jumps in and leads the discussion. Charles and Sid sit quietly watching Lon, who tries to organize the "fishbowl" group for decision-making. Arthur makes occasional comment. Lon comes on strong; he is extremely well organized, which is important because only 10 minutes have been allotted to solve the problem. The fishbowl group decides that each member in the total group should change partners. Lon and Jerry take the honors for seeing that the decision is made within the time allotted.

The rest of us critique the fishbowl group. Our main criticism is that the decision to change partners was made even though one of the partnerships (Jim and Paul) was not represented in the group that made the decision.

Jim, Paul, Ray and I are told to take a "dip" in the fishbowl. Since the four of us have been vying for leadership (Jim and Paul have made late, but strong, bids for the crown), the machinations of our decision-making method should be interesting.

Guru announces the problem to be solved: Two members of the entire group must leave. We must pick the two who have either contributed the least to the group conversations or who have the least to gain from the group. There is only one ground rule. No man is allowed to pick himself.

I quickly suggest that each of us gives his own two choices and the reasons for them. The suggestion is accepted. Paul jumps up and lists our choices on the black board. Except for Jim, all of us have arrived at the same two choices. Although Jim disagrees with one of our choices, he submits to the majority, and changes his choice. We are now unanimous in our choice of choices, and we have made our decision well within the time limit.

Paul asks Guru to give us another problem. Guru tells us to cnoose a spokesman to tell the two men we have chosen that they must leave.

Jim asks if there is one among us who wants to be the spokesman. I volunteer. Jim and Paul back me up, but Ray is adamant: Either he feels we should allow for more discussion or *he* believes he is the best man to break the news. Jim tells Ray that we don't need his vote, since he's outvoted by 3 to 1, anyway. I threaten to deadlock the vote, however, if we fail to reach a unanimous decision. Ray submits to the majority. Our second decision has been made within the time limit that was allotted for the first.

Paul asks for another problem. Guru tells me to carry out the spokesman's job. I do, and the two men we have chosen tell me that they agree with our choices.

During the critique that follows we are given high marks for organizing for the decision, for productivity and for the decisions we made. We are also told, however, that our group has had a "steamroller" effect; that we pushed so hard for a decision, we rolled over anyone who disagreed with the majority. Jim is cited for being "ruthless" for trying to force Ray into a decision by telling him that his opinion wasn't needed. Ray is accused of not wanting to make any decisions at all, because he was revolted by the premise of the problem. Paul is said to have been interested only in the productivity of the exercise. I agree with the critique.

Conclusion: Although our "fishbowl" group was effective and decisive, we were ruthless in our approach to the problems. We failed to even consider our option to refuse to deal with the problem.

How I impress the group: 10:30 am

Guru tells us that we will assess each other. He lists the following points of focus:

- Assess behavior, not personality (what the man did, not what he is).
- Be descriptive, not evaluative.
- Be specific, not vague.
- Use your own data.
- Adopt a problem-solving attitude; try not to advise, sermonize or philosophize.
- Tell the truth kindly.

We are now told to write the three most

Thursday, May 22

negative adjectives and the three most positive adjectives we can think of next to each group member's name. My impressions of each group member follow:

Ray: image-minded; self-centered; sensitive perceptive; helpful; astute.

Paul: stubborn; self-conscious; image-minded humorous; self-critical; earnest.

Jim: disorganized; self-centered; immature involved; industrious; competitive.

Arthur: image-minded; selfconscious; confused earnest; questioning; reasonable.

Lon: impressionable; self-conscious; habitual forthright; well-intentioned; emphatic.

Sid: narrow-minded; smug; a loner concerned; respectful; courteous

Charles: blunt; stubborn; narrow-minded sincere; frank; positive.

Frank: self-conscious; impatient; immature direct; natural; positive.

The group's impression of me (I list the six most often quoted adjectives) are as follows:

egotistical; guarded in self-disclosure; evasive

flexible; emphatic; helpful.

Before and during my assessment, I fluctuate between a feeling of gratitude and a feeling of fear. The gratitude stems partly from the positive things the group has to say about me and partly from my feeling of brotherhood for the group. My fear stems only from the thought of the negative things the group might say. But my fears are never justified. Most of the negative attributes I have impressed them with, I am all too aware of myself. I have, however, taken stock of one negative impression. They say that I am somewhat evasive, guarded in self-disclosure; I am guilty of shallow relationships. I will have to find a cure for that. They have struck a nerve.

Arise   : 7:30 am

Breakfast: 8:15 am

Self development program: 9:30 am

We are relaxed now. The assessments are over, and we are looking forward to going home. We have one more task to perform. Guru tells us to fill out our Performance and Career Development Plan. He says that this guide will assist us in crystallizing goals and actions on the job, and he recommends that we use it as a progress review reference and as a basis for career planning.

The program is finished. From Monday through Friday we have introduced ourselves to the group; been introduced to the group by our partners; critiqued each other on our introductions; been assessed by our supervisors; assessed each other, and supposedly planned a better future based on the feedback we have received here.

The LDA program is effective because it is spontaneous and directed to a positive goal. I wonder, though, if most of what I have been impressed with this week will continue to impress me when I get back on the job. It takes considerable impression, it seems to me, to change behavior. ▪▪

The second article in this series will present on-the-job feedback from members of the LDA workshop, whether or not the experience has helped them to be more effective and whether or not they would recommend it to others.

Yes, you can develop your creativity

Engineering staffs can be guided toward more original solutions,
if the working climate in the company is right.

Dr. Wilmer C. Anderson, Director of Research, General Time Corp., Stamford, Conn.

"Life without any problems is not paradise; it is hell."

The quote has been attributed to Confucius, and some engineers may dissent. Life is certainly full of problems in engineering, and elusive solutions can raise hell. The key to paradise in the engineering plant is creativity.

Can creativity be taught? Or is it something innate that a person either has or lacks?

Within limits, enlightened engineering companies are finding that the creativity of their staffs can be improved or developed. But managers must establish the climate for such progress, and the individual must apply himself. You may not develop a team of Einsteins from your present engineering staff, but it is quite possible to improve their creative abilities with suitable training.

Let us see first how the creative process works and then examine how it may be nurtured. In engineering, creativity can be divided into five basic steps:

1. Recognition and analysis of the problem.
2. Saturation with information and suggested solutions.
3. Incubation of ideas.
4. Illumination.
5. Verification of the solution and modifications to it.

An important consideration in creativity is that at the outset the problems to be solved should be stated in functional requirements that are as basic as possible. How many times have we seen good ideas thrown into the wastebasket, only to be retrieved later on when it was found that initial marketing specifications were more restrictive than necessary! Supervisors can be equally guilty if they set the specifications so early in a project that they really reflect a preconceived solution in their own minds. If a solution is left open and purely *functional* specifications are given to the project engineer, he may come up with a better solution than the supervisor had originally envisioned. This is the creative way to *recognition and analysis of the problem.*

Following such functional specification, the engineer should *saturate* his mind with background information on the problem—information tapped from every possible source. As part of this process, he explores many tentative ideas, but not necessarily real solutions in themselves.

Then the engineer should let the problem *incubate.* Some authorities recommend that he actually drop the problem and work on a second project, while the first one is incubating in his subconscious.

One day (or night), hopefully, a solution appears—the so-called *illumination.*

There follow many hours of patient engineering and experimentation to optimize the solution —*verification and modification.*

Promoting creative thinking

What can company managers do to help this process? Here are some practical ways to promote creative thinking in your organization:

■ **Broaden the staff's background of experience.** Creativity is certainly not a universal characteristic. Persons with creative abilities in one field, such as art or music, are not necessarily creative in another—science, say. Yet it is not unusual for a scientist in one discipline to carry over his talents into a second technical field. An engineer can solve problems more easily if he is equipped with basic knowledge in several technical fields. This background will enable him to recognize the merits of a variety of solutions.

Assign engineers to work on projects in teams. One man may be a member of several different teams in any one year, and each team should include men of different technical backgrounds. By close association, each engineer can obtain a working knowledge of other fields and thus broaden his own base for creativity. Obviously a man cannot find an electronic solution to a problem if his whole experience has been solely with mechanical devices. This system is used at the General Time Corp. plant in Stamford, Conn., and the proof of its success is the number of electronic patents created by mechanical engineers and of mechanical patents generated by electronics engineers.

Avoid these six common barriers to creativity

There are mental blocks to creative engineering. They include:

- **Difficulty in isolating the problem.** A very common trouble with engineers. Frequently what appears to be the problem may not be the real basic problem. It is the old case of not seeing the forest for the trees. How often does an engineer struggle with interfacing two circuits over wide voltage and temperature ranges when, if he examined functional requirements, he would realize that more than likely either one or both of the troublesome stages could be completely eliminated with a slightly different approach.

- **Difficulty in narrowing the problem.** Here the engineer tries to carry too much forward simultaneously, with the result that he is never able to focus on the individual parts of the over-all problem. A good cook is able to focus her attention on critical segments of her dinner—the dessert, say—while still keeping the other elements of her dinner on schedule, so that all will be perfect for eating at the correct time. Contrast this with the inexperienced cook who burns half her food while the other half gets cold because of her inability to keep the different segments of the whole dinner in proper perspective.

- **Closing the door to alternatives too soon.** Another common fault, particularly of development engineers. They are so anxious to get on to the "hardware" stage that they grab the first solution that comes to mind and run with it. One way for the manager to counter this is to take the first solution offered and say: "Fine. Now forget this one and give me a brand new one." Do this several times until four or five solutions are available. Then have the engineer evaluate them himself. He will often discard the first ideas suggested. After a while he will develop the habit of offering alternative solutions before taking them in for evaluation.

- **Difficulty in seeing remote relationships.** This is among the most difficult blocks to overcome. Practice and work with others who have this ability is the only remedy many authorities can suggest.

- **Failure to record "trivia."** Engineers are prone to skip over details that are obvious to them and frequently are guilty of not recording items that may seem inconsequential at first but may later have an important bearing on the solution. Frequently experiments have to be repeated because certain critical circuit details not considered important at the time were omitted.

- **Failure to distinguish between cause and effect.** This is a stumbling block even among the best scientists. Edison discovered electron flow from a heated filament to an anode, but it took deForrest to recognize what Edison had actually discovered and then improve it with a control grid.

- **Insist on good research habits.** Convince your engineers that a well-kept notebook improves not only their record-keeping for possible patents but their work as well. Many engineers have a standard excuse: "Let me put the data down on scratch paper first, then copy everything neatly into a notebook." This is nice in theory; it fails miserably in practice. Such scraps of information are frequently never copied into the research notebook. As a result, earlier discarded approaches, which could prove valuable later, often are thrown into the wastebasket and forgotten.

- **Use simple, but formal, invention disclosures.** Writing up an idea for the patent department makes an engineer think about his solution more thoroughly. Frequently this leads him to alternate solutions. Some of these may even be superior to his first one.

- **Have frequent internal idea sessions.** Let engineers get together to exchange thoughts.

- **Permit "free" time for personal work.** Many companies now grant their research staffs as much as 10 per cent free time to explore ideas on their own. This is time that does not have to be accounted for or rigorously charged to some formal project. The only stipulations are that it be spent on ideas of company interest, and that the results be presented to management in a reasonable period.

- **Encourage the storing of idea materials.** This is like a squirrel storing nuts for winter food. Clippings from papers, trade journals, magazine articles, references and technical journals, advertisements of unusual materials, and samples—all are filed for future use. They become the mental "food" that may supply the missing vital link in a solution; they may spark an idea for a new product.

- **Have periodic give-and-take conferences at which outsiders are guests.** Invite staff members and guest speakers to discuss new developments in various technical fields. Such talks, followed by informal discussions, can prove extremely stimulating. The talks do not have to be long or formal. A half-hour talk, with equal time for questions and answers, is enough to start several minds thinking in new directions.

■ **Discuss the creative techniques used by others.** Tailor such sessions as you do an applications forum. Show engineers the methods and techniques used by others, and discuss how these can be applied to their own work.

■ **Develop practical incentive policies.** Some companies give awards to outstanding men. This is tricky ground from a personnel point of view and must be handled carefully to prevent more damage than gain to the company. Make sure that all team members are properly rewarded; otherwise disgruntled members may quit or refuse to cooperate as a team.

These are basic, universal ways to spark creativity in the engineering plant. Some companies have also found the following to be valuable:

■ Input-output schematics.
■ The technique of "forced relationships."
■ Checklists.
■ Morphological analysis.
■ Brainstorming.
■ Creative thinking exercises.

The *input-output method* is especially useful in systems engineering. A little "black box" is drawn, with input signals and the corresponding output functions desired. It is then up to the engineer to fill in the connecting links that must appear in the black box to produce the results depicted. The mere putting down on paper of such a form helps to clarify the problem.

Forced relationships is a technique that can be helpful in innovating new consumer products and gadgets. Catalogs of existing products are forcefully related to a list of properties or materials from new technologies, so as, hopefully, to arrive at some new and useful product. For example, cooking utensils may be matched with Teflon, baking wear with pyroceram used in satellites or ice jugs with foamed plastics.

A *checklist* for creativity contains key words and a series of questions. It may include:

1. *Modify:* Change color, form, shape, motion?
2. *Magnify:* Additions, more time, greater frequency, larger, stronger, thicker?
3. *Minify:* Smaller, condensed, miniature,

lower, shorter, lighter, streamlined?
4. *Adapt:* What other idea does this suggest? What could I copy? Anything similar in in the past?
5. *Substitute:* What else can be used? Other materials, other processes, other power, another approach?
6. *Reverse:* Transpose positive and negative, turn it backwards, turn upside down, reverse roles, opposites?
7. *Rearrange:* Interchange components, new layout, change schedule, pattern, sequence, transpose cause and effect?
8. *Combine:* Blend, alloy, assortment, ensemble, combine units, purposes, ideas?

In other words, take some present product and consider what would happen if you did any one or more of these things to it. Would a new and useful product result?

Morphological analysis is a method developed by Dr. Fritz Zwicky of the California Institute of Technology. It consists of first defining the problem, then listing every conceivable theoretical solution and finally evaluating each of the suggested solutions. Thus a problem having, say, three variables, each with five possibilities, would have a total of $(5)^3$ or 125 theoretical combinations. Of course, perhaps only two or three of these might prove worth pursuing further.

Brainstorming may be summarized as follows: A group of eight to 10 people of varied backgrounds is assembled for a session lasting no less than 15 minutes or more than one hour. Rapid-fire suggestions are made. There is no evaluation of ideas during the session and no criticism. The group suggests ideas as fast as possible, and they are jotted down on a blackboard for visual stimulation and reference.

Brainstorming differs from the *idea session*. For the latter the general rules are: The chairman alone knows the true objective. There is a general discussion at first of the subject matter, without regard to pinpointing a specific area of interest. Gradually the discussion is narrowed toward the goal, and finally the goal is considered in the light of earlier suggestions. ■■

Managerial sensitivity training works

So alumni say, as they rate Leadership Workshop program a month after 'graduation day.'

How do you feel about the sensitivity training program you completed?

"I had a ball."

"I feel indignant about it."

"We worked like hell."

"I didn't know I was such a bastard!"

"I have more confidence now."

"Wait till you get there."

As this sampling of comments suggests, a wide range of opinion about management sensitivity training programs exists among former participants. The remarks above are by "graduates" of one of those programs, called "Leadership Workshop." It is a two-phase program for supervisors, managers and executives, designed by Leadership Development Associates (LDA) of Westwood, N.J., and conducted by two industrial psychologists, Kenneth H. Recknagel, president of LDA, and Jerry Judd, senior associate. The two phases of the program are called "Self-Development" and "Management Interaction."

Four weeks ago I participated in the Self-Development phase with eight other managers. I was assigned to a workshop at secluded Mount Hope Farm, Williamstown, Mass. For five days, without interruptions, we saw ourselves as others see us as we assessed our own behavior, examined our boss's written assessment of us and, finally, assessed the behavior of one another. On the last day of the workshop we were guided by our instructor to formulate a plan for self-improvement on the job.

Only as good as the follow-up

The purpose of a program like this, according to LDA, is to secure a constructive appraisal of the individual's leadership skills and the impact his behavior and attitudes have on others, so that he can become more effective on the job. But for the program to be completely effective, especially for those who have a number of behavioral adjustments to make, what follows the workshop assumes paramount importance.

The follow-up recommended by LDA calls for the workshop grad and his boss to confer immediately to discuss his training experiences. It's recommended that the boss do a good job of listening to his employe, as well as openly sharing his own feelings, opinions and suggestions. Only through the boss's efforts to identify his man's improvement goals, and to discuss his plans with him, LDA says, can his experiences be converted into long-term improvements. Only then can he help his employe work out a realistic plan for personal development and career advancement.

What our survey says

To determine the effectiveness of the LDA approach, I recently asked the eight managers who were in my workshop four weeks ago how they rated the effectiveness of the program today. My survey turned up the following points of interest:

- The program gave six of the participants insights into behavioral blind spots that they had. The other two participants said the opinion they held of their having "negative" behavior was verified at the program.

- At the conclusion of the workshop, five participants were "enthusiastic" about the program; two were "satisfied;" one was "satisfied and confused." One month later, six are "enthusiastic" about the program; one is "satisfied;" one is "very enthusiastic."

- Seven members of the group said that the program had helped to make them more effective on the job. One said it was too early to tell. Those who believed they were more effective at work said it was because they had been able to improve personal communication with superiors, peers and subordinates—mainly because they're now more aware of how they're coming across after being assessed at the program.

- Seven group members reported that a better understanding existed between themselves and their boss. (One man has not yet talked to his boss about the program.) The basic reason for the improved relationships, the members said,

Feedback from the 'graduates'...

Feedback Sheet & Analysis	Frank (Research Engineer)	Charles (Shop Foreman)	Ray (Personnel)
Opinions at conclusion of program			
Examine feedback you have received (boss-group).	eye-opening; stunned for a week by negative feedback	not surprised; need more education	my defensive barriers aren't as good as I thought
Select the critical attitudes cited that you accept as belonging to you.	non-aggressive, uncommitted, not critical enough	non-participatory, stubborn	self-centered, superiority image
When were you aware of these attitudes? What sparks behavior?	at program lack of self confidence	at program quiet among strangers	after marriage need to be accepted and recognized
What could you do to adjust this attitude?	experiment vs. practice; help from wife & boss	learn that others are important	put the needs of others first
How do you feel about the program? enthusiastic—satisfactory—confused	enthusiastic	satisfied	enthusiastic
In what ways did you find the course helpful to you?	opened my eyes to personal problems	helped me communicate —don't let lack of education stand in way	meaningful introspection was accomplished
Identify any features of the program which got in the way of your learning?	prior warped anticipation	none	none of a serious nature
Would you recommend this course to your company, associates or friends?	yes	yes	yes
Current opinions of program			
How do you feel about the LDA program now?	enthusiastic	enthusiastic	satisfied
Has LDA training helped you be more effective on the job?	yes; I have implemented changes in behavior—am now more critical of subordinates; now getting better results	yes; communications with peers and subordinates have improved	too early to tell
Has the program been harmful to you in any way?	no	no	no
Would you recommend the program to our readership?	yes	yes	yes
What was the outcome of the conference with your boss after the program?	much better understanding between us—knowing why I impressed him the way I did makes me understand his reactions	have not talked to him in detail	we jointly recommended the program for our company

Arthur (Systems Analyst)	Sid (Accountant)	Jim (Chief Engineer)	Lon (Packaging Engineer)	Paul (Research Physicist)
verified my fears about my negative attitudes	shed light on behavioral blind spots	shed light on blind spots, some surprises	accurate	paradox between what I thought and what I learned
defensive, vague	narrow-minded	ruthless, conscious of youth	lack confidence, not critical enough	nauseatingly precise
at program self-centered	at program don't know	at program youth in high position	knew them not confident	at program personality conflicts
take advice; think of audience	have to think about it	listen to others	take speaking and writing courses	people-oriented file to keep current
enthusiastic	enthusiastic	enthusiastic	satisfied	satisfied and confused
exposure to others; feedback highlighted previous blind spots	a reassessment of my standards and values is required	exposure to behavior patterns that could have affected my career adversely	verified understanding of myself; brought other attitudes to my attention	threw light into behavioral blind spots
none	lack of communication on my part got in the way of my learning	long hours at times produced tired-type boredom	instructor should keep group more on course	too much BS tolerated; should have been cut off more often
yes	yes	yes—with reservations; would not recommend for emotionally unstable person	yes	yes—with reservations; would not recommend for emotionally unstable person
enthusiastic	enthusiastic	enthusiastic	enthusiastic	very enthusiastic
yes; have improved communications with peers and superiors	yes; have decided not to leave job—am working out misunderstanding with boss	yes; I am more tolerant of the opinions of others now that I know I was ignoring peoples' ideas	yes; I've picked up more confidence, because I found out I lacked it at the program	yes; I'm more sensitive to needs of others
no	no	no	no	no
yes	yes	yes	yes	yes—with reservations; would not recommend for emotionally unstable person
better understanding between us because I try to communicate better	my boss is going to take the program	better understanding between us—got to know boss better	better relationship	went on long business trip together

Personnel man critiques the LDA program

The following report of the strengths and weaknesses of the "Leadership Workshop" program conducted by Leadership Development Associates of Westwood, N.J., was prepared by Ray, a personnel recruiter. He submitted the findings to his company two weeks after he had participated in the training program.

Strengths

■ *High degree of professionalism*—There are many amateurs in the sensitivity game, and some of them do a great deal of harm. LDA is run by two experienced people, Kenneth Recknagel and Jerry Judd. They can add much insight to our understanding of our company's management personnel.

■ *Greater personal awareness*—This was the strongest asset of the program. Although no one in the development group gained a great deal of new knowledge about himself, he did become more aware of how his behavior affects others in both a positive and negative way. From this experience, he can adjust his behavior enough to effect a more positive attitude and response in relating to others.

■ *A complete, semi-structured program*—The objectives of the week were reasonable and obtainable. I was able to see progress towards results in a relatively short period of time. I had the feeling that an invisible hand was guiding the ship but that the group members always had options to change the course to suit their own particular needs.

■ *Constructive criticism*—An attitude of helpfulness to the individual prevailed throughout the week, mainly due to the subtle guidance and influence of the instructor. This atmosphere helped each person to be frank and open and not to fear the others in the group.

■ *Effectiveness of group identity*—I became

much more aware of the power to achieve positive results by way of group motivation and participation. This development group approach gives a person more confidence in using the team approach when he learns to effect "cohesiveness." The individual learns not to fear the sharing of ideas and opinions. Once he experiences group interaction that projects identity and support, he will be more receptive to suggestions from groups he may supervise. This approach could build morale in our company.

Weaknesses

■ *A lack of direction and control*—It seemed at times that not enough professional control was exercised, that the group dominated the direction and effectiveness, not always to its own good. However, this did not seriously impede the group's progress.

■ *Clarification of course objectives needed*—Companies sent people to the program for a variety of reasons. Perhaps course objectives should be more thoroughly spelled out. At this point I'm not certain of my reasons for suggesting who should attend, but some clear-cut objectives should be reached as to what we would hope each person would gain from attending.

■ *More time for needed goal-setting*—This is a very important aspect of the week, but not enough time is devoted to it. This could be a major part of the man's follow-up on the job.

If more time is allotted for career planning, then, generally speaking, the week is well worth the cost and time, especially for persons who have spent little time in introspection and self-study.

was their efforts to turn negative attitudes that were uncovered at the workshop into positive ones. One man's boss is going to participate in the workshop himself; another boss took a 20,000-mile business trip with his employe, in part to help establish a better working relationship with him.

■ None of the participants thought the program was harmful to himself. All recommended its use in industry, with two having the same reservation—that of not recommending it for any person who is emotionally unstable and who might be harmed by too much negative feedback.

Two participants also thought that people who know themselves well, and communicate well, would not really benefit too much from the program.

My fellow LDA alumni—six of them engineers—have been open-minded and extremely accurate in their assessment of themselves. On the last day of the workshop, our instructor told us that as a group our hallmark was "conscientiousness." That attribute, the expert guidance of our instructor and the LDA approach made our training week a beneficial one for all concerned. ■■

Do you like your job?

An attitude survey can pinpoint the causes of any discontent; then it's up to your company to resolve the problem.

Dr. Keith Tombrink, Industrial Psychologist, Lockheed Missiles and Space Co., Sunnyvale, Calif.

"I could be doing so much more for my company if they would only let me."

"Any half-intelligent high school graduate could do the work I'm doing."

"How can I get management to understand that my skills are not being used?"

Do any of these statements have a familiar ring? Or maybe you're a manager and seek the answers to these questions:

"Am I realizing maximum productivity from my engineering manpower?"

"Are my engineers finding maximum job satisfaction?"

"Why is my manpower turnover so high?"

Underlying all of these questions and statements is this fact: Some engineering managers and some companies do not know what their employes really think and want.

For the sake of convenience, let's restrict the discussion to engineers. The engineer, the manager and the company—all stand to benefit, if everyone knows whether the staff engineers are satisfied in their jobs. The assumption is that a smart company, once having learned the truth, will take steps to remove any employe dissatisfaction.

The truth is closely allied with whether or not the engineer is being properly motivated. How do you find out if an employe is properly motivated? It's simple—just ask him.

Yet very few companies do it. Relatively few conduct attitude surveys to find out what the employes think about their company, their supervisors, their jobs. This is unfortunate because such a survey can have many benefits, including the following:

■ Providing a measure of over-all morale of employes.

■ Identifying specific motivational problems.

■ Indicating to employes that management is concerned about their problems.

■ Giving employes a means of communicating their thoughts and feelings to management, perhaps even venting a little steam.

■ Showing the extent to which employes understand and support company policies.

A stimulus to action

Some managers and companies may feel they already know what the morale level is and that nothing can be learned from an attitude survey. The experiences of most companies that have conducted surveys, however, do not bear this out. Even if major motivational problems are known to exist, a survey is still worthwhile, because it frequently is just the stimulus needed to trigger corrective action.

Top management at the Lockheed Missiles and Space Co. wanted to know if there were any serious morale problems. While the company turnover rate compared favorably with area industries, it felt it could be better. A company-wide attitude survey was prescribed to help find the remedies.

The opinion survey that the company conducted is shown on pages 99 and 100. Employes were asked to rate general management policies (Questions 1-8), the effectiveness of the company communications program (Questions 9-11), their own job (Questions 12-19), their working conditions (Questions 20-22) and their supervisors (Questions 23-27).

Employes also were asked to rate 13 of the company's special programs and services, such as the credit union, company newspaper, retirement plan, group insurance, cafeteria and vending-machine products.

Corrective steps begin

As soon as the results were analyzed, action was taken on two fronts:

■ The results of the survey—from the most favorable to the most critical—were published and discussed at great length in the company newspaper for employes.

■ Corrective action was begun to eliminate or at least improve the greatest problem areas cited by the employes.

By publishing all the findings, top management showed the employes that they were interested in their welfare and were willing to admit that the staff had some legitimate complaints.

Corrective action began in the most easily correctable areas.

For example, there was a feeling among management that "we really took a beating" on Question 22, concerning "housekeeping." (See Fig. 1). Immediate steps were taken to strengthen the janitorial staff and put it on an accelerated clean-up schedule. The company even changed the brand of floor wax that it was using when it received several individual complaints about the brand on the floor.

The cafeteria received a poor rating. The company got in touch with the concessionaire and action was taken to improve the food services.

Though the salary ratings (Question 20 and Fig. 1) were not as critical, improvements were initiated on this front. Managers and salary personnel were encouraged to look for inequities.

When the survey results showed significant employe dissatisfaction with company communications (Questions 9-11 and Fig. 2), managers at all levels were encouraged to expand their staff meetings and to have more of them. The company also increased its number of publications for employes. And managers were encouraged to attend meetings with other departments and sections. Finally, informal professional associations were encouraged.

When a high percentage of employes indicated they were dissatisfied with the amount of responsibility given them in their jobs (Question 16 and Fig. 3), superiors were asked to reassess their practices of delegating responsibility and to make certain that the work assigned was suited, as well as possible, to employe capabilities.

In short, steps were taken to improve employe morale. Follow-up random surveys, taken after the corrective actions, showed the company's ratings had improved. The employes were more satisfied.

Planning the survey

Is an attitude survey difficult to conduct?

One thing is apparent: It's not a project for a do-it-yourselfer. Attitudes can be even more elusive to measure than electrons, and the techniques involved in assessing them are complex. Most companies turn to an outside professional consultant to do the job. Even if the capability is present within the company, it's considered wiser to engage a consultant to give employes the assurance of complete anonymity. The ideal setup is to have a company man and the consultant work together on the survey. The former can provide an intimate knowledge of the company, and the latter can look at the company with fewer preconceived ideas.

No single survey can accomplish all things. Unless management's objectives are carefully determined in the beginning, the researcher may find himself trying to glean information from a

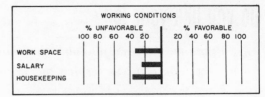

1. **The company fared poorly** in employes' ratings of their working conditions. For example, nearly 40% of the sample was critical of the "housekeeping." As a corrective measure, the company strengthened its janitorial staff and accelerated the clean-up schedule.

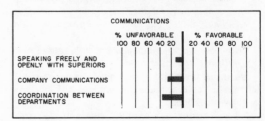

2. **Coordination between departments** received a low employe rating, with as many being critical as there were others reacting favorably. As a result, the company encouraged managers to expand their staff meetings and to conduct more of them.

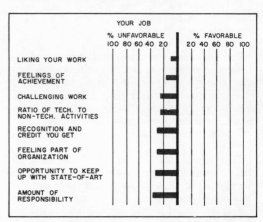

3. **In rating their own jobs,** employes gave the "amount of responsibility" the lowest rating. As a corrective measure, management urged supervisors to reassess their practice of delegating authority and make certain the work assigned is suited as well as possible to the capabilities of the employe.

survey that it was never intended to yield. Thus the question should be: "What conclusions do we want to draw from the survey, and what statistical tabulations will be required to make these conclusions?"

The two most common methods of collecting data in an attitude survey are the questionnaire and the interview. The easiest type of questionnaire con-

How would you rate your company, supervisor and job?

Here is the attitude questionnaire that Lockheed Missiles and Space Co. asked its employees to fill out.

Please show how you rate each of the following by placing an "X" in the appropriate box. Skip any item on which you don't have enough information to base an opinion.

- 1. How do you rate the company as a place to work for?
  ☐ Very Good   ☐ Good   ☐ Neutral   ☐ Poor   ☐ Very Poor

  2. How do you feel about our policies and procedures?
  ☐ Very Satisfied   ☐ Satisfied   ☐ Neutral   ☐ Dissatisfied   ☐ Very Dissatisfied

  3. How satisfied are you with your opportunity for advancement at the company?
  ☐ Very Satisfied   ☐ Satisfied   ☐ Neutral   ☐ Dissatisfied   ☐ Very Dissatisfied

  4. How do you rate the company's technical capability?
  ☐ Very Good   ☐ Good   ☐ Neutral   ☐ Poor   ☐ Very Poor

  5. How do you feel about management's concern for employees?
  ☐ Very Satisfied   ☐ Satisfied   ☐ Neutral   ☐ Dissatisfied   ☐ Very Dissatisfied

  6. How satisfied are you with self-development opportunities available through the company's training programs and courses?
  ☐ Very Satisfied   ☐ Satisfied   ☐ Neutral   ☐ Dissatisfied   ☐ Very Dissatisfied

  7. How do you rate management's overall operation of the company?
  ☐ Very Good   ☐ Good   ☐ Neutral   ☐ Poor   ☐ Very Poor

  8. I feel part of not just the company but the total corporation.
  ☐ Strongly Agree   ☐ Agree   ☐ Neutral   ☐ Disagree   ☐ Strongly Disagree

COMMENTS

- 9. How good a job does management do in communicating about company activities and matters affecting your work?
  ☐ Very Good   ☐ Good   ☐ Neutral   ☐ Poor   ☐ Very Poor

  10. How good is the coordination between departments?
  ☐ Very Good   ☐ Good   ☐ Neutral   ☐ Poor   ☐ Very Poor

  11. Do you feel you can speak freely and openly with your superiors?
  ☐ Almost Always   ☐ Often   ☐ Half-the-time   ☐ Occasionally   ☐ Almost Never

COMMENTS

12. Do you like the kind of work you do?

☐ Strongly Like ☐ Like ☐ Neutral ☐ Dislike ☐ Strongly Dislike

13. I get a feeling of achievement from my work.

☐ Strongly Agree ☐ Agree ☐ Neutral ☐ Disagree ☐ Strongly Disagree

14. How satisfied are you with the recognition and credit you get for your work?

☐ Very Satisfied ☐ Satisfied ☐ Neutral ☐ Dissatisfied ☐ Very Dissatisfied

15. How satisfied are you with the ratio of technical to non-technical activities in your job?

☐ Very Satisfied ☐ Satisfied ☐ Neutral ☐ Dissatisfied ☐ Very Dissatisfied

16. Under present conditions, I am satisfied with the amount of responsibility I have.

☐ Strongly Agree ☐ Agree ☐ Neutral ☐ Disagree ☐ Strongly Disagree

17. My work is challenging.

☐ Strongly Agree ☐ Agree ☐ Neutral ☐ Disagree ☐ Strongly Disagree

18. How satisfied are you with the opportunity to keep up with the state of the art in your field?

☐ Very Satisfied ☐ Satisfied ☐ Neutral ☐ Dissatisfied ☐ Very Dissatisfied

19. I really feel part of things in my organization.

☐ Strongly Agree ☐ Agree ☐ Neutral ☐ Disagree ☐ Strongly Disagree

COMMENTS

20. My present salary is appropriate for the work I do.

☐ Strongly Agree ☐ Agree ☐ Neutral ☐ Disagree ☐ Strongly Disagree

21. How do you rate your work space?

☐ Very Satisfactory ☐ Satisfactory ☐ Neutral ☐ Unsatisfactory ☐ Very Unsatisfactory

22. How do you rate the housekeeping?

☐ Very Good ☐ Good ☐ Neutral ☐ Poor ☐ Very Poor

COMMENTS

sists of succinct questions and statements to which employes respond by making a simple check mark or by writing a number. It is relatively inexpensive; it can be administered to large groups at one time; it presents questions in exactly the same way to all respondents, and it permits direct comparisons to be made between groups of employes.

Its disadvantages are that it usually does not allow for personal introduction and hence may not achieve the best rapport with respondents; it does not permit freedom of expression available in less structured methods, and it usually suffers from relatively poor response rates.

Another type of questionnaire consists of open questions, to which the respondent is asked to write his opinions. This is more laborious for the employe and more laborious and costly to analyze the results.

The interview permits a richness of response beyond that achieved in questionnaires. It also ensures that the questions are properly understood, probes deeper into attitudinal areas as the need arises and generally establishes a level of rapport that elicits the willing cooperation of the respondent. On the other hand, interviewing is expensive and is subject to many difficulties and errors.

Lockheed attempted to combine the best parts of different methods. Its survey consisted of items to be rated on some continuum of satisfaction and favorableness, coupled with interviews conducted on a small sampling basis.

Interviews at the beginning of the survey can be used to determine which items to include in the questionnaire. Interviews at the end of the survey can help verify and interpret the responses to the questionnaire.

Preparing the questionnaire

Once management knows what it wants to ask, the questionnaire can be prepared. Professionals usually keep these guidelines in mind:

■ Keep the questions short—less than 20 words, if possible.

■ Use language that the employes understand.

■ Avoid questions that contain more than one concept. A respondent may agree with one part but not with the other.

■ Avoid double negatives.

■ Avoid leading questions—ones that indicate what the answer "should be."

■ Avoid loaded questions—ones that create emotional tone or suggest feelings of approval or disapproval.

If comparisons are to be made between groups, individuals should be identifiable on pertinent characteristics. A good way to accomplish this and still maintain anonymity is to include questions about a person's age, level of education,

sex and salary level.

It may also be desirable to ask questions about specific personnel policies or suspected problems.

Obviously, a survey should reflect specific conditions—possible morale problems—at your company. Other possible questions, in addition to those shown on pages 76 and 77, might include:

■ How does the pay here compare with other companies in the area?

■ How much encouragement does the company give for me to take outside courses?

■ How effective is the company's management training program?

■ How do you rate the company's attitude toward engineers who want to remain as "working engineers" rather than as managers?

Pre-testing is the only way to insure that questions are properly worded and that respondents can answer them in a reasonable period of time. Thus the questionnaire is administered to a small, representative sample. If substantial changes are made after this test, the survey should be pre-tested again.

Conducting the survey

It is best, most professionals believe, to survey the entire work force, especially if a company is conducting one for the first time. This gives every employe the opportunity to participate, which in need to select a precise sample. Subsequent surveys are usually conducted on a sampling basis.

Questionnaire surveys frequently are sent directly to the employes' homes, accompanied by a letter of explanation and a self-addressed return envelope. To encourage a high rate of returns, a publicity campaign may be carried on in the company just prior to the mailing.

If it is still feared that the return rate will be too small or perhaps not representative, the questionnaire can be administered on company premises. The survey can then be introduced personally and the questionnaires collected immediately upon completion.

In all situations, participation must be on a *voluntary* basis.

Interviews usually are conducted on the company's premises.

Analyzing the data

The statistics should be separate for each employe subgroup, as well as for the working force as a whole. This will permit between-group comparisons and possibly indicate where specific corrective action should be applied.

Processing write-in comments can be laborious. First, a sample of comments is selected and carefully studied. From these a classification system is derived, whose categories represent the different concepts contained in the responses. The remaining comments are then analyzed, either on a sampling basis or in full, by coding them according to the derived categories. Finally the number and percentage of comments are computed for each topical category.

Reporting the results

It is the researcher's responsibility to interpret the findings as completely as possible and provide management with an appropriate verbal report.

Typical write-in comments and quotes from interviews should be sprinkled liberally throughout the report to illustrate the points of view. This gives management the feeling of reading the "real" opinions of employes. Care must be taken in using quotes, however, since it will be assumed by management that these attitudes are typical of the employe group in question.

There will always be some employes who do not believe that management will publish negative findings. Much is gained by making a full and forthright report to employes once the survey is complete. It will show management's sincerity, and will, in itself, be a form of corrective action towards improving communications.

Caution must be exercised in drawing conclusions from attitude surveys. It is important to avoid drawing cause and effect conclusions when the study design and the result data do not support them. Just because two factors are found to be related does not necessarily mean that one is the cause of the other. A particular survey may be good for identifying undesirable conditions, but it may be necessary to treat it only as the starting point for investigation to determine underlying causes.

Unless sincere attempts are made to correct undesirable conditions, employes will likely become suspicious of management's intentions, and the ironic result will be that the attitude survey will

Taking corrective action

serve to worsen company morale rather than help to improve it. When employes have made a wrong conclusion because they had incomplete or erroneous information, the true, full facts should be explained. When it is impossible or impractical to correct a problem, this fact and the reasons for it should be known. Most employes realize that not all problems can be solved immediately and will accept logical explanations.

Factors to consider in setting priorities for corrective action include: the degree of unfavorable responses to an issue, the importance of the issue to employes, the extent to which the causes of the problem have been clearly identified and the difficulty and costs correcting the problem.

When a particular corrective action is taken, a way should be included to measure its effectiveness. Only through evaluation can management be sure that the action resulted in the greatest benefit to both employes and the company.

Are surveys expensive?

The cost of a survey may run as low as $2 an employe or as high as $30 to $40, depending on the methods used and the size of the company. The average is in the area of $3 to $5. In a large company, the total cost could easily exceed $50,000.

But when evaluated against the outcome—a key to higher productivity—it can be a worthwhile investment. In an average company, an increase in productivity of just 1 or 2 per cent probably would offset the cost of both the survey and most of the follow-up corrective actions. ■ ■

Money is not the only motivator

*There are personal satisfactions that every engineer must get at work,
and the wise manager makes them available.*

Dr. Burt Scanlon, Associate Professor, University of
Wisconsin Management Institute, Madison, Wis.

If you think that money is the only incentive that motivates people to do a good job, your career as a manager is not likely to be successful. Money is a strong motivator, but it's only the beginning.

When an engineer doesn't work to his peak performance, it is because he isn't motivated to do so. He has no incentive to do his best—no matter how generous your company's salary policy may be.

Practical motivating incentives help people to satisfy their basic social, psychological and self-fulfillment needs. And such incentives are things that you, the manager, have control over.

Nonmonetary incentives get people ego-involved in their jobs and are the cornerstone of a positive approach to managing engineers.

These incentives represent nothing new or different; the challenge lies in adapting them to your managerial policies and then putting them to use on a consistent basis.

It's significant that these incentives were drawn up by men from all levels of management, not by a group of psychologists.

Inform him where he fits in

If an engineer doesn't know where he and his department "fit in," he can't have any sense of importance or identification. If a maximum contribution is to be made, everyone must have a clear picture of what the department's objectives are and how these objectives relate to the rest of the company.

Involve your engineers actively in the determination of departmental objectives, as well as in tying these goals to over-all company progress. This process of involvement creates a sense of identification in the individual.

Another successful practice is to let the engineer coordinate the job or project on which he is working with other departments, such as production or sales. In this way, he is exposed to the rest of the organization, and his job takes on significantly more practical meaning. In turn, you, the manager, can devote more effort to coaching, counseling, coordinating and over-all controlling, rather than to doing the detailed work.

Explain why his job is important

Closely related to, and an extension of, this point is the need to emphasize the importance of the job. Every engineer should have a clear picture of exactly *what will happen if his job is not done adequately.*

The engineer should know why the project is being undertaken, the relationship of the project to potential sales and other projects, and the specific conditions that led to its inclusion in the work schedule.

Managers should take the engineer beyond the simply physical accomplishment of his work and show him how and why his job is vital to the total company operation, especially succeeding operations.

Emphasize the problems that will arise if the job is done wrong or is late, and let the engineer meet some of the coworkers who are depending on his performance.

Let him know what is expected

People will generally perform at the level demanded of them only if it is within reason. Unless you have clearly outlined *what you expect and the specific standards by which performance will be judged,* you cannot reasonably expect any more than you get. Letting them know explicitly gives them something to work for. It gives direction to their efforts and they can see tangible results in terms of accomplishment.

Managers, who take the time to sit down with their engineers, reach a common agreement on the key elements of the job and set specific performance standards for each element, get significantly improved results. In fact, when engineers are actively involved in this process, they often will set standards higher than you will.

It is not uncommon for an engineer to spend considerable time and effort to complete a project, only to find that the results don't coincide with what his boss had in mind. The supervisor, another engineer or the man himself starts backtracking. Additions, subtractions, rework and revisions are needed to get the effort into the desired shape. The outcome then is wasted time, duplication of effort, strained relations, frustration and, perhaps most unfortunate, a demoralizing effect on the engineer who did the work.

Usually all this could have been avoided if the

manager had only looked before he leaped — if he had initially determined specifically what results he was looking for and outlined and discussed these with the engineer before he began, not after the job was done.

Offer the engineer a challenge

Not only do people generally perform at the level demanded of them, but they also respond more favorably when there is a real challenge. One of the strongest needs people have is *a sense of achievement*. If there is no challenge, this need cannot be satisfied.

Make the challenge reasonable and have it represent attainable goals. When, as a manager, you set goals for your staff that are far above what can reasonably be accomplished and beyond what you really expect, there are severe long-range repercussions:

- Staff members become frustrated, because they can never reach the goals.

- There is no sense of achievement.

- Employees are constantly on the defensive, trying to justify their unrealistic performance levels.

'Where do I fit in?' Every engineer should know where he and his department fit into the total company.

Give bouquets for a good job. Engineers, like everyone else, like to receive praise for a job well done.

- Padding of budgets, schedules, etc., takes place.

- The superior-subordinate relationship breaks down in antagonism.

A manager should pause periodically to analyze the strength of his staff. Review the work of each man and ask the questions: "Am I using his talents fully? Does he have something to work for, something to stimulate his mind?"

Too often managers view the challenge for their staff members solely in terms of how much work each man can do in a physical sense. What is needed is work that stretches the mind, that leads to new learning, new growth and development on the job. When the work of an engineer becomes boring and routine, motivation disappears. A formal program, with the objective of progressively moving professional people up to higher levels of work as they exhibit the required abilities, can go a long way toward motivating these people.

Tell him where he stands

How many times have you heard a manager complain about an engineer's performance, only to learn that not only has the manager never let the engineer know what was expected of him but also never informed him of his progress on the job? The idea behind this incentive goes back to the basic philosophy that, if given the opportunity, most people want to work and do a good job. If they don't know where they stand or if they find out only after the situation has deteriorated substantially, the manager cannot expect improvement. *The relationship between the manager and the engineer must be a continuing one in terms of what is being accomplished.*

When problems arise in this area, the cause may well be that the manager has not done a good job of defining key areas of accountability, establishing meaningful measures of performance, setting objectives and standards, and evaluating people on the basis of results achieved.

These performance measures can be established for any job, either by a specific yardstick or a series of statements that describe the conditions that will exist when a given phase of the work is done adequately.

Delegate authority, responsibility

Every manager should consciously assess both his own and the department's activities with this question in mind: *"What jobs am I doing and what decisions am I making that might just as well be done by one of my engineers?"* The result could be to relieve the manager of some activities and decisions while, at the same time, to make a subordinate's work more meaningful.

Another point: When subordinates come to you with questions or problems, it might be advantageous to get their ideas on how to handle the situation. This shows respect for the subordinates' judgment, fosters their initiative and confidence and makes them feel more important. Instead, many managers are prone to express "their ways" and never give the subordinate a chance to express his views.

Make a commitment to give your staff members freedom to work in their own ways toward agreed-on goals. By doing this, you'll achieve a higher level of departmental achievement, higher morale and a less hectic schedule for yourself.

Delegation of authority can be destroyed by always detailing the "how to" or by overcontrolling on a day-to-day basis. The man who usually knows a job best is the one who does it every day. He is more sensitive to the problems that hinder accomplishment and is more likely to have ideas and suggestions on how to overcome them.

Give credit where credit's due

How often have you taken stock at the end of the day or a week and asked yourself: "Who in the department did a particularly good job or accom-

The written word is powerful. A letter of praise in an engineer's personnel folder is a strong motivator.

Every job is important. A wise manager ensures that every engineer knows why his specific job is important.

plished something that deserves a pat on the back?"

Good performance happens more often than you realize. Too often the manager is vocal when things go wrong or when he exerts pressure to get results, but never acknowledges the achievements of the department and the individuals who contributed to them. A positive approach in a sincere and meaningful climate tends to beget positive results. When you accentuate the positive rather than the negative, the chances are that your engineers will follow the example.

Sometimes it means giving credit in the form of written recognition. Often there is a need to formalize credit in this manner, because it means much more to the individual being praised.

A recent company study of the personnel folders of 3974 employes revealed that there were 3241 cases of written memos of discipline and warning compared with only 338 cases of written recognition in a four-year period. This imbalance exists in a great many companies.

The written word is a powerful motivator when used properly. It can be the little extra that makes the difference.

Show a personal interest in him

Somewhere along the line, the manager has to *establish a personal relationship wih his staff members that goes beyond the purely technical or job relationship.*

This does not necessarily mean socializing with them. Rather it means that, if you are going to get maximum performance from your people, you must relate to them as individuals in a sincere way. You must develop a genuine interest in them in terms of things that are important to them.

Most of us have had the experience of meeting someone for the first time and walking away with a very favorable impression. In analyzing why that person impressed us, we very often find it was because he showed sincere and keen interest in us. In short, our ego received a boost. Engineers are no different.

When an employee feels that his boss is sincerely interested in him, his problems, his future and his wellbeing, he is more likely to be a high producer. Every manager should ask himself: "How much time do I spend interacting with and giving support to my subordinates, so they can conceive to their highest level of capability?"

Support means helping your subordinates overcome problems that hinder accomplishment, working to diminish interdepartmental barriers and coaching and counseling your engineers.

Allow your engineer to participate

Participation plays a large part in gaining commitment. When people participate, *they become mentally and emotionally, as well as physically,*

Offer him a challenge. Give the engineer an opportunity to put his abilities to work on a challenging assignment.

involved. Their role is active rather than just passive. Participation involves actively seeking the ideas and suggestions of people, encouraging them to voice their opinions and to get involved, and allowing them to contribute with their minds as well as their skills. Here again, it is worthwhile to ask if there are areas of your operation where it would be possible for employees to take a more active role.

A manager can take a problem to his staff, seek their ideas and suggestions, and come up with a list of specific actions that could be taken. Such lists often contain suggestions that the manager was oblivious of.

Bridge the communications gap

Failure to communicate is one of the most frequently cited complaints that subordinates have of their bosses. And the problem may not be a lack of knowledge of how to communicate effectively; rather it may be one of not *realizing the importance of communication and how people feel when communication is lacking.*

A useful experiment in communications is to sit down with a group of your peers and build a list of all types of information that your staff absolutely must know to do their jobs. After listing from 5 to 10 points of information, each man evaluates himself on how effectively he is communicating these essentials to his staff. Some managers have their subordinates do the evaluation and, by so doing, add to the list areas that the manager may have overlooked. A smiliar procedure can be used to identify the types of information people would like to know.

Provide opportunity for growth

A man is never fully satisfied until he is working toward or has reached that level of the job that is consistent with his ability. What a man can be, he must be. This self-fulfillment need is strong and can be satisfied only when the employee is provided with the opportunity to grow. If these opportunities are not forthcoming in his present job, he will most certainly look elsewhere.

Potential for growth is a very important consideration in engineering. There is a big need for companies to examine and classify the engineering work that they are doing. This work must be categorized according to degrees of difficulty, challenge and abilities required. After this is done, a program of continual personnel evaluation must be established, to identify the engineers who have met the requirements and are ready to move to the next level of work. A formal program for the growth and development of the professional engineer must be established. ∎ ∎

Don't wait for brainstorms

Organize for creativity. Structured 'idea sessions' can lead to new thinking—and new, successful products.

Dr. Wilmer C. Anderson, Director of Research, General Time Corp., Stamford, Conn.

New product ideas pop up in many places—sales, the engineering department, the customer's imagination. Most of these ideas, however, are usually one-shot affairs that do not lead to a new product line.

Is there a way to organize the creative talents of your staff to insure a steady flow of new, successful products? At General Time Corp., we have found the "idea session" to be of valuable assistance. Instead of relying on random inspirations, we have set up planned sessions at which our research staff attempts to create new products through the interchange of ideas. Such a program might work for you.

Let me show you how two important products emerged at General Time from this organized creativity: Incremag and Mu-Chron.

Incremag is an electronic/magnetic counter that can be used for dividing or multiplying the frequency of an oscillator into a fixed number of counts to provide specific pulse output. Incremag products were used in some Ranger moon probes, in the first six Tiros weather satellites and they are being used in many other military, industrial and oceanographic devices.

Mu-Chron is a square-wave, magnetic oscillator, especially valuable in the low-frequency range. It operates on the saturating-core-magnetic-multivibrator principle. The unit's advantages lie in the square wave, its small size and low cost for the frequency range involved. Optimum frequency range is 10 Hz to 1 kHz. Mu-Chron is accurate in the first cycle after power turn-on; first half-cycle polarity can be controlled. Output frequency is a function of the transformer's saturating time.

As director of research at General Time, I am helmsman and catalyst of the on-going innovation program in which we developed these products. We start with idea sessions—not to be confused with brainstorming, which is different in form and content. We have tried brainstorming, but with little success. In an idea session:

- We discusss only one major topic—thoroughly and fully—including technical aspects.
- We notify participants of the topic at least

two weeks in advance of the meeting, so they can read and think about it.
- We choose participants carefully from all levels, using their demonstrated creativity as the criterion.
- We mix as many different disciplines as possible, to cross-pollinate the thinking.

An idea session in action

Here's how an idea session operates in practice. You have just come to work for General Time. As the name implies, the company makes timepieces and is interested in new and improved methods of timekeeping and related matters. With this background, what could be more appropriate for the first idea session than the topic of time? So, among other points, we discuss (1) What is time? (2) How is it measured? (3) What are its uses? The session begins:

Although all of us speak of time in some form every day, nobody can say what time actually is. Yet we use it. Just as we do not know what electric, magnetic or gravitational fields are, yet we use them in thousands of products.

For our second session, we decide to concentrate on the second question—How is time measured?

Man has probably been conscious of time passing from his earliest intelligent moment. Even the cavemen knew that after so many moons the seasons would change. Or that the stars would look different in the night sky. The first men might even have used a "timepiece" by watching the shadow of a tree as the sun appeared to pass overhead.

Getting back to business, we start the second session with the four major categories in which time can be measured: astronomical, physical, chemical and biological. Each can be a whole topic for discussion. Briefly though, astronomical methods would include such things as sun and moon cycles and the earth's rotation. Chemical methods might include chemical reactions, burning ropes or candles, or electroplating. Biological methods—say, incubation or gestation periods—are known to be accurate within 5 per cent. Many

"How is time measured?"

people have internal "alarm clocks" that awaken them at almost the same time each morning. Further, we all can estimate time intervals more or less accurately.

In our second session, we discard these major categories—except for the physical. We choose it for the next session. And in doing so, we open a Pandora's box. To mention a few major sub-categories: fluid flow, mechanical methods, electrical methods, atomic methods. Again, any one is material for another study.

Don't junk old ideas—update them

Under fluid flow, there's the old water wheel and Chinese water clock, and the hourglass. Just to prove you should never discard old ideas, we look at this last principle. I passed a store window recently and saw an hourglass advertised. About 30 inches high, built of plastic, with plastic beads in place of sand, it served as a table on which individual drinks could be placed. It was sold as the "Cocktail Hour"—for $50.

Similarly the latest thinking in fuzing missiles and ordnance pieces, and even computers, is a fluid timer based on a fluid oscillator, flip-flops and other logic elements, all fluid driven. Some are extremely small, etched out of glass. A stack of them is about as big as a sugar cube. The point of both examples is that it pays to review what has been done and to update it for modern needs.

On to mechanical methods. They include many common vibrating or oscillating devices. For example: tuning forks, pendulums, a watch's hairspring balance wheel.

We decide to postpone discussion of electrical methods. We go on to atomic methods. How can we use the atom to keep time? Four rather obvious ways are atomic, molecular, crystalline or lattice oscillations, and radioactive decay. We pick radioactive decay (incidentally, this was before the maser-laser days) as the next topic for investigation.

Among the many ways to use radioactivity as a time source are: the integration of the charge from released particles; counting the particles given off; collecting the derived products, such as radon gas, lead or Carbon 14 concentration. We choose to discuss counting of disintegrated particles at the third session. When we do, the topic leads to possible detectors to use, counting methods and alternate ways to display the results that would indicate time.

Attracted to magnets

We select "counting methods" for the fourth session. Again, we break this topic down into several categories: electrochemical, electronic, magnetic, chemical. We choose two: electronic and magnetic. Later we shelve the electronic approach when the magnetic proves very successful. We hope to pick up the electronic approach again, since we are getting into several rather unusual concepts.

Magnetic counting methods open up several possible avenues. After reviewing each briefly, we decide to consider the idea of a multiple-count core that uses incremental magnetization. This means counting on frequency-dividing with fewer components. For instance, we can use two transistors instead of eight to get a binary countdown. Also, of course, we do not have a power drain, because the magnetic core remains in a stable state without any power input. This seems unique to us, and besides, it offers considerable appeal and potential for proprietary developments.

After normal laboratory breadboarding of counting circuits, we go to applications in counting and timing devices. This leads us to our present Incremag product line and gives us our first entry into the space program that was born after Sputnik I.

Now you may ask what would have happened if we had chosen a path other than the one that lead to Incremag? We did just that—after Incremag was fully launched. We went back to the point at which we were discussing how time can be measured by physical means.

This time we pick the road labeled "electrical methods." First, we subdivide the subject, listing electrolysis, oscillators, ionization and many electromagnetic devices, such as motors and steppers. We look more closely at oscillators.

Here again we have a wide range. We happen to like the "magnetic saturation type"—probably because of our prior work with Incremag systems. The same magnetic core that makes the Incremag a stable counting device is used to make a stable oscillator. We see a lot of flexibility in this circuit. It provides oscillators with variable-duty cycle and frequency (voltage controlled).

The choice again is a happy one, since it leads us directly to another product line—Mu-Chron. We have only begun to scratch the surface of Mu-Chron's numerous variations and uses.

Random creativity won't work

The value of Incremag and Mu-Chron has been tremendous. With them, we have been able to do such formerly impossible things as:

- Obtain a count of 50 per stage over a military environment; formerly only a count of 2 per stage was practical.
- Divide a 5-MHz frequency down to 200 Hz in two stages; or drive a 50-Hz synchronous clock

from a 1-MHz source with only two dividing stages. By other methods, this normally takes six to ten stages.

- Have frequency discrimination over any given bandwidth with extremely sharp edges—and without the use of any resonant circuits.
- Divide a frequency by as much as 1000:1 in a single stage. Even our own Incremag group considered this impossible to achieve.

Our idea sessions taught us a lot, particularly about imagination and how to stimulate it to produce practical products. But perhaps the most important general concept we learned about innovating is that the random method won't work in the long haul. Often not even in the short haul.

You must work in a disciplined, though flexible, structure. For us, that structure is the idea sessions, which have proved themselves an outstanding way to spur creativity—and to produce successful new products. ■■

Stop the revolt in the labs!

Engineers demand more than pay to be content. Learn how to 'involve' them in their work.

Alfred Vogel, Director of Employe Relations and Management Research, Opinion Research Corp., Princeton, N.J.

Unlike the college campus, on which students are resorting to picketing, faculty lockouts and riots to gain participation in decisions affecting their careers, there is no visible revolt in the nation's laboratories.

Yet numerous opinion studies among engineers and scientists in industry reveal that, like the students, many feel that their wishes on the job have been receiving short shrift. Like today's students, they're seriously dissatisfied with the situation. Only their dissatisfaction shows up, not in wrecked classrooms, but in such symptoms as turnover and just-enough-to-get-by performance.

Surveys show that basic managerial practices may be to blame for much of the problem. They can be corrected, in some cases relatively painlessly, but in others, only by reversal of ingrained policy.

Why pick out engineers and scientists? Do they

need more say-so in their work than other groups? The answer is yes, as indicated by a number of studies conducted by Opinion Research Corp., Princeton, N.J.

In the excerpted ratings of the importance of various job factors to the employes of three companies (Table 1), compare the way electrical, mechanical and chemical engineers feel with the way clerical and hourly rated employes do. Such factors as pay and job security were deliberately omitted to gain insight into the satisfactions that employes seek once these basic needs are met.

More so than clerical or hourly employes, engineers seek personal involvement in their work. On the other hand, they are less sensitive than other employes to fringe factors of the job such as a clean house, a one-big-happy-family atmosphere and the like.

Note the shift of engineers' interest away from

areas that supervisors and company personnel structures traditionally stress as the survey continues in Table 2.

In yet another study that covered only research scientists and engineers most respondents rated work enjoyment and the authority to make decisions second and third behind pay as of major importance on the job.

Fit management to the men

Results like these, which have been confirmed in numerous studies, carry a clear message to the engineering manager: A "we know best what you need" style of supervision simply falls short of the mark with engineers. Leaning on it invites, in sequence, apathy, noninvolvement and minimal productivity.

Conversely, a strong clue to gaining maximum productivity from engineers lies in their openly expressed desire for job involvement. Giving serious consideration to engineers' views, letting them assist in making decisions involving their work and seeing to it that they're given meaningful responsibilities and the chance to make the most of their talents could open the door to new heights of achievement.

What continues to surprise, however, is the continued apathy of many companies toward meeting these expectations of their professional employes. In 1959, Opinion Research Corp. published a study, "The Scientific Mind and the Management Mind." This report documented the widespread discontent among scientists and engineers with how they were being treated in industry. In it substantial majorities of engineers and scientists in six companies noted that they were forced to overspecialize, that they weren't given enough freedom on the job, that too often they were immersed in detail, that their abilities were being too closely channeled to what had already been proved—in short, that they were poorly utilized.

Today, as new studies are undertaken, the same problems are turning up in many companies, some of which are constantly recruiting new talent in the market. Quite often little or no attempt has been made to give the talent on hand an opportunity to reach full potential, according to scientists and engineers.

Education breeds disbelief

The evidence is mounting through opinion surveys that younger, better-educated employes tend, in fact, to be more dissatisfied with their experiences in industry than older, less educated employes. There is, of course, a high correlation between age and education. Younger people, by and large, have had more schooling, and three factors cause them to question managerial attitudes that they encounter in industry.

(1) A product of today's education is an attitude of questioning "the establishment." The more recently schooled employes tend to ask of high-sounding management policies, "Is it so, or is the management only giving lip service to it?"

(2) There is a rising trend in society, especially among young people, toward favoring democratic values. And young people have learned to equate participation in decisions that affect their lives with democratic values.

Table 1. Engineers want involvement

"It's of top importance to me—	Engineers	Clerical employes	Factory employes
That I make the most of my talents."	73%	57%	50%
That I feel my views are taken seriously by those above me."	63	51	44
That I have important responsibilities."	41	20	16
That I be allowed to make important decisions affecting my work."	34	18	15

Table 2. Job-fringe factors rate low

"It's of top importance to me—	Engineers	Clerical employes	Factory employes
That I get along well with fellow employes."	38%	56%	62%
That I have clean working conditions."	25	50	59
That I work with people I like."	24	39	38

Table 3. Management short of expectations

"I rate my company 'poor' on—	Better-educated employes	Less-educated employes
Taking employe interests into account when making important decisions affecting you."	49%	27%
Understanding employes' point of view."	39	24
Respect shown employe as an individual."	33	22
The ability of management and employe to work together."	26	15

Table 4. The more-educated are critical

"I agree that—	Better-educated employes	Less-educated employes
There is not enough opportunity for employes to let the company know how we feel on things that affect us and our work."	62%	54%
Management does a good job of explaining the reasons behind important business decisions."	43	67

(3) Young people today have higher expectations regarding work than previous generations. A job is regarded as more than just a way of earning a living; it's a means of achieving psychological satisfaction.

The results of a study of all employe groups in a large company (Table 3) illustrates the relationship between education and employe attitudes. The better-educated group includes engineers and other who attended or graduated from college. Note that better-educated employes consistently give their company lower ratings .

A second example from a study among employes in another company (Table 4) touches on other areas and further points out how the "acceptance gap" widens with education.

Both studies show that better-educated employes are more critical. Indications are that this trend will grow and that widespread frustration and discontent among them will increase.

Lack of outspoken resentment should not be taken as an indication that a manager's decisions meet with his engineers' approval and support, as the companies sponsoring the preceding surveys learned. And the manager seeking to avoid the effect of frustration and discontent on the job will do well to consider delegating to his engineers certain important decisions affecting their work. It may make the difference between a group which merely "puts in time" and one that more fully cooperates in reaching goals.

At the opposite pole from the engineer who "puts in time" is the one who comes up with creative performance. A prized commodity, creative performance calls for a high degree of voluntary self-commitment to the job by the engineer, which one would think an employer would go to great lengths to generate through his chains of command.

But studies show that in more than one company *preventing innovation* has become an institutional feature; it's part of the company's reward structure through which engineers and managers alike take their cues as to what is legitimate and what is prescribed behavior. Results of an opinion survey in one such company are shown in Table 5.

While major upheavals may be called for to reverse the anti-creativity climate in such companies, two steps are basic:

(1) Rewards for innovation must be incorporated into the compensation structure.

(2) "Change-mindedness" must be institutionalized through strong management actions. The higher up the ladder they begin, the more effective.

Table 5. A monument to status-quo management

		Engineers	All management employes
Many managers here practice a don't-rock-the-boat philosophy, rather than attacking problems aggressively	Agree Hard to decide Disagree	95% 1 4	84% 3 13
One can get by in this company merely by keeping one's nose clean	Agree Hard to decide Disagree	97% 0 3	80% 16 1
Good ideas for improving performance often don't get to the people who have the power to make decisions	Agree Hard to decide Disagree	86% 4 10	71% 22 7
There is too much emphasis on established procedures, not enough on providing new ways	Agree Hard to decide Disagree	81% 3 16	68% 6 26
Many people here are against change—they prefer to keep things the way they were in the past	Agree Hard to decide Disagree	73% 1 26	68% 3 29

The above judgements were expressed in an opinion survey made among engineers (largely EEs) and management personnel of one company.

Back-talk is not a waste product

The fond delusion exists among some top managements that professional employes consider themselves "one of us" and are more willing than other employes to exert themselves for company goal as a result—"Aren't they allowed more freedom of motion, consultation and expression than the man on the machine or the clerk at the desk?"

But this feeling is frequently unfounded. Surveys show that engineers, often only to a slightly lesser extent than other employees, feel left out when it comes to shared confidences with management.

In many companies, management stands to cut away layers of resentment that block fuller job commitment on the part of engineers by diverting some of the attention now lavished on elaborate house organs and programs designed to communicate *to* or *at* employes into encouraging questions from employes and listening to their views.

One 10-plant company discovered this when these survey responses were returned from its employes:

Generally, management is more interested in telling us what they think we ought to know than what we want to know.

	Agree	Disagree	No Opinion
Clerical employes	73%	25%	2%
Production employes	67	29	4
Engineers-scientists	68	31	1

There is not enough opportunity for employes to let management know how we feel on things that affect us and our work.

	Agree	Disagree	No Opinion
Clerical employes	78%	21%	1%
Production employes	75	22	3
Engineers-scientists	61	38	1

Manage creative engineers creatively

Give them room to innovate on the job and add the personal touch. Here are some hints.

Dr. Daniel E. Noble, Vice Chairman of the Board, Motorola, Inc.

Creative workers have surface traits that sometimes bother other people. Some wear wildly printed neckties or sport long sideburns or a handlebar moustache. Some go to the other extreme and dress extraordinarily slovenly. The first impression many managers get is:

"This guy is a kook. Watch out."

You could, as a supervisor, lose a gifted talent if you handle creative engineers this way. Supervisors who would work effectively with creative engineers must be creative managers. You can start by shucking off extraneous personal biases.

To provide working conditions that will yield the maximum output from creative engineers, know how the creative process works and what the creator's outstanding traits are.

But that isn't all you need to manage innovative engineers. You must add understanding, tolerance and encouragement—frequently encouragement of traits and behavior that may seem to be adding a wrench to the cogs of a smooth-running organization.

The personal touch helps

How a manager gets along with his creative engineers has little to do with rules and regulations. He is dealing with people who think of themselves as different—and they are different. So the supervisor's personal touch—his ability to empathize with other people—is the key to success. Most management experts agree that the *creative person's relationship with his working supervisor is more important in motivating him than any other factor.*

That's a surprising statement. It may topple completely a few shaky assumptions you already have—for instance, that money is the major magnet for creative people with talent to sell; that creative people tend to ignore their supervisors and go it on their own; that the manager should cut himself loose from the creative man.

All these ideas go overboard. What remains is this: the manager is not a time-oriented boss, but an advisor who works with his creative engineers. He learns what they want, what will help them turn out better solutions faster—and he gets it for them.

What do creative engineers want? The same things, in large part, that all engineers want. But in the case of the innovator, they are vital to his productivity; he won't function well at all without them.

Here are 11 guidelines for managers. The creative engineer wants:

- A permissive atmosphere where he is trusted to be productive. He believes in himself, and he wants his manager to.
- Freedom to pursue problems he finds intriguing. This not as risky as it sounds, since studies indicate that more-creative people are more concerned with practical values than less-creative people.[1]
- The chance to talk freely and frankly with his supervisor.
- Freedom from routine jobs—filling out reports, for instance—that pull him away from his problem research.
- Colleagues of his caliber with whom he can mix on the job. Of course, this does not mean that all creative engineers are "groupers." Some prefer to work strictly alone.
- Information on the company policy under which he must operate. This does not refer to narrow procedures; rather, the company's broad aims.
- Appraisal of his work by his supervisor soon after it is submitted.
- Time—and a place—where he can be alone without looking like an oddball or a loafer.
- The option of having professional colleagues and contacts who are not in the company. This includes membership in professional societies, lecturing, writing.
- Special consideration for harmless idiosyncrasies that might upset strait-laced managers.
- Freedom to fail—or to suggest far-out solutions without being ridiculed.

Ways to keep creative engineers content

Corresponding in a rough way to the creative engineer's wants are positive steps that a manager can take to create a good working atmosphere. These actions apply, incidentally, to less-creative engineers, too.

Here they are:

- Be honest. Creative engineers want straight answers that they can rely on. Most really are not interested in "office politics."
- If you have a criticism or comment to make about the man's work, tell him and not your fellow managers. And tell it to him privately.
- Use personal conversations, rather than elaborate evaluative forms and reports, to get a fix on the status of a project. Conversations with your engineers may take more of your immediate time, but you'll get fuller, straighter answers in person—and you won't tie your engineers up filling out forms you haven't time to read."
- Keep your engineers informed of developments in the company. You don't have to have the whole story, if company security is involved, but your men should hear the significant facts from you, not from the office grapevine.
- Show concern for your engineer's personal welfare and problems. Don't pry, but if a death in the family, illness, even a divorce occurs, express your willingness to overlook a temporary drop in the man's productivity.
- Consciously try to develop a warm and affectionate attitude toward your men. Many managers are stunned to learn that their subordinates think they are cool, indifferent or brusque. Consider how you handle daily contacts with the staff. Are you interested, abrupt, friendly, businesslike? Put yourself in their shoes.
- When you evaluate an engineer's work, balance criticism with praise. One good technique is to pick out the good elements and mention them first. Then, establishing confidence, move into the points that need improvement.
- Give your engineers feedback from the top when there is favorable comment on their achievements. If there is criticism, talk it over with the engineer without saying that the dissatisfaction originated higher up. If you think the criticsm is invalid, go to the top and find out why it was made. Perhaps blame is falling on the wrong man.

So far so good. But what does the manager do when Mr. Creative balks at a rule or attracts unwanted attention? Let's look at two problems a manager might encounter with his creative engineers. Each problem situation is followed by action choices. Pick as many as you think are solutions. The answers are on p. 129.

Note: The choices are by no means the *only* actions a manager could take, but they are to help you see if you are moving in the right direction. Pick the best solutions of those available.

Who's who in creativity: eight types

Creative people don't fit into molds. Yet when researchers at the Institute of Personality Assessment and Research, University of California, Berkeley, studied 45 engineers, and scientists who were working on space or missile problems, they found eight discernible creative types.

But—as a report by Wallace B. Hall, associate research psychologist at the institute, makes clear—no one person fits any one type perfectly. The traits overlapped, so that each creator had some of the characteristics of several of the eight types. Researchers classified the people they were studying by noting the *predominant* traits.

Harrison C. Gough at the institute lists the eight creative types as follows:

1. Zealot. Dedicated, driving, indefatigable, with a lively sense of curiosity. Others see him as tolerant, serious-minded and conscientious, but not as getting along easily with others.

2. Initiator. Begins at once to generate ideas; stimulating to others and a good team man. Seen as ambitious, well-organized, industrious, a good leader, efficient and not a worrier.

3. Diagnostician. Sees himself as a good evaluator; finds strong and weak point quickly in any problem, a good troubleshooter. Not critical of others' mistakes. Observers label him forceful, self-assured and unselfish.

4. Scholar. A man with an exceptional memory, looking for detail and order, but not a perfectionist. Seeks help when needed and ad-

apts to others. Well-informed in his own field, not a bluffer. Described as conscientious and thorough, dependable, lacking somewhat in confidence and decisiveness.

5. Articifer. Sees himself as good at perfecting ideas that others suggest; does not attempt to do what he cannot. Seen as direct, honest, getting on well with others, observant and responsive to cues given by others' behavior.

6. Ethetician. Favors analytical thinking, prefers problems leading to elegant solutions. Has widespread interests and tends toward impatience with too much order and detail or if results are slow. Observed as clever and spontaneous, with a degree of immaturity, impatience and indifference toward deadlines and obligations.

7. Methodologist. Vitally interested in methodological issues; open about own work and enjoys discussing his plans. Has little competitive spirit and is tolerant. Characterized by others as considerate, not too ambitious but occasionally difficult.

8. Independent. Dislikes and avoids administrative details; not a good team man nor a driving one, but has a lively sense of curiosity. Prefers to think in reference to physical and structural models rather than in analytical and mathematical ways. Seen as active, robust, hard-headed and forthright in judgment. May behave abruptly or impolitely, but has little self-doubt.

Here are the two problem situations:

Case A. *Bill Creative makes a point of coming in an hour late and leaving two hours early. He deliberately attracts attention when he does this, irritating other department employes who work 9 to 5. Yet he consistently comes up with good insights and problem solutions. He is valuable, but he is causing trouble among the other employes. What does the manager do?*

Action choices:

1. Ask him in and tell him he is doing outstanding work. Then explain to him that though he may not know it, he is causing a problem. Could he come in at 9 a.m. and, if he must leave before 5 p.m. could he do it only occasionally—and without fanfare?

2. Publicly embarrass him one morning by telling him he is late and note that he has been leaving early while all the other engineers are working full hours.

3. Invite him in and tell him he is doing an excellent job, but you have some pressing problems you'd like him to put his talents to. Could he arrange his schedule so that in the future he

could stay until you leave—usually not later than 6 p.m. Let him know that if he follows through successfully, he could get a substantial raise.

4. Tell him privately that he is doing fine work but would he please keep the department hours. If he comes in late next day (without excuse or explanation) fire him immediately.

5. Ignore your department's reaction and do nothing. You are dealing with a highly temperamental person and to say anything will only create more problems and worsen the situation.

Case B. *Several engineers have made it known to you that Charles Creative sits at his office desk for long periods with his feet up as he taps the side of his head with a pencil. Recently two engineers, thinking he was killing time, walked into his office and tried to strike up a conversation. Each was met by blank, rather cold stares. Is something wrong with Charles? The office conversation about him is beginning to embarrass him. What do you do?*

Action choices:

1. Mention casually in presence of all engi-

neers that Charles is doing an excellent job on this or that problem.

2. Suggest to Charles that he be more receptive to other staff members.

3. Have a door put on Charles' office or move him to a more secluded area.

4. Warn your other engineers not to bother Charles because he is doing creative thinking.

As you can see, there are many possible solutions to each management problem. Obviously, there is no pat formula that will guarantee that creative engineers will hurdle obstacles and create for you, while the rest of the staff happily carries on the less-innovative assignments. There always will be problems. But some of the major roadblocks can be removed when they are in your personality or management manner, or when they are the result of popular misconceptions and fears about creative people.

The cardinal rule for the manager of creative engineers is: Work *with* them and be willing—almost eager, in fact—to change the job environment and the rules to suit their needs. ∎∎

Reference:
1. M. R. Feinberg, "Fourteen Suggestions for Managing Scientific Creativity," *Research Management*, Vol. XI, No. 2 (1968).

How to upgrade group job performance

Coach your men so that they, as well as you, look for top results in their work.

Dr. Burt Scanlon, Associate Professor, University of Wisconsin Management Institute, Madison, Wis.

Most engineers have no trouble describing their jobs in a physical sense, in terms of the various activities they perform. But just ask the average engineer to describe his job in terms of *results expected*. Then compare his description with the views of his manager on the same subject. You'll gain a fresh understanding of the term "communications gap."

You'll also be putting your finger on a root cause of individual performance gaps—lack of mutual understanding and agreement between engineer and manager on the expected outcome of the work activities in which the engineer is involved.

Without such mutual understanding and agreement as a base, the success of even the most painstaking work a manager does to raise the performance of his staff will be limited.

With it, the manager can undertake a man-by-man coaching and development program for subordinates that will build his own stature in the company as it steps up the accomplishments of his work unit. Such a program can produce these benefits:

▪ It can close individual performance gaps under his supervision that reflect unfavorably on his work unit's total efficiency and his proficiency as a manager.

▪ It can prepare the employe reporting to him to handle greater job responsibilities, with less demand on his supervisory time.

▪ It can promote his employes' growth in terms of possible future advancement, thus enhancing his reputation as a leader.

Mutual agreement is the key

The key point in coaching and development is that there be mutual agreement on goals between manager and employe—an agreement that fosters commitment on the part of the employe. If he does not honestly commit himself in terms of the importance of performing certain activities as they relate to his job, in terms of agreeing to what factors his performance should be judged on, on how his performance will be measured in each area, and of what minimum standards he is to meet, it is very likely he will pour considerably more energy and effort into resisting the manager than into working with and for him.

The way to get the needed mutual agreement is not through a telling-and-persuading approach but rather one of mutual interchange, where the employe himself is involved in setting up the criteria for his performance and development.

So far, the manager has set up what he wants from the employe. But things the subordinate looks for in his job must be integrated with this to get mutual agreement and desired results. He wants such things as recognition, job importance, achievement, new experiences, freedom to work, growth opportunities and dollars. After the manager interprets desired improvements in his work performance to the employe in terms of these wants, a settlement can be made on:

- The work and major activities for which the employe is responsible.

- The factors upon which his performance will be judged, such as quality, schedule-meeting, cost, innovation, self-development, service to other people or departments, and so on.

How much to expect?

Setting the stage for a coaching atmosphere that will achieve maximum levels of performance on the part of subordinates involves, first, a performance analysis by the manager. Crystallization of information regarding performance expectations begins with his listing the names of all the people over whom he has direct supervision.

After this listing is complete, he must set up in his mind, as a second step, what would constitute a 100 per cent level of efficiency on each job. (If, with respect to a job in question, the man were performing at a 100 per cent level, what would he be accomplishing?) In the absence of existing measurable standards, judgments must be made.

The third step in performance analysis, is to rate each subordinate in terms of the 100 per cent standard for his job. Essentially, what is being done is to ask the question, "How well is the man doing?" Typical ratings will range all the way from a few in the upper 90s to a few in the 70s. The point of concern is not how well the man is doing in terms of what the manager thinks his potential might be, but rather how well he is doing in terms of what the job requires.

The rating is not an end in itself but rather a means to an end, improving performance. Ask the question, "Why this level of rating for this man?" You'll begin to spot the major areas of each man's performance that need improvement, as well as those areas where strength is being exhibited.

Following analysis of the man and his performance, set up performance improvement goals that present a challenge to him—an increase from a 75 per cent to an 85 per cent level in one area, from 80 per cent to 90 per cent in another, and so on. Goals must give him something to work for by stretching him and requiring some special effort. Those that are set too low will tend to result in apathy and disinterest on the job. A man easily becomes accustomed to putting forth

The manager as a catalytic agent

half-way effort and achieving half-way results.

Goal-setting in action

"Negotiation" of individual work goals between the manager and those who report to him is at the heart of General Electric Company's highly successful work planning and review meetings.

These man-manager meetings seek joint commitment to the individual's work goals and the means of meeting them, according to Marion S. Kellogg, the company's manager of individual development methods service. She notes, "Employes who help set their own goals have an extra incentive to reach them."

Centering of attention on goal-setting replaces a traditional pattern of dwelling on the need for improved performance in such meetings. Miss Kellogg explains that "Emphasis shifted to goal-setting after studies indicated that productivity more than doubled after an employe's effort was directed toward specific, measurable goals."

GE trains its managers in the skills of negotiating work goals with their employees, and managers strive in work planning and review meetings to get each employe's agreement to widen his skills and job knowledge in at least one area, thus preventing the employe's own development from being crowded out of the picture by emphasis on straight improvement of routine performance.

As the employe progresses, goals for his further progress are established. His development is continuous, and his interest in it gets little chance to lag.

At the same time don't neglect the above-average performers to concentrate only on those who are at or below average. They, too, need challenge to prevent them from losing interest in the job because of the feeling that the work has become routine and repetitive.

The percentage improvement goal that is established should be related to a specific area of accountability where improvement of performance is sought; it should bear some relationship to the individual's present level of performance as well as to the type of work involved. And it must be reasonable and realistic.

Improving results on the job is very seldom a single-handed, do-it-all-yourself proposition. Engineers will require assistance and support from any number of sources, including their immediate superior.

The superior can act as an important catalyst in helping the engineer identify the problems and difficulties that are hindering his accomplishment in a particular area of job accountability. His emphasis, however, should be placed on listening, counseling and helping rather than on

EMPLOYEE PERFORMANCE ANALYSIS
AND
IMPROVEMENT PLANNING CHART

I. EMPLOYEE'S NAME	II. HIS PRESENT EFFICIENCY LEVEL (IN TERMS OF 100%)	III. AREAS IN WHICH HE NEEDS IMPROVEMENT	IV. SPECIFIC IMPROVEMENT OBJECTIVES (BY AREA)	V. HIS OVERALL EFFICIENCY RISE SOUGHT (IN %)
1. *Adleman, R.*	85	*Fails to adopt constructive criticism*	*work-in-progress reviews to prevent tangents*	5
2. *Lea, J.*	70	*New man: Does not organize time, X-check refs.*	*1. Re-schedule time 2. Require alt. ref. ratings*	15

		WORK GROUP EFFICIENCY GOAL		
GROSS TOTAL COLUMN II.	822	ADD	GROSS TOTAL COLUMN V.	80
DIVIDED BY NO. OF NAMES	10		DIVIDED BY NO. OF NAMES	10
EQUALS THE PRESENT AVERAGE EFFICIENCY OF WORK GROUP (%)	82	*equals 90%*	EQUALS AVERAGE EFFICIENCY IMPROVEMENT SOUGHT (%)	8

A single form used to arrive at improvement objectives set for individuals and the entire work unit. It shows present efficiency ratings for both, efficiency goals for both, and sets out the plan for reaching goals.

Column I lists each employee in the work unit. Column II lists the present efficiency rating of each on the basis of 100 per cent. Column III lists areas for each individual's improvement. Column IV lists objectives of improvements to be made by each. Column V lists total improvement percentage expected of each man.

An additional column (not shown here) can show each man's strengths as an aid to the manager in arriving at a figure for the man's present efficiency level (Column II).

Total Column II and divide this total by the number of employees listed to arrive at the present average efficiency of the work unit. Total Column V and divide this total by the number of employees listed to get the work unit's average improvement objective. Add averages of Column II and Column V to determine the work unit's over-all efficiency goal.

telling. We must begin with the assumption that because the man is closer to the job, he is in the best position to identify problems and difficulties that exist for him, as well as to suggest ideas about things that could be done about them. A telling approach very often elicits a defensive reaction rather than creating a climate where the man wants to improve.

In addition, if there is over-control in terms of detailing exactly how and when everything is to be done, the results actually achieved do not reflect the full efforts of the individual. Within broad limits he should be allowed to exercise his own initiative and ingenuity in determining how to achieve certain objectives.

The manager should not get bogged down in the detail of "how" but rather should concentrate on control in a broader sense. The confidence and trust he exhibits will usually be rewarded by successful performance. When mistakes do occur, they should be used to contribute to future growth and development. Emphasis should not be

on the mistake itself, but rather on why it happened and what can be done to avoid it in the future.

Chances are good that performance improvement objectives will not be accomplished if the manager's appraisal dwells too heavily on the negative. People have a maximum tolerance for the amount of criticism they can accept, whether it be leveled at several areas of performance or just one or two.

The man undergoing coaching and development must receive feedback on his performance in all levels of his accountability. This enables him to gauge his own progress and make his own adjustments where needed—a process that frees the manager from the distasteful role of a policeman who watches performance, notes deviations and "issues tickets" when necessary.

Performance appraisal, as an essential part of the coaching and development activity, is not a once- or twice-a-year activity—not if it is to bring worthwhile results. ■■

A manager can't do it all himself

Learn to delegate authority, and you'll be coordinating a highly successful project group.

Louis S. Saiia, Director, VALTEC/Value Technology, Sunnyvale, Calif.

Maybe you're not a manager now, but you may be tomorrow. Your chances of success will be immeasurably improved if you follow one basic principle: delegate work wisely.

A manager's effectiveness depends upon his ability to get work done through people. He must delegate work so efficiently that high productivity results, with profits to his company. To achieve this, a healthy, cooperative atmosphere must exist between employee and manager.

Delegation of work is an art. It takes conscious effort to cultivate certain attitudes. If you aspire to be a successful manager, here are three rules to start with:

- Keep an "open mind."
- When an employee makes an honest mistake, try to turn it to advantage.
- Don't overdirect subordinates.

The manager must be receptive to new ideas, new methods. This does not mean that all managerial decisions must be subject to debate by employees. But there is such a thing as listening to suggestions from them. There is such a thing as tact in issuing orders and seeing that they are carried out. And what employee doesn't appreciate praise for a job well done?

One of the easiest things in the world is to fly off the handle when a subordinate makes a mistake—particularly a mistake that looks costly at first glance. It takes a trained manager to analyze the mistake for possible gain. How many discoveries, after all, resulted from "mistakes" in the laboratory?

Of course, we all know how irritating it can be to be assigned a flexible job and then have the supervisor stand over us and hound us until, step by step, the job is finished in precisely the way he would have done it himself. Such a manager wants automata, not people, on his staff.

Let's observe a good manager in operation. John is the engineering chief of an electronics plant. One day he had to supervise a fairly tough job: the mechanical attachment of a 0.003-in.-diameter tantalum wire to an OFHC copper base. He set down his guidelines for a proposed method and discussed the problem with Harry, one of his engineers. Harry suggested that a swaging meth-

od—quite different from John's approach—might work out better. John listened. The idea seemed to have merit, but he cautioned Harry on several difficulties that could arise. He mentioned the extremely tight work schedule that the plant had to meet, but gave Harry the green light to try his idea.

Within a day, when John checked the progress on the job, Harry admitted that dimensional tolerance of the copper had been lost with the swaging method. Discouraged, he was about to scrap his idea. John took stock of the situation and discussed the positive aspects of Harry's method. He particularly noted that the swage method did a better job of fastening than had been achieved before and that the dimensional loss in the copper was due only to upsetting the material in the wrong direction.

"What can you do to your swage tool that will move the metal down and in toward the lead wire?" John asked Harry.

A day later Harry came in with a handful of parts that were better than any ever before produced by the company. And within a week there was a bonus: an automatic wire feeder, spinner and cut-off mechanism—made possible by the original swage tool.

A little encouragement goes a long way.

Ralph J. Cordiner, president of General Electric, has passed this bit of advice on to those who would be good managers:[1]

"The work of the manager requires conscious selection of the tasks reserved for himself. Then it requires deliberate delegation of everything else to others in the organization within the framework of his well-designed organization pattern, *no matter what wrench this will require* from his working habits."

Steps to follow for successful delegation

Planning

- Determine the objectives of the work to be performed.
  - Analyze past and present trends.
  - Elicit ideas and participation from person to whom you intend to delegate work.
- Establish policies and goals.
  - Determine priorities for the objectives.
  - Anticipate obstacles or difficulties to be encountered and select practical steps to overcome them.
  - Anticipate interface with other organizations and devise means for coordinating with them.
- Formulate ideas, schedules and standards of performance; be realistic in your planning with respect to time schedules, budget and manpower.
- Make the objectives and plan known to all who will be affected.
- Use the results of Measuring to adjust the work of Planning.

Integrating

- Show the common purpose that integrates all aspects of this work.
- Obtain sincere voluntary acceptance of the assignment.
- Encourage individual self-development.

Organizing

- Determine and classify the work required by dividing it into manageable components.
  - Classify into logical and easily understood kinds of work.
  - Don't overload subordinates with responsibility and work.
- Assign the proper authority needed to accomplish the work.
  - Define responsibility, accountability and authority (both that required for the job and that which will be reserved).

Measuring

- Establish a measuring system that has an orderly recording and reporting method (informal oral reports; weekly, semimonthly or monthly written reports; and a formal quarterly report).
- Create an interpreting, analyzing and appraisal system.
  - Appraise by comparison with other projects that are similar in nature.
  - Determine performance and deviations.
- Adjust the Planning stages to reflect the measured results.

Executives like Cordiner have found that, though there are no absolute laws for dealing with people, there are general methods of good management that are effective.

The American Management Association lists 15 problem areas to avoid in delegating authority.[2] Here they are, rephrased into five "don'ts" and five "do's":

■ Don't use vague language when you delegate work. For instance, suppose you want a contract reviewed. Don't just ask your engineer to review the specifications. Clearly establish what the objectives are and set down guidelines in clear, readily intelligible language.

■ Don't use haphazard and poorly organized ideas. Many managers have a tendency to say that it they want anything done right away, they have

to do it themselves. Actually, this is merely a cover-up for their own shortcomings and false starts, for each of their own abortive beginnings helps them to clarify more exactly what they in fact want. Now, if they plan carefully before any work commences, they will avoid most mistakes regardless of who does the job.

■ Don't assume that the person to whom you delegate work automatically knows what you want done. Spell it out for him specifically, and include background details, if these are important.

■ Don't talk down to employees. Listen to their suggestions. Many of us have spent so much time in classrooms, either as students or teachers, that we tend to revert to the classic professorial role when we become managers in industry. Employees resent being treated as dense students. So do managers, only they sometimes forget how irritating it can be.

■ Don't nag after you have delegated work. Establish your reporting and follow-up schedule before you delegate the task. That's the time to make it clear that the schedule will be adhered to, unless something unforeseen occurs to change it. Explain that if something should threaten the deadline, you must be informed.

The moral of these "don'ts" is clear: if you want to delegate work successfully, you must first get your own house in order.

Then make these "do's" part of your routine:

■ Do select the proper employee for the job. Know the abilities, limitations and work needs of your staff. Assign projects and work within an employee's capacity but also keep him stretching for new knowledge and skills.

■ Do use examples and demonstrations, if necessary, before turning a subordinate loose on his own. Good delegating practice is a training tool. By informative examples, visual aids and effective presentation, the manager sets the pace of his organization.

■ Do limit the number of orders given at one time. There is no set rule on this, but if the length or complexity of the job warrant it, break down the instructions into small, logical parts.

■ Do allow reasonable time schedules. Take into account contingencies aside from the time that it might normally take to perform the task—the ability to procure scarce materials, for example.

■ Do follow up in an orderly fashion. Demonstrate a genuine involvement with your staff. Tour the shop, look over the work in progress, tackle on the spot any special problems that your employees

might be having. Save open criticism of work for private meetings in your office.

When Harry S. Truman was President, he had a now famous sign on his desk: "The buck stops here." The sign was a reminder that some jobs, some responsibilities can't be delegated to others. You alone must face these. You simply cannot, for example, delegate to anyone else the responsibility for disciplinary action or for matters of standard company operating policies.

Finally, remember this: the fact that you delegate authority doesn't mean that you are no longer answerable for your subordinates' mistakes. Upper management will still hold you at fault. And that's why it's to your advantage to delegate authority wisely. ■■

References:

1. "Professional Management in General Electric," *Better Business Management Course* (Schenectady, N. Y.: General Electric Co., 1954), Book 3.

2. M. J. Dooher (ed.), *Pointers on Giving Orders* (American Management Association, 1956).

Appraisal programs can be effective

Both supervisor and employee need to learn the rules of the evaluation game before the day of judgment arrives.

Robert Vijil, Jr., Engineering Instructor, Alabama A & M University.

In appraising the work of an actress in a play, a certain theater critic once wrote: "She was the epitome of eloquence and grace—a gifted performer indeed." Across town another critic saw it this way: "She gave the sort of performance that would have induced the audience in Shakespeare's day to shower the stage with an overabundance of well-ripened fruit."

Where appraisals are concerned, whether in the theater or in the engineering department, there will always be a certain amount of controversy, because the appraisers and those being appraised are, after all, only human.

However, much of the misunderstanding about appraisal systems can be eliminated simply by knowing why appraisals are necessary, how to conduct them, and what systems are used.

Pointing up the need to close the communication gap that exists between supervisor and employee is the result of a survey conducted recently at an electronics company.

In answer to the question, "How often does your supervisor conduct an appraisal review with you?" half of the employee respondents said never. When the respondents were questioned further, in an attempt to uncover the appraisal procedure that had been used, supervisors replied that they considered daily casual remarks made to the employee as part of a formal counseling process. The employees, however, considered these off-the-cuff remarks as being irrelevant. To them, a formal appraisal interview had never been held.

When employees were asked if they were satisfied with the appraisal system currently in use, 50% of them said they didn't know what system was in use. (For complete results of the survey, see tables 1 & 2 on next page.)

Why evaluations are made

You may ask, "Why do employees have to be appraised at all?" There are three main reasons:

- Employee's viewpoint: "An appraisal not only tells me how I'm doing on the job and what's expected of me in the future, but it gives me the opportunity to express my needs, ambitions and goals. It also gives me a chance to complain, criticize and gripe."

- Supervisor's viewpoint: "It tells me whether or not a man is right for his job, and helps me to select his successor if he's not. Appraisals also help me to distinguish between the 'livewires' and the 'short-circuits' on my staff, and gives me a better understanding of the job and goals of the department and a yardstick for measuring individual and group progress."

- Company president's viewpoint: "If we are to grow, we must determine whether or not our employees have the skills necessary to increase the quality and quantity of production. We should not only provide an opportunity for our people to practice these skills within the organization, but we should also motivate them to acquire these skills by setting goals that have as much meaning and value to the employee as they do to the company. The purpose of the appraisal interview is to inform our employees of these company goals."

Conducting a proper appraisal

The supervisor who wonders just how he should go about conducting an appraisal can be guided by the following five principles:

1. Assume that the employee knows more about himself than the boss does.

2. Understand that it is the employee who sets preplanned objectives with the help of the boss and not the other way around.

3. Realize that what is going to happen is more important than what has happened.

4. Put the accent on the employee's strengths, not his weaknesses.

5. Accept the idea that the boss should be a coach, not a psychoanalyst.

Once the supervisor is fully versed on the guidelines for evaluating an employee, his next logical step is to adopt a procedure for appraisal. Although the application of company-established evaluation procedures will naturally vary among supervisors, there are three elements common to all: setting standards; making judgments; and informing the employee.

Setting standards: Before a supervisor can evaluate an employee, both parties must under-

Table 1. Employee survey

1. How often does your supervisor conduct an appraisal review with you?

   Never, 50% of respondents answered. The remaining answers varied from every six months to every two years.

2. Do you discuss salary at these reviews?

   The 50% who answered negatively to question No. 1 said no to this one. The remaining answers generally fell into a yes category.

3. Does your supervisor make definite recommendations for improvement in your work?

   Yes, said 80%, while 20% answered no.

4. What do you feel is accomplished by a performance review?

   The majority of respondents replied that a review would give them an insight into how their supervisors felt about them. They wanted to know where they stood.

5. Does your supervisor make a point of mentioning your good qualities?

   Yes, said 100%.

6. Are you satisfied with the review system currently in use?

   Half of them said they didn't know what it was. Only 10% expressed satisfaction with the present system.

7. Do you know what the salary evaluation procedure is?

   The answer was 100% no.

8. Do you have good rapport with your supervisor?

   Approximately 75% replied in the affirmative.

9. Do you know what is expected of you in your job?

   Most of the responses were affirmative, but almost all respondents said the understanding was not on a long-range basis.

10. Do you feel you can offer recommendations for improvement in the appraisal procedure?

    All responded yes—they should be held more often and at regularly scheduled intervals.

Table 2. Supervisory survey

1. How often do you hold performance reviews with your employees?

   Approximately 25% claimed to hold reviews every six months, 60% said annually, while 15% said never.

2. Do you discuss salary at these reviews?

   Most respondents answered in the affirmative. Some claimed that salary discussion was the only purpose in holding a review.

3. Do you make definite recommendations for performance improvement to the employee?

   The replies were a categorical yes.

4. Does your employee know the significance of an appraisal review?

   Yes, said 50%. Many supervisors considered this to be a poor question.

5. What do you try to accomplish during an appraisal review?

   To let the employee know where he stands, almost 100% responded.

6. Are you satisfied with the review system currently in use?

   Only 10% said they were satisfied.

7. Do your employees know what the salary-review procedure is?

   Some 80% answered negatively.

8. How often are you appraised and interviewed by your own supervisor?

   All but one answered never.

9. Do you have good rapport with your supervisor?

   Almost 100% answered in the affirmative.

10. Do you have good rapport with your employees?

    The reply was 100% affirmative.

stand what performance is expected from the subordinate. To determine that, the supervisor must know what the reasonable requirements are for the jobs under his direction. Each employee must know how the supervisor interprets these requirements. And these standards must be fair and attainable.

Making judgments: Many supervisors assume that their workers are doing all right unless they make some serious mistakes. A supervisor is not in a good position to appraise the job performance of employees unless he has all the facts.

The appraisal of an employee should represent the honest effort of a manager to collect sufficient relevant information about a particular application and evaluate it to the best of his ability.

Informing the employee: After the employee has been judged, the supervisor should tell him in a personal interview what he thinks of his performance.

Three methods used

In order to accomplish the objectives of an appraisal program, some of the major rating systems should be considered. Various methods used are:

- Chart or form, which lists a number of traits or personal characteristics.
- Rank-order, in which the supervisor places all employees under him in order from best to poorest.

- Forced distribution in which employees are rated on only two characteristics; job performance and promotability.

With this system a five-point scale is used. One end of the scale represents the poorest. The supervisor is requested to slot 10% of his employees to the best end of the scale, 20% to the next category, 40% to the middle bracket, 20% in the bracket next to the low end, and the remaining 10% to the lowest category.

Last things first

Evaluation periods vary: quarterly, semiannually, annually. Recent trends favor quarterly action. To evaluate performance at more frequent intervals can cause the supervisor to remember "last things first," thus creating a critical incident that may be out of proportion with the employee's true performance record. ■■

Bibliography:

Brown, Milton, Effective Supervision, The MacMillan Co., New York, N.Y., 1961.
Bittle, L. R., What Every Supervisor Should Know, McGraw-Hill Book Co., Inc., New York, N.Y., 1959.
Drucker, P., The Practice of Management, McGraw-Hill Book Co., Inc., N.Y., 1961.
Famularo, J. J., Supervisors in Actions, McGraw-Hill Book Co., Inc., N.Y., 1961.
Kellogg, M. S., What to Do About Performance Appraisals, American Management Association, New York, N.Y., 1965.
McGregor, Douglas, Human Side of Enterprise, McGraw-Hill Book Co., Inc., New York, N.Y., 1960.

4   MANAGING PROJECTS

Primer for a project manager
The management behind Apollo
Short-interval scheduling cuts design time
Learn the basics of contracts

During the course of his career almost every engineer will manage a number of projects. Managing any project, whether small or large, involves similar factors: scheduling, budgeting, engineering problem solving, motivating people, working with suppliers, and so on. Each project manager will develop his own style for getting things done. There is no substitute for experience, so the wise engineer will take advantage of his opportunities at project management to try different methods.

One smart way to pick up some useful techniques is to talk to a number of successful project managers to find out how they handled their assignments. The first three articles of this section do this. The past decade marked man's first ventures into space. Our achievements in the space program are some of the best examples of imaginative engineering management of all time. Three of the most significant projects were the Surveyor moon landing series, the Apollo manned lunar landings, and the international Intelsat communications satellite program. Surveyor, in its early

phases, was in such deep trouble that it was almost cancelled. The management techniques used to bring it from near-failure to unqualified success are discussed in "Primer for a project manager." Then, one of the managers responsible for the success of the first Apollo "man on the moon" shot, talks about his approach to running a project.

These interviews are followed by a description of a highly successful management technique called "short-interval scheduling." This breaks the milestones of PERT or CPM down into smaller pieces, and allows a manager to spot trouble early and to turn his attention to the right areas as work progresses.

Finally, for the engineer who gets in government contract work, or in any job involving contracting or subcontracting, "Learn the basics of contracts" describes the details of various types of contracts and shows why and where each might be applicable.

Primer for a project manager

Dynamic leadership based on sound principles can even rescue a failing project.

Morale was low and dropping lower. Congressional criticism was mounting rapidly. Costs were soaring over the budget. Delays were multiplying at an ever-increasing rate.

That was the state of the Surveyor project in 1964 when Dr. Robert L. Roderick became program manager for the Hughes Aircraft Co. of Culver City, Calif., which was responsible for building the unmanned lunar spacecraft under contract to Jet Propulsion Laboratory, Pasadena, Calif.

Three and a half years later, the seven scheduled launchings to the moon were completed, and the project was being hailed as this nation's most successful space venture—so successful that despite the early troubles the Surveyor team received the Robert J. Collier Trophy for 1967. This prize is awarded annually by the National Aeronautic Association for the greatest American achievement in aeronautics or astronautics.

What happened between 1964 and early 1968 to effect this dramatic change? Was Roderick an industrial magician?

Not exactly. Things didn't change overnight. In 1965—a year after Roderick took over—a subcommittee of the House of Representatives called Surveyor one of the nation's least orderly and most poorly executed space projects. Nor did Robert Roderick reverse this finding all by himself. But probably no one person was more responsible than he for the eventual success of Surveyor.

A personal interview with Roderick was conducted to find out what produced this dramatic turn-about. The replies can almost be called a "Primer for Project Management."

Though Roderick was still with Hughes at the time of the interview, he spoke with frankness about the project, the people and the organizations involved. Since then he has become president of the Advanced Marine Technology Division of Litton Industries, Inc., Culver City, Calif.

What was the state of the Surveyor project when he took over in 1964? Not very good, Roderick recalled.

"For one thing" he said, "morale was very poor at Hughes. The continual changes in redirecting the program since its inception in 1961 had created the impression among our people, including management, that maybe we really couldn't do it.

"This lack of direction meant we really had no clear way to go. The series of problems and setbacks had rendered our schedule meaningless.

"NASA and JPL were really bugged at us, to say the least. We were really at the bottom of the list. NASA even discussed the possibility of cancelling the program at that time."

Roderick's approach, which is valid for any engineering program, made use of these rules for good management:

▪ Make sure that all portions of the system will work together to form a compatible whole. Expect the unexpected in engineering problems as the program progresses, and be prepared to make technical compromises to solve them, even to using occasional unorthodox practices.

▪ Create a climate for work in which the employes tell their superiors what the problems are instead of trying to hide them.

▪ Organize an integrated work schedule, with the help of PERT or some other system, and reorganize it as the program progresses.

▪ Make allowances for human frailty. A flexible work schedule recognizes that not everyone will do his job well in the shortest time—"you have to define the job in terms of what your available people can do."

▪ Set up efficient communications. Keep all employes on the program, including all subcontractors, informed of the value of their contribution to the full program.

▪ Be prepared to work round-the-clock to overcome design problems and keep your schedule. In this total effort, two 10-hour work shifts can be more effective than three 8-hour shifts.

▪ Ensure that the good men stick with the program until it is finished. Good management is the best way to keep them from leaving the company for other jobs.

First a good system

One of the first management decisions in a program like this, Roderick said, is to create "a good systems engineering organization" that will detect early both the human and technical problems in any subsystem.

From Surveyor's inception in 1961, weight was the major design problem, he said.

"There was just almost nothing that we wouldn't sacrifice to get a few ounces out of the spacecraft," he continued. "And this led in a number of cases to what you would call unsatisfactory design practices—you know, not necessarily wrong, but everything was shaved to the closest. The fittings were machined to hold tubing together, rather than having them cast or done in a simple way. They had to be machined carefully out of hard metal which gives you the greatest strength.

"Another significant thing," Roderick said, referring to a decision that was made before he took over, "was that the amount of filtering used in the spacecraft was held to an absolute minimum. In other words, you know, you have a wire that goes from one place to another, and maybe there's some noise that you get on it. The conservative thing to do is to put a good cathode follower or equivalent impedance matching devices between the two, so that this noise doesn't matter. But they didn't do that; they just let them go between, and hoped the noise wouldn't be too serious, in order to save weight."

The planned experiments, or payload, went through the weight-saving wringer, too.

"Roughly speaking, it started out with a very large payload—300 pounds or so," Roderick recalled. "That rapidly came down to something reasonable, but still significant, early in the program. But it wasn't until January of '63 that it was formally recognized that the thing was just out of hand, and the lunar drill was formally dropped from the program."

And still other technical headaches arose.

"In late '63," Roderick said, "it became apparent that there were significant problems in the development of the variable thrust vernier engines. The problem was severe, and finally in March of '64, at JPL's request, we terminated [a subcontractor], who was the manufacturer, and went scrounging around, trying to find someone else to make an engine. It was pretty late to find a new engine. At the same time [the subcontractor], having been shaken by this action, made a supreme effort to try and solve the problem with their own money. And, in fact, they did solve it."

Compatibility can go too far

Achieving compatibility between the various parts of the total system was not just a matter of seeing that connectors fitted together and interference was minimized. It involved interaction between the people and different design groups, Roderick explained.

This interaction was particularly important between the scientists whose experiments were to make up the payload and the engineers who had to put the whole system together. Too much communication could backfire.

"There sometimes is a tendency for the experimenter—who is a kind of wild man, so to speak—to get pretty friendly with the spacecraft design people, when they work together, and to start making changes all over the place. And that worries everybody up the line—the contractor, the program management, the agency directing the program and the Government headquarters agency."

Roderick did not shy away from this interaction, however. In fact, Hughes insisted that the key experimenters look at the spacecraft frequently and work closely with the engineers, he said. Both groups came to understand the problems that each faced. And the solutions reached were reasonable ones. The program manager must see to it that he keeps involved in this communications link, since it is one of the hardest to close.

Early identification of the most difficult design problems is a prerequisite for a well-managed program, Roderick said. One such problem in the Surveyor program was the doppler radar to be used in the landing. All doppler radars are tricky, he pointed out, but this one was even trickier because it would use a split dish, radiating from one side and receiving with the other. Hundreds of dB of isolation would be required between the two halves.

Because the potential trouble was recognized early, Hughes sent a team of engineers to work with the engineers at Ryan, who were the basic developers. The design proved extremely difficult at first, and no "breakthroughs" were in sight. The problem was solved with two principles that could apply to many such engineering tasks—attention to detail and repeated testing. This involved learning how to lap things, trying various materials and then learning how to use the right materials. Gradually the feedthrough was reduced to an acceptable point.

But then the unexpected struck.

The plume of the main retro engine was very hot, and it would radiate right back toward the vehicle—including the doppler antenna. Since a radar antenna is parabolic, it focused the heat right on the feed, which was made out of epoxy. Under the conservative, worst-case conditions used on the project—statistically speaking a 3-sigma condition—the feed would melt. This wasn't a simple problem. If such a condition held for 10 to 15 minutes, according to Roderick, there was no question that the radar would have been ruined. But the retro would be on for only 40 seconds. It might or might not cause damage.

"So we ran a whole series of tests," Roderick

said, "and we concluded that probably it wouldn't wreck it. But we finally found a nice, neat solution. We put a snoot over it. Just a piece of cloth like you put over the top of a jar when you put it in the refrigerator. Just a rubber band around the sides and a special cloth that didn't flap, wasn't to thick, didn't out gas, etc."

Engineers are often accused of favoring highly sophisticated, very expensive solutions to problems on programs like this when much simpler approaches would do. Roderick said that he did not find this to be a particular problem. In fact, he commented, the ingenuity of designers at Hughes and Jet Propulsion Laboratories often resulted in substantial savings.

An experiment to sample the amount of magnetic material in the lunar soil was a case he cited. A device could have been designed to obtain highly accurate measurements of magnetic material content; it would have taken years to build at a cost of millions. Instead, two pieces of metal—one magnetic and one non-magnetic—and a surface scraper filled the bill. The scraper threw over both pieces of metal and a measurement was then made to determine if the percentage of magnetic material was less than a certain amount.

On one of the landings the scraper was not available. But during the landing the vehicle skidded in such a way as to throw lunar material over the pieces of metal; so the experiment was run anyway.

Once into the program, Roderick said, a major thing the program manager must look out for "is to be sure that a climate exists whereby people are free and feel the compelling necessity for identifying technical problems, and that you, as program manager, are not creating an atmosphere where people hide problems."

"Instead," Roderick emphasized, "you're creating an atmosphere where people tell you what the problems are, where problems are brought out into the open. Then you attempt to solve them in a real way, so that you and your customer are able to work them out as early and as effectively as possible."

Roderick admitted that this advice is easier to give than to follow, "because the external pressures are unsympathetic to the internal problems, since they either mean money or schedule change or some other unpleasantness."

A successful manager, however, must overcome these obstacles, he said, "and create a climate not only for your own shop—which usually isn't too difficult, since your guys are basically problem solvers—but also within the company management, external management, government management. You must create an atmosphere where no attempt is made to bury problems, where

people don't point fingers, where people say, 'Okay, hit us over the head for a few minutes, and then let's see what we're going to do about it.'"

Next. get organized

Once this climate is created, Roderick said, the next thing is to "get organized."

"And I mean very specific things," he explained. "One, you must have an integrated schedule which shows, in one place, everything that must be done. Some use PERT, which will do it, if it's complete. The important thing is completeness, that you're not leaving something out because it's too hard to work. And you must maintain that schedule.

"If someone says, 'I can't make that schedule,' don't fire back, 'Make it,' and go away. You sit down with him and say 'Now why can't you? Is there anything we can do?'

"You work it out with him, and if he turns out to be right, you change it. And that effect is allowed to propagate throughout the system. But it doesn't mean that you agree with anyone who says he can't do it!"

For the Surveyor project, Hughes used PERT for engineering scheduling, line and balance for manufacturing scheduling and "a top level book of 200 pages that formed the master schedule."

"It was a very detailed master schedule," Roderick said, "re-exercised and revalidated every two weeks. And I reviewed it page by page every week."

Tying in with this organizing are financial controls, he continued. "You must have a complete and meaningful work breakdown structure. In reality it is the heart of organizing a project.

"It sounds real simple, but isn't because things change. Your work statements change, your content changes, your problems change. But as you do with your schedule, you must align the structure to your contract and to the way you are actually doing the work. And for the sake of good organization, make sure there is only one man responsible for each work package."

The signs of success? "We knew by Monday what we had spent the previous week," Roderick noted. "Everyone knew where he stood. Each person started off the week knowing whether he was going over or under budget, what job he had to do."

This is about as much as a project manager can do "in an administrative sense," Roderick went on. "You create the structure in which people can work, but the structure, in itself, does not solve the day-to-day problems. It can give no general guidelines for specific problems.

"Is this man competent to do the job? Is there the right mix of employes on a specific job?

"Only the one who's running the program and the people helping him can assess people and can fit them to the jobs that have to be done," Roderick said.

Periodic reorganization essential

During Roderick's tenure as manager, the Surveyor program at Hughes was reorganized about every six months. "If we found a man was not good enough for one job, but was good enough for a lesser job, we accommodated him," he said. "If a guy wasn't good enough to hack it at all, you got rid of him."

What if a particular department couldn't do the job assigned to it?

"You take away the work from them and give it to another department—or, as we did on many occasions, you take people out of another department and put them in the department that needs strengthening," Roderick said.

The program Roderick ran at Hughes had, at its peak, 2700 employes, of whom 800 worked directly for him.

Roderick elaborated on some of the differences between a large and small project.

"On a very small project," he noted, "it's possible for one or two guys to do most everything. And it's an extremely efficient organization if they have good, clean guidelines. Two or three people can do fantastic things.

"But when a project gets above a certain level —say around several hundred people—you have to break it into a bunch of different parts in order to do the job. And as soon as you do that you have to worry about the sum of those hundreds of different parts. You may have a good man on each one of those parts who, by himself, would be fine, but it may not work together because of different interactions going on in the system. And so you have to add— in an understood way—a superstructure on top of all that makes it possible for all these parts to fit together.

"It's a frustrating and difficult process because your men feel there are still more people on top of their backs preventing them from doing the job. And to some extent they're right; but at the same time, this superstructure is doing one function that can't be delegated: It is making sure all the parts fit together.

"Another thing that happens is that in a 3000-man effort, you can't have all good guys, not even in a company with as deep a technical staff as exists at Hughes. That many don't exist, and so you have to define jobs in terms of what your available people can do."

Pad the schedule

The best type of schedule, Roderick stressed, is one with "lots of balance and a known degree of pad that is not quite visible to anyone."

He explained that a schedule may be planned for eight hours, "but the guy who planned it knows that it takes only six hours.

"It is likely that if a problem occurs, it would happen within that period," Roderick said. "If the procedure is just a routine thing, you may schedule it right up to the minute. There are maybe a million things that could possibly occur, and you plan for a hundred or even maybe a thousand of them; so to accommodate all the problems that could occur, you plan the schedule with enough time to solve these problems and still remain on schedule."

In some cases parallel development is called for to insure that schedules will be met. This approach was used on a number of Surveyor systems, including the transmitters and the antenna-solar paddle positioner unit. Separate groups at Hughes and at JPL carried on this parallel design work. In most cases the back-up approach was not used at all. But in others either the secondary approach was used or parts of it were incorporated into the primary system.

"A parallel development should not be taken lightly," Roderick advises. "It takes away from your ability to do the prime one you are betting on. Also, it is something that costs money."

Relations with subcontractors

Another possible problem area is in relations with subcontractors, Roderick noted.

"The real problem you face with subcontractors is a possible breakdown in communications," he said. "They may be in trouble that you know nothing about; so you can't help them. This creates an emotional reaction within the subcontractor and within your own organization. You have to get everyone working together in an effective way. This is the hardest part about working with subcontractors. There is a tendency to build walls around them."

One technique Roderick used when he entered the program was to invite every subcontractor— usually the company president—to a dinner and presentation. "It involved a complete presentation of the total Surveyor program," he recalled, "so they could see where we were going and its importance to the nation. We also had NASA and JPL people there to emphasize that this was crucial to the landing of man on the moon."

Part of the evening was spent "socializing and talking with individuals, answering their questions in a more in-depth way." Roderick said this technique had a "very beneficial" long-range effect in relationships with the subcontractors.

Another project of Roderick's was to make up a mailing list "containing the names of every company that had anything to do with Surveyor."

"We kept feeding them material that they could use for publicity of their own firms and for motivation within their companies," he said.

Roderick also sent out a team to all the major subcontractors, giving presentations, "telling them what was really going on—how the equipment was designed, how their equipment fitted into it, the importance of schedule dates, the whole bit."

The end result, Roderick said, was "a publicity program that really paid off."

"You can't do that with every program," he noted, "but this was one on which it was really effective. We had men just breaking their backs on their part of the job. At some companies we had the president working on a $2000 item."

Once into a contract, Roderick continued, "you must make sure your supplier [subcontractor] is getting a clean deal—that is, make sure he understands what he is supposed to do."

"Say, your supplier gets into a situation where this guy hasn't a chance of making any money," Roderick explained. "It is a fixed-price contract, and he is badly overrun. You analyze the situation and discover you are penalizing him more than is reasonable under the situation. Perhaps it was a tougher job than you should have placed on him, or we did a bad job of spec'ing it. There is usually some fault on your part that related to the subcontractor's bad performance. You are better off in readjusting to give him a new start.

"This happened with one subcontractor. We provided them with an opportunity to make significant dollars if they performed better. And that helped, I think. It helped not only in the dollars but also in the attitude. They felt they had somebody they could work with, rather than a constant pounding on their backs."

Roderick recalled that a similar program was set up within Hughes.

"We started by giving a presentation to the several thousand people on the program, by myself and each level of company management right up to the top—a big pep rally. We tried to communicate to these guys how the whole program fitted together. Subsequent to that—especially in the manufacturing areas, where people could easily have been decoupled from the program—I went around personally and gave presentations. I got primed on what each one was doing and tried to relate their problems to my problems and to the total program. I did that every six months or so in some areas. I think it was effective."

A company newspaper—Lunar Landmarks—was another public relations effort aimed at boosting and maintaining morale. Published twice a month "for the critical period of time,

the paper emphasized the contributions of people."

"It doesn't matter what technique you use—whether it is an open house or a house organ, having dinners or special meetings," Roderick emphasized. "The important thing is that you do something. It is important that you create the excitement, knowledge, communication, interest. You must be able to communicate in some manner. You want to make them feel a part of the program. And that's what they want, too."

On 24-hour call

Hughes had a policy whereby everyone was on 24-hour call. "Everyone on the program had to leave a number where he could be reached," Roderick said. "I would estimate that about every other night I had to get up at 2 in the morning to do something—either talk to someone, make a decision, go to the plant. That program ran during the critical 18-month period."

A design error that cropped up in the high-voltage power supplies for the transmitters illustrated the importance of working this way, according to Roderick. These power supplies were within thermal compartments, and everyone had assumed all through the program that these would quickly out-gas once the vehicle was in space; because of the resulting vacuum, there would be no need to provide any protection against arcing.

When tests were finally run, it took several hours for these compartments to come down in pressure. This was totally unexpected. The compartments weren't sealed; in fact, they had big holes in them. But the flow rate turned out to be very slow anyway. And, unfortunately, the transmitters would be in a high-power mode of operation during this out-gassing period.

This was discovered very late in the program. So at a critical time a significant design change had to be made.

"When we had to redesign the transmitter," Roderick said, "I got personally involved in it. I didn't do the design, but I stayed there, around the clock, until we had something that made sense. The important thing about my presence was that others felt, 'Gee, if the boss is willing to be here on Saturday night, rather than go to a party, and is here until 2 in the morning, how can I call in and say I can't come in because I'm going to a party.'"

During this tense period some four or five design alternatives were studied, according to Roderick. The solution was to fill the high-voltage power-supply compartments with foam.

Hughes had an around-the-clock operation to get the program back on schedule. "We found out, however, that a man cannot work every day for more than a month, no matter what the schedule is," Roderick conceded. "We worked out a scheme where everyone got at least one day off a week. We didn't start out that way—initially everyone worked a seven-day week. We also eliminated the third shift and went to two 10-hour shifts.

"We found it was the most effective way to utilize personnel. The trouble with the three-shift arrangement is the handover problem. In a three-level handover arrangement, the first-shift man gives instructions to the second-shift man, who didn't quite understand the problem. He then gives instructions to the third-shift man, and by the time the first-shift comes on again, things are really screwed up. You may have lost a day before the guy who really understood the problem comes back on. If you have two shifts, there is really only one handover, and it makes a tremendous difference in the way they are able to treat the problems."

Once a project is under way, a manager is continually faced with the prospect of losing his good men. How do you keep them from leaving? Roderick answered this way:

"I would say that the most effective way to keep good people on a program is to do a good job of managing it. They must feel that they are needed, that they have a direction to go and the whole program is moving in a reasonably satisfactory manner. That is the strongest thing.

"If you take a good man and he is working on something that needs to be done, he isn't worried about leaving. You can work him seven days a week—do almost anything you want with him as long as he knows that what he is doing is needed. We were also unusually generous in the Surveyor program with the pay they got, with the newpaper that we initiated, and the special awards program, where we honored guys who did something unusually well.

"The key to keeping people is to make sure they have something real to do and they understand what it is and they can see that the program is going somewhere. As soon as that stops, you will lose them." ▪▪

The management behind Apollo

Coordination, planning, and one step ahead were success formula for lunar module project.

Immediately before Apollo 11's module scored a lunar touchdown, most of us back on earth were huddled around TV screens nervously anticipating all the mechanical and electrical functions that could go wrong. The happy fact that nothing did go wrong is a tribute to NASA's Lunar Module program in general, and to those responsible for the success of the LM assembly and test program in particular.

Because we think engineers are interested in knowing exactly how such a program was managed, we interviewed Paul Butler, Grumman Aerospace Corporation's Assistant LM Program Director for SCAT (spacecraft assembly and test). Mr. Butler is currently working on the company's space station project. NASA awarded the LM contract to Grumman in January, 1963. The company accounted for about 45% of the cost of the project, with over 7000 suppliers accounting for the remaining percentage.

Our questions and Butler's comments follow:

What were your emotions when the LM was approaching a lunar landing?

The landing didn't worry us, especially when Armstrong said that systems were still "go." The alarm light that came on didn't bother us because we knew the astronauts had more than 30 seconds of fuel left.

What worried us most was the launch from the moon's surface. During the landing the astronauts had an abort capability at any given time.

Once they were on the moon, however, the engines had to work the first time. It bothered us that a man couldn't take over until the LM engine lit. I guess all of us were mentally going through the things that had to function to allow the ascent stage to leave the moon.

How is the LM project organized?

Dr. Ralph Tripp, LM Program Director, reports to Joe Gavin, Vice President, Space Programs. Five assistant program directors serve him through (1) engineering; (2) manufacturing; (3) spacecraft assembly and test; (4) ground support equipment; and (5) quality control.

What was SCAT's responsibility?

SCAT's responsibility was to assemble and test the LM to delivery for launch. Manufacturing produced the basic structural shell and wiring harness of the LM, and our job was to install all the black boxes, outfit the cabin, test all the systems, and take it up to the point where it could be flown. When the vehicle left Grumman it was absolutely complete, except for the fuel and the computer programs that were designed for the moon mission.

How did you maintain quality control?

Grumman representatives were present at each vendor's plant. We changed the mix of engineering and quality control constantly; we let it pulse as a function of what we were after. The vendors checked their parts out of their plant, and we checked them into our plant. We ran what we called a PIT-test (pre-installation test) every time we got a new piece of equipment. We'd check every piece before installing it in a vehicle to make sure it had not been damaged in transit.

Every time we broke, say, a connector, before we placed it back in its box we had to go back into the circuitry and exercise every copper path that went through that plug to be sure that the pin .mated, and to be sure that when it didn't mate it didn't bend or come loose. Every single wire had to be functioning and have continuity from end to end.

How did you coordinate the work?

Coordination was the most effective key to the entire program. I happen to be a nut on planning and scheduling. Planning, to me, isn't tracking. Tracking just tells me where I am today, and I never want to know just that. What I want to know is—based on where I am today—what's left, and how do I get there from here. So I denied the 1200 people of SCAT the chance to tell me what they did yesterday.

The LM engine ignites! Grumman engineers congratulate each other as the lunar module kicks off the moon.

I think the key is this: I could quiz three group heads, and each head could say that he's one day down (one day behind schedule). One or two of the three might mean they were going to be down only one day three months .from now. But one day down for the third man might mean he was going to miss by a month, or cause another group to miss by a month.

We constantly assessed the impact of the current position. LM is not production, it's development in the truest sense of the word; for each LM mission is a stepping-stone to the next one.

Let's consider two philosophies to explain the basic difference between development, and production. I can use the philosophy that says I want parts on the shelf: if something breaks, I can take it off the shelf and put it into play. This indicates a production program. But in development, the first time you have an anomaly you want to find out right away what failed, why it failed, and how you can fix it so it doesn't fail again. When you determine the cause of the failure, you then modify all the subsequent boxes . . . And you have to be careful not to overhandle the box because you're likely to destroy its integrity.

How did you work out the timing of the deliveries for subsystems so that related pieces would be ready at the proper time?

A master schedule was the real heart of the timing. I like to pace parts coming in slightly ahead of my needs. One ahead of need—never two, just one. Installing one part triggers the scheduling system to produce the next one, or deliver the next one as the case might be. Of course, we had confidence in some of the hardware, and we'd go ahead and install it. But we couldn't do that with some of the active pieces like the radar, which we'd been working with constantly.

Now where this "one ahead of need" system gets to be significant is if the LM on the pad, with it maximum priority, lays a requirement on us for a part. We'd take it from the last vehicle on the line or, if it wasn't there, from the next vehicle up the line, and so on. We had three vehicles on test here at all times, and there were three vehicles at Cape Kennedy.

Our job, in addition to moving vehicles out, was to support the Cape. I could pull a part from the No. 1 vehicle in Bethpage, figuring that I had more latitude to employ a "work-around" than they had down there. We had 24 hours; at the Cape they had only one hour.

What would you avoid doing again?

Nothing really stands out in my mind. We're constantly improving the system; better management methods were spawned by an evolutionary process. Once we put the LM together we had to hook the ground support equipment to it and check it to see if it was functioning. We're constantly refining this check-out system. When I get smarter I expect to be able to check some major system, knowing full well that if I get certain parameters out of it all systems must be working.

The development program is, by nature, one that teaches us what to avoid doing the next time. For example, we took 80 days of electrical subsystem testing and cut it to 20 through better test logic and experience. If we were going to work on LM for 10 years we could check it out in a short time. Weight is important. If you knew some circuitry in a given component was required by another one, you'd use that same circuit rather than repeat it.

What is the cost differential between manned and unmanned space vehicles?

The human being can handle emergencies. Neil Armstrong could probably have landed on a rock and got away with it. But he saw it so he came down and moved over away from it. Some of the unmanned Surveyors landed, and some didn't. The cost would depend mostly on what the vehicle is sent for. The cheapest way to go is in a manned LM with no backup system.

What element of chance was there in designing the LM to land and take off from the moon?

We weren't certain how large the landing gear should be. We asked ourselves: Does radar reflect and bounce off the lunar surface, or does it penetrate x amount of feet and then bounce back? Would there be dust on the surface or not? What was the composition of the surface, and how big a footprint did we need to support it? We were extremely conservative. We made the pads three feet plus. We learned later, of course, that the pads penetrated the lunar surface by 1/4 inch.

What was your most serious problem in assembling and testing LM?

Water glycol. How was it used? You have to get rid of heat. On earth you can turn on the fan. But in the vacuum of space you don't have this capability. The thermal characteristics in space are extreme. In the absence of any atmosphere, the sun side of the vehicle gets very hot and the shade side gets very cold.

If I want to cool a piece of hot radio equipment I can suck the heat off through a cold plate. Now I've got the heat in the cold plate, but I still have to get rid of it some way. So I transfer the heat from the cold plate into a hollow tube containing water glycol. Then it passes on through sublimators. I'll boil off some water and pass the heat off into the hard vacuum of space.

The main problem with glycol is that it forms a residue. Many times we'd be working up on top of the LM and break a line. If we spilled the glycol we had to keep washing the LM down with distilled water and wipe the surface with litmus paper to make absolutely sure that the residue was off. If we didn't get it off and the water hit the thermal-shielding blanket it would injure it. Then we'd have to take the blanket off and change it. A water glycol spill was serious because it took time to correct the mistake, and time was our most important commodity.

How were employes motivated to maintain the high reliability of the LM?

A staff can build an airplane and watch it fly, and then they can work on it some more and watch it fly again. But after a LM is finished,

"LM is built inside-out because in outer space the vacuum is on the outside, and the atmosphere is on the inside,'' Butler tells interviewer Richard Turmail as they inspect a mockup of the LM innards.

your staff will never see it again except on TV. This kind of engineering makes it difficult for management to motivate a man to admit he's made a mistake. We overcame this problem through a fortunate selection of people over a long period of time. We chose people who had a human desire to do a good job.

If one of them goofed, I would talk to him and ask him if he had learned something from the mistake. I would ask him what he was going to do the next time. I like to know why people do things. Many will give you "reasons" when they're really only trying to convey a thought. The key to good management is in trying to determine your staff's mental process rather than the words they're using. If you understand the mental process, you can begin to solve their problem.

In development, all I can really guarantee is that I will never make the same mistake twice. That guarantee automatically means that I will keep getting better.

Does Grumman have any incentive bonus program for engineers on the LM project?

No. Everybody says, "What are you going to do for your people?" From my own warped personal point of view—nothing. We already did it. You pay a guy a salary to do a professional job. If he does a good job, why do you have to reward him? I like to think that doing a good job is part of the professionalism of being an engineer.

Some companies believe that the only way to hold onto their best people is to give them a piece of the action.

I don't believe that. The only way to hold onto the best people is to give them a challenge. If you have the moxie it takes to be a good engineer today, you don't want to sit back; you want to create. If an engineer doesn't have a challenge, more money isn't going to help him.

When the LM approached the moon's surface, the alarm light that came on with 30 seconds of fuel remaining was reported as having been the result of an overloaded computer. How do you overload a computer?

Everything that's fed into a computer has a priority. The LM computer was saturated by low-priority programs. When a computer is programed, it has a built-in circuit that says, "Hey, I'm so saturated I can do only one program at a time." When the alarm lit up, it simply meant that the low-priority programs were not being interrogated by the computer.

Neil Armstrong wasn't concerned about those programs anyway; the computer still had the capability to match anything he was going to do.

We knew we had 90 seconds of overfuel against his time-line; 30 seconds represented one-third of his overfuel left. That's a pretty good margin. You don't want to carry a lot of fuel anyway. For every pound you want to land up there, it takes four pounds on the pad to get it off. From a safety and economy standpoint, you don't want to land something you're not going to bring back with a large safety margin.

Did NASA breathe down your neck?

Sure. Sometimes we expected it—sometimes we didn't. I'll say this: The relationship I enjoyed in SCAT was closer and on a higher technical plane than any I've ever known. The problem we had to solve forced a much closer relationship; we didn't just talk contract ties, we talked technical problems and solutions.

What kind of engineering talent are you interested in for the future?

That depends on the direction the company wants to take in the future. What is the post-Apollo space program?

Whatever it is, it will include an orbiting space station. Most of the cost right now is in getting from earth into orbit. Of course, we'd still have to get up to the station, but I could get there with a bulk of fuel and run back and forth from the moon many, many times before I'd have to go back to earth. I could always send the spacecraft back to an orbiting space station, repair it, and stick it back in orbit.

Three things will drive the space program: Performance, cost and time. Apollo definitely had time as its driver, but it also had to perform. Cost? No one knew how to land on the moon at a lower cost and still do it in this decade. Time? Post-Apollo programs will be willing to let time slide.

Do you have any regrets about the LM program?

One regret I have is that the descent stage is on the moon forever more, and the ascent stage is orbiting the moon. We'll never get them into the Smithsonian Institution for future generations to see. ▪▪

Short-interval scheduling cuts design time

Breaking jobs into small subtasks can improve engineering output significantly.

Raymond J. Behan, Operations Manager, Heinemann Electric Co., Trenton, N.J.

Several years ago the engineering design section of a manufacturing company was employing a permanent staff of about 25 designers, but at the same time it was finding it necessary to contract for a "temporary" staff of more than 30 job-shop personnel to help it meet its commitments.

Temporary! For over three years, top management had been carrying this crew of 30 extras to bail out the design section—with no end in sight.

Management went to work on the problem. Seven months later, after trying the technique of Short Interval Scheduling (SIS), the temp-

orary staff of 30 was cut to 13, with no reduction in the volume of design work. The company estimated annual savings of $320,000.

SIS—the division of work into short-term goals, with timetables for employes to meet—has gained wide acceptance in American industry in recent years. Application of its principles to the work of designers and other engineers in the electronics industry can be particularly rewarding. Improvements of up to 30 per cent in engineering and design performance have been shown to be quite possible (see example).

And applying and reaping benefits from use of this tool for managing time in the realm of "the scientific mind," "think time" and "one-time occurrences" is easier in many ways than in manufacturing, clerical and service operations —once engineering management lets go of a few pet myths and misunderstandings.

The tradition barrier

Ordinarily the return on a dollar spent on research and design in the electronics industry meets little criticism. Rapid product obsolescence and intense competition make expenditures in these areas necessary, as in few other industries. So a "Do nothing that might rock the boat" caution tends to temper management attempts to increase the output received for the research and design salary dollar.

Traditionally the establishment of managerial controls and time standards for the work of electronic engineers has called for a light touch or even a hands-off attitude. But, with allowance for individual work habits, SIS need not create resentment on the job.

Oversimplified, the typical assignment of a designer is to reach goal X by date Y. Like anyone else, a designer works better when he has recognizable "mile markers" with which to measure his progress on his way to goal X, and a timetable with which to pace himself along them in meeting date Y. The typical assignment overlooks these considerations.

Short Interval Scheduling supplies the designer with both needs.

Design supervisors also often direct their planning attention to goal X and date Y, viewing their intermediate functions as expansions of their pre-management work. They supply their designers with assignments, stand-by technical know-how and practical assistance if and when it's asked for, but tend to throw up their hands when it comes to establishing realistic control over expenditures of design manpower under their supervision. Unless their project completion dates are liberally budgeted, they can be easily overshot.

What's missing? Like their designers, supervisors need small-package estimates of what work is involved between one mile marker on the way to a designer's goal and the next. They can't make reliable estimates in advance of the amount of total work a project will require without estimates of individual elements that go to make up the whole.

In addition, they need a device that alerts them to any inadvertent false starts or misdirection in their designers' work, so they can correct such situations before compounding of errors sponges up excess design time.

Short interval scheduling supplies design management with both needs.

SIS in action

In the case of the manufacturing company that relied habitually on 30 outsiders to rescue a permanent staff of 25 designers, the SIS attack went like this: Two staff supervisors were selected to evaluate all current jobs in process and all existing backup work. Time estimates for the segment-by-segment completion of these jobs were laid out on a calendar (Fig. 1) to get a picture of total manpower utilization. The chart showed that while 30 job-shoppers were needed to help out at the beginning of the project, only 13 were needed by the time the work had reached its final stages; the surplus helpers could be eliminated as they completed their parts of the total project.

To be sure each helper and member of the permanent staff completed his individual task on time, a second control (Fig. 2) was established. Through it management could ascertain whether

---

'Test drive' the SIS system

You can make a trial run with SIS, using a stripped down version of it, on one of your own jobs in your own design section. You can try it on a small-risk basis, and the results of the test are rapidly available. Here's how:

- Select two designers of similar ability and experience in any field.
- Assign each the same one- or two-week project, making sure they don't communicate during the project's duration.
- Tell designer 'A' to report back with his results at the end of the five-day (or 10-day) period established.
- Break the assignment down for designer 'B', establishing daily goals toward its completion over a *four-day* period (eight days for a two-week project). Check his progress daily.

Time and again, when this experiment has been made, the outcome has been similar to this:

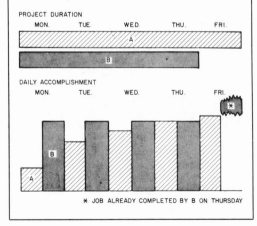

✳ JOB ALREADY COMPLETED BY B ON THURSDAY

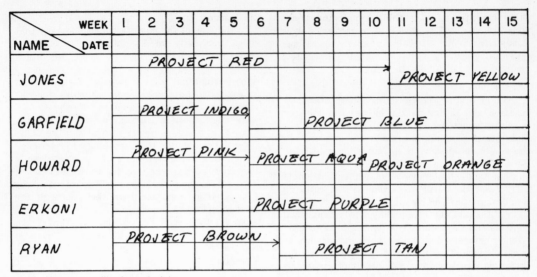

	WEEK	1	2	3	4	5	6	7	8	9	10	11	12	13	14	15
NAME	DATE															
JONES			PROJECT RED								→	PROJECT YELLOW				
GARFIELD			PROJECT INDIGO					PROJECT BLUE								
HOWARD			PROJECT PINK		→	PROJECT AQUA			PROJECT ORANGE							
ERKONI							PROJECT PURPLE									
RYAN		PROJECT BROWN				→	PROJECT TAN									

Fig. 1. Manpower utilization schedule

the required hours for the job were expended by each individual as planned.

Designers and helpers filled in their progress on charts each day, and so were continuously alerted as to whether they were on schedule. The supervisor got the assignment forms back at the end of the week for review and any corrective action that might be required.

Two-way advantages result

The company found after seven months that SIS increased not only the productivity of designers and helpers but also that of its managers.

When a manager breaks down a project for his designers into a series of short-range accomplishments and supplies them with an estimated arrival time at each milestone, he is making it easier for the designer to visualize the end goal—completion of the project at a certain time. The psychological effect is to instill in the designer a continuing sense of challenge and urgency about arriving at each of the intermediate goals on time. This replaces the single urgency that the designer working without short-interval control begins to feel only as the date set for project completion nears.

The designer finds it easier to pace himself to meet a series of daily goals than to proceed toward meeting a "lump sum" goal in the distance. And this puts the manager in a position where he can perform in the role of true management rather than as a fighter of brush fires.

Vital to the manager's devising and assigning of short-range goals is his checking to see that they are met. Each goal met on schedule means that the track is clear for the designer to pro-

ceed to the next and for the manager to direct his attention to other areas.

Only in a "schedule miss," when routine checking reveals that a current short-range goal has not been met, is it necessary for the manager to do more than check a worker's progress. The schedule miss is the manager's cue to go into action and correct the cause before the small miss, if not caught in time, gets the chance to develop into a big one.

The manager working in this manner is availing himself of a modern management technique known as "management by exception." His man-supervising efforts are no longer spread across the board, but are continuously refocused onto areas most urgently needing his attention.

As smaller parts of the project are brought under control, this control adds up to control over the whole, from the standpoint of both the manager and his designers.

How long is a short interval?

SIS should be used discriminately. The areas where control is most necessary are those where lost time is most costly. The application of SIS to the file section or the reproduction room is not likely to bring the return that it will when applied to a roomful of designers and draftsmen, who are more numerous, higher priced and more important in the total operation of the company.

Likewise, the length of the short interval to be scheduled and the frequency of supervisory checking should be realistic. Hourly intervals and checking pay off in some warehousing, assembly and clerical jobs, but a daily interval is more likely to fit the electronic engineer's need for a

PROJECT: *INDIGO*	WEEK ENDING			DESIGNER: *GARFIELD*

THIS WEEKS SCOPE

1. *Lay out infra-red holding fixture — 16 hours*
2. *Rough design on feed mechanism - 9 hours*
3. *Finalize cam turn device — 15 hours*

	MON.	TUES.	WED.	THURS.	FRI.
SCHEDULED HOURS	8	8	8	8	8
ACTUAL HOURS	8	8	8	8	8
% COMPLETED	15 %	36 %	58%	80 %	100 %

Fig. 2. Assignment and report form

recognizable unit of accomplishment by which to gauge his own progress.

For the supervisor who is checking the engineer's progress for schedule misses, an interval of a week between checks may not be unrealistic in some cases.

In Short Interval Scheduling for design work, precision and expert determination of the work-time relationship is not necessary. "Reasonable expectancy" is the key. How much can the average designer, with a given complexity of work, produce over a given period under normal conditions? The design supervisor, the management arm closest to the job, measures the work load in terms of known and estimated factors, sets up reasonable expectations, and schedules the design task into short intervals.

Unscientific determination? Leaves too much room for error? Even if they are still subject to some "puffing," estimated work goals, established under monitorable methods and that result in decrease of design expenditure and more rapid output, are better than no goals at all. Ask yourself this question: At the outset of a design project, can you pinpoint within 24 hours when each man on it will become available for the next project? This is a goal of his own the manager should be able to meet through short interval scheduling.

Objections—and how to meet them

Engineering managers often object to the installation of work-control procedures, such as SIS, fearing that they might place emphasis on the schedule at the expense of quality and creativity. This attitude has nipped many promising work-control plans in the bud.

Let's examine some of these objections and answer them.

The scientific-mind objection: "You can't estimate stages of work that involve creativity."

Answer: You're estimating it right now—whenever you establish research or design budgets. You estimate total hours of engineering time, designing time, drafting time and so on to arrive at a project budget. You're already breaking it into segments at this point; break it down further, so you can control the sum by controlling its parts.

The added-paperwork complaint: "Determining, recording and reporting on short-interval segments of work turns supervisors into paper shufflers and takes them away from their real job."

Answer: The reports and records that go with SIS are tools that the supervisor uses to decrease the incidence of costly, unplanned work. Through them, he begins to manage the time of his subordinates, which is a part of the supervisor's job that is at least as important as that of supplying technical know-how to his men.

The "thinking time" mystique: "An engineer's progress toward his work goal does not just involve so many computations and so many hookups on a breadboard. Much of his work is unmeasurable—done in his head."

Answer: The design supervisor needs to know how his employe is progressing so he knows when to step in to expedite progress—even in "thinking time." Thinking may involve determining the problem, determining alternative solutions, investigating and analyzing alternatives, and selecting and presenting a basic design before finally developing a workable design in detail. Each activity can be assigned a tentative number of hours, and scheduled checks will reveal when a segment is getting off-schedule and calls for attention.

The question of conflict with PERT and CPM: "SIS will throw off our carefully worked-out PERT and CPM techniques for planning and co-ordinating research and design work."

Answer: SIS supplements these devices. It furnishes better control over the smaller parts of projects and establishes interim goals, schedules and check points between the broad "events" basic to PERT and CPM.

Short Interval Scheduling is not designed to work at peak efficiency in a vacuum. The benefits from its use in a small area are multiplied when schedules are coordinated with those of other contributing areas in the company. The greater the company management interest and support, the tighter the coordination, and the larger the benefits. ▪▪

Learn the basics of contracts

Here's a primer of contractual agreements and their relative effectiveness.

John A. Bianchini, Vice President, Jovin Industries Corp., Farmingdale, N.Y.

In 1962, the Whirlpool Corporation supplied Sears Roebuck with more than $300 million worth of appliances, including all of Sears' washers and dryers. In itself this may not be too startling, but when you consider that Sears is Whirlpool's largest customer and that Whirlpool, conversely, is Sears' largest individual supplier, the fact that the relationship has endured for years without benefit of a written contract is unusual, if not unique.

At one time or another, all of us in the contracting business wish the same informality characterized Government buying. We'd avoid a lot of red tape and possibly progress a little more rapidly then we seem to now. But human as we are, abuses would be bound to creep in. We are in actuality compelled to resort to some sort of written agreement—cost-plus-fixed-fee, firm-fixed-price, or incentive contracts.

A simple graph has been developed (Fig. 1) which can be used to study these contractual relationships in a given procurement situation. We call it a "cost-profit chart" and have found that it can describe a whole variety of contracts.

On this graph, the horizontal axis represents profit-loss. Price is not shown directly, but happens to be the algebraic sum of the measurement on the two axes that describe a point. Though our later discussion will relate incentives on performance and delivery to this chart, we will first discuss the cost-incentive aspects, because these determine the type of contract and will often be the only incentive aspects in it. Performance and delivery incentives are never included unless cost incentives are also built in.

CPFF contracts encourage inefficiency

Figure 1 shows a cost plus fixed-fee (CPFF) cost-profit relationship. The fee (profit) is a fixed dollar amount which does not vary as costs increase. This CPFF line represents a contract where the estimated cost was 100 and the fixed fee 6. Under this agreement, the Government will pay all of the reasonable allowable and allocable costs incurred in fulfilling the contract. This is called a 100-0 sharing situation, since the Government pays 100% of the cost. Whether the final actual cost is 80, 100, or 120, the contractor's fee is the same. Obviously, there is little motivation in this contract to minimize costs: profit is guaranteed. In some procurement situations, this contract form is necessary because minimizing cost is not a prime consideration.

Both DOD and industry officials agree that

CPFF contracts not only fail to provide incentives for economy, but actually deaden management efficiency by removing the need for either the Department or the contractor to estimate costs accurately and to plan and control programs tightly.

In the 10 years between 1951 and 1961, DOD dollars spent under CPFF contracts rose from 13% of total expenditure to three times that figure. Accordingly, in 1962, the Department of Defense assigned to each military department a specific goal for reducing CPFF contracts during fiscal years 1963, 1964, and 1965. The goal for 1963 was to reduce such contracts to 25.8% of total contract awards (compared with 38% in the first nine months of 1961). By the end of 1966, the CPFF contracts had gone down to around 12% of total contracts.

The Armed Services Procurement Regulation (ASPR) now tends to restrict CPFF contracts to research or study programs, where the level of effort is unknown, and to development work for which an incentive contract is impractical.

Firm-fixed-price contracts involve high risk

ASPR has also taken a new look at firm-fixed-price (FFP) contracts. In the past, the government contracting officer justified the use of the FFP contract by extensive competition or historical cost data; now he must try to identify the risks involved and negotiate a price that reflects a reasonable division of these risks between the contractor and the Government. Even though costs may vary widely from the estimate, a contract providing for "high profit potential and concomitant contractor risk" may still be used. Government negotiators have been directed to use the type of contract best calculated to "stimulate outstanding performance." For this purpose, the firm-fixed-price contract is still preferred when costs are predictable with a fair degree of accuracy. See summary for contract-type definitions.

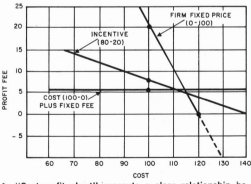

1. **"Cost-profit chart"** presents a clear relationship between the three basic contract agreements in existence.

The FFP cost-profit line in Figure 1 represents a contract where the estimated cost is 100 and the profit at this cost is 20. The line portrays a relationship where every dollar of cost reduces profit by one dollar. We call this 0-100 share; the contractor pays 100% of the cost, whatever it might be. The fixed price to the Government is 120 and does not change. When actual costs exceed 120, the contractor loses money. This loss is represented by the dashed line. Such a contract places maximum emphasis on reducing costs. The Government considers it a most desirable contract form when it can be used.

Basically, the factors that restrict use of the FFP contract are:
- Inability to establish a realistic cost objective within acceptable tolerances. If the cost estimate is not sufficiently close to what the actual cost will be, the potential for windfall profit or loss is greater than either the Government or the contractor can accept.
- Inability to define the work in the detail needed to permit enforcement of the contract. This is related to the first problem. If the Government cannot define exactly what it wants, as opposed to defining something to do, then the Government cannot estimate the cost fairly or be sure it is getting what is paid for.

Incentive contracts are tailored to a problem

When conditions preclude the use of FFP contracting, the Government must try to balance the uncertainties in a procurement by using a form of incentive contract. Any number of incentive arrangements could be made, with their characteristic curves falling between the FFP line and the CPFF line in Figure 1. The one shown describes an arrangement where the estimated cost is 100 and the profit at that cost is 8. But actual costs may vary from this target. Some formula is used for sharing the increased or decreased costs between the Government and contractor. In this case, the cost-sharing formula is 80-20, which means that the Government pays 80% of any added cost, the contractor 20 per cent. Similarly, cost-savings are shared according to the formula. For example, if the actual cost is 90, the profit is 10. This is arrived at by adding the bonus for cost reduction to the target profit as follows:

Profit at estimated cost (target)	8
20% of the cost reduction (10)	+2
Earned Profit	10

Likewise, if the actual cost were 110, the profit would be 6, a reduction of 2 from target. Another way to say this is that for every dollar of added cost the contractor spends, his potential profit is reduced twenty cents.

The sharing arrangement could be anything from 99-0 to 0-99, although these extremes are theoretical. Usually, real sharing arrangements will fall between 50-50 and 95-5 or some combination of these shares within different cost ranges. The sharing arrangement determines the slope of the curve drawn through the target point.

There are three basic forms of incentive contracts—cost-plus-incentive-fee (CPIF), fixed-price-plus-incentive-fee (FPIF) and fixed-price-plus-incentive-fee with successive targets (FPIS).

Let's examine the CPIF contract first

Figure 2 shows a CPIF contract that may be described as follows:

Target Cost   = 100   Profit Ceiling   = 12
Target Profit =   8   Profit Floor   = 4
              Sharing = 80-20.

We have introduced a new term on this chart—"range of probable actual costs." Remember that incentive contracts are used, as opposed to the most desirable form, the FFP contract, because it is difficult to establish a cost estimate within the tolerances that are acceptable to the contracting parties. In the situation portrayed in Figure 2, it is agreed that 100 is a reasonable estimate for the cost of the effort, though the actual cost may be as great as 120 or as little as 80. It the contractor produces at a cost of 80, he has performed in an outstanding manner.

The profit ceiling and floor prevent a windfall profit or loss when the final actual cost is less than 80 or more than 120. Though the basic assumption is that the final actual cost will fall somewhere in the range of probable costs and that the contractor will have produced a product of desired quality at minimum cost, the share line is constructed to cover the whole range of actual costs.

Summary of the major contract types

Type of contract	Definition	Where appropriate
CPFF—Cost plus fixed fee	Government pays all costs plus a fixed fee.	Where cost and management efficiency are not prime objective; e.g., to meet a vital system need.
FFP—Firm fixed price	Price remains the same regardless of costs.	Maximizes cost incentives, hence is preferred by Government. Can only be applied if: • Cost estimates are quite accurate (otherwise windfall profits or big losses are possible). • Performance can be strictly defined.
CPIF—Cost plus incentive fee	Profits linked to costs, but floor and ceiling profit levels set.	Where tolerances are needed in cost estimates. Has the disadvantages that: • Government doesn't know in advance how much it will have to pay. • Contains no incentive for cost-cutting once profit floor is reached.
CPA—Cost plus award	Minimum profit set; additional award decided by impartial board on basis of costs and performance.	Where cost and performance estimates are virtually impossible to make in advance. Vagueness to both parties is disadvantage.
FPIF—Fixed price incentive fee	Profits linked to costs; profit ceiling set but no floor. Fixed maximum price means contractor can lose money if costs run high (Fig.3).	Similar to CPIF, except that contractor has much greater incentive to cut costs lest they climb above target level.
FPIS—Fixed price incentive with successive targets	Same as FPIF except that profit floor set. Under specific conditions, whole contract may be revised as work proceeds; e.g., if some system component doesn't work and needs further development.	Where system design involves some unknown factors. Must be used with care since contractor could purposely keep early costs high to gain higher profits through renegotiation.
Performance incentive	Similar to previous types but with additional incentives tied to these factors: • Performance. • Schedules. • Weighted combinations of these plus costs.	Where factors beyond costs are vital. Requires careful definition of goals and methods of testing performance.

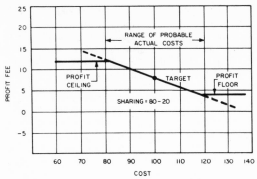

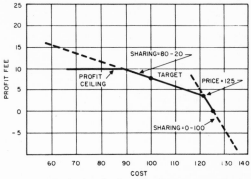

2. Simple incentive curve converts to a CPIF contract by adding a profit ceiling and profit floor. Note that these limits exist outside the range of probable costs.

3. In the fixed-price-plus-incentive-fee contract, the incentive curve becomes a firm-fixed-price curve when a specified total price is reached; in this case, 125.

Without changing the incentive arrangement portrayed on the chart, we could keep the same profit ceiling and floor, the same share (80-20), the same range of probable actual cost, and state the target cost as either 90 with a target fee of 10, or 110 with a target fee of 6. As a matter of fact, when we leave the negotiating table, the incentive arrangement is the pricing provision of the contract. The price of the contract to the Government will be the actual allowable and allocable cost of performance, plus a profit determined by the curve at that cost level. The Government, therefore, won't know precisely what the contract price is until after the work is done.

The cost-plus-award contract is merely a variation of CPIF. Instead of setting up yardsticks ahead of time which, by mechanical application, will determine the profit to be paid, this contract suspends the decision regarding profit until the work has been completed; the judgment required in setting targets is deferred from before the fact until after it.

Under the cost-plus-award concept, the Government does not predetermine the target cost of the sharing formula. A floor is set under the profit. After paying all allowable and allocable costs incurred in fulfillment of the contract, the Government agrees to pay a minimum fee of 2 as profit.

Where does the incentive come in? After establishing the minimal profit, the contract states that, upon completion of the project, an impartial board will review the manner in which the contractor has performed. Based on its evaluation of efficiency, quality of workmanship, timeliness of fulfillment, and any other pertinent considerations, the board is authorized to award an additional fee, ranging perhaps up to 6 or 8.

Half of this fee may depend upon costs alone—upon how efficient the contractor was in keeping them down. The other half of the award may be based on the quality of the product and/or its delivery schedule. If it is delivered ahead of time, the contractor may be awarded an extra 2. If its quality is better than expected, he may be given from 1 to 8 units of profit for superior quality control.

The award fee emphasizes only one aspect of the procurement, such as cost alone, but at the expense of all other aspects, which may be of equal importance. It is useful when the problem of predetermining target costs, target fees, and cost-sharing formulas is too great to permit application of the usual CPIF provisions.

Fixed price incentives involve greatest complexity

Now a brief look at two other incentive forms. Figure 3 shows the profit-cost relationship for a fixed-price-incentive-fee (FPIF) contract with firm targets. This is a contract that has:

Target Profit = 8 Share = 80-20
Target Cost = 100 Ceiling Price = 125% of
                          Target Cost

The Government has established a fixed price ceiling of 125 on this contract and so draws a

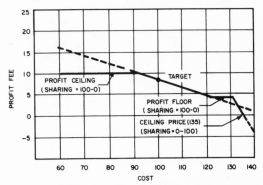

4. Profit ceiling, profit floor and ceiling price are added to the simplified incentive curve to form the more involved fixed-price-incentive contract with successive targets.

fixed-price share line. This line starts at the profit = 0, cost = 125 point. Note that when the actual cost reaches approximately 121, the 80-20 line through the target point intersects this line, so that the contract really becomes a fixed-price contract. Beyond that point, the contractor is paying 100% of increased costs. The ceiling price and the sharing formula see to that. Above 125, the contractor pays out of his pocket, actually losing money.

The other type of incentive contract is known as a fixed-price-incentive contract with successive targets (FPIS). This contract is also subject to change as time goes on. It differs from the FPIF contract by setting an initial floor and ceiling for profit, an initial target cost, and an initial target profit, all of which are subject to revision.

Though the Government begins with an initial formula, it may be renegotiated at a specific point in time or in the event of some specific event. There are occasions where the revision may be done more than once.

Figure 4 shows an initial formula for a procurement where the estimated cost is 100, the target profit is 8, the off-target cost sharing 80-20. To this, we add a minimum profit of 4, a maximum profit of 10, and a price ceiling of 135. All the limiting features of the CPIF and the FPIF contracts are combined in this initial formula. If the costs overrun the estimate by 31%, the contractor is working on a fixed-price relationship. This fixed-price ceiling cannot be increased when the Government reviews the formula. It may be decreased.

At revision time, the Government negotiates a new target cost for the contract. The initial formula applied to the new target cost determines the new target profit. For example, if the new target cost were 90, the profit would be 10. If the new target cost were 120, the profit would be 4.

With a new target profit and target cost thus established, the Government can now make an FPIF contract, using any sharing arrangement desired and a price ceiling of 135 or less; or the Government can convert to a FFP contract, in which the price would be the new target profit plus the new target cost. Generally speaking, the new cost-profit arrangement negotiated during revision will always be one of these two contract forms.

The FPIS contract has to be used with considerable discretion. Like the renegotiable type, which it closely resembles, the FPIS contract is subject to some exploitation. The contractor may keep costs high, up to the point of negotiating the reset, in order to ensure a higher firm target cost. Initial targets, therefore, should be conservatively set by the Government.

Performance incentives are also valuable

Before 1962, incentive contracts applied the incentives to dollars of cost alone. Presently, they also apply to performance reliability and to scheduling as well, and are used in both the development cycle and the production cycle. For example, in July, 1963, the Government committed $460 million on incentive contracts; 25% of these obligations were on contracts that contained performance as well as cost incentives.

This is in line with the basic principle of incentive contracting, which holds that a contractor should be motivated, in calculable monetary terms, to:

▪ Turn out a product that meets significantly advanced performance goals.

▪ Improve on the schedule of progress, up to and including final delivery.

▪ Reduce the cost of work by substantial amounts.

▪ Accomplish the project under a weighted combination of some or all of these objectives.

Though no specific rules exist for setting performance incentives, there are three general rules that should be recognized. For our discussion, these are termed identification, definition, and balance.

Identification determines what specific qualities in the performance of the product, or of the contractor, the Government may wish to emphasize. It may be the time of delivery, to insure compatibility with other items entering the defense system. Or it may be the altitude, or the payload, or the mean time before failure, or any of a thousand other things. Generally, an attempt is made to specify the factor, or factors, that would contribute most to making the total system a success. This decision is not made by the Government people alone. The technical people have a large say in it. Once the factor is identified, however, the Government has to include it in the contract.

After the factor is identified, it must be defined in measureable terms. How else will the Government know whether the contractor has been successful? This means that the technical staffs (Government and contractor) must together establish a definite guideline for the testing of performance. Usually a test document is developed and incorporated in the contract. It will define specifically what is being measured and how. Too often this step is neglected; the results are some awful tussles.

One thing further remains to be done: the balancing of the performance-incentive arrangements with the cost-incentive arrangement. The Government has to assign properly weighted values to each of the identified parameters. If the cost is most important, it should bear the greatest

Table 1. Performance Incentives

	Reward or penalty ($)	Limit ($)
Delivery		
On schedule	0	——
Early	+10,000/day	+300,000
Late	−10,000/day	−300,000
Performance		
Aircraft flies at 100,000 ft	0	——
Above	+40,000/1000 ft	+400,000
Below	−20,000/1000 ft	−400,000*

*If aircraft does not reach 80,000 ft, the system is unacceptable

Table 2. Profit Possibilities*

	Max	Target	Min
On cost	$11,300,000	$7,300,000	$3,300,000
On performance	800,000	400,000	0
On delivery	600,000	300,000	0
Total profit	$12,700,000	$8,000,000	$3,300,000

*Taken from the three points plotted in Fig. 5.

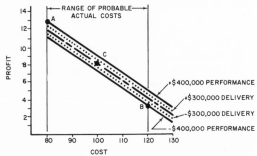

5. **Performance and delivery incentives** can also be added to the cost-profit chart. In this particular case, the major profit motive is still dependent on cost reduction.

weight; likewise, delivery and system-performance weighting should show their relative standing. Obviously, there are trade-offs to be made. The Government does not want to write a contract that says, "Spend as much as you like for performance and we'll give you a big bonus for it." Likewise, the Government does not want to pay a big bonus for cost reduction at a sacrifice of quality. Significantly, performance and schedule incentives may no longer be used in DOD contracts unless appropriate cost-control incentives operate at the same time.

Performance incentives can be shown in the cost-profit chart. Usually they are stated as an adjustment to the fee that is otherwise payable. Let's assume a very simple example. The contract is for an aircraft that has an estimated cost of $100 million, a profit (at that cost) of $8 million, and a share formula of 80-20. Performance incentives are on delivery and flying altitude and are characterized in the accompanying tables. The cost-profit chart, shown in Figure 5, can then be drawn.

Looking at this relationship another way, we select three points on the chart for comparison: the maximum profit at the lowest point in the range of probable actual cost (A), the minimum profit for the highest point on the range (B), and the target (C). We now add up combinations of these extremes (see Table 2) to illustrate the balance of incentives.

If the aircraft is delivered late (zero profit), flies at only 80,000 ft (zero profit) but is manufactured at a cost of 20% under target, the contractor realizes a profit of $11,300,000 and (see Table 2) this is still better than meeting target on all three elements. Obviously, the weighting of incentives in this case says that delivery is not too important; that the government can get along with an 80,000-ft performance; but that, above all, costs have to be watched.

This is a simple illustration, but one can see the importance of balancing incentives so that they properly motivate the contractor to achieve what the Government wants. Once the effort is launched, the contractor is continually confronted with trade-off decisions that affect his profit. ("Should the Government spend the extra $372,000 to carry out an effort that has 87% probability of adding 1000 ft to performance?") By adding in ten, twenty, or more performance parameters, each of which interrelates with the others, the situation becomes even more complicated. ■ ■

5 MANAGING FINANCES

Profit by learning cost analysis
Good budgeting can boost profits
Profit/volume analysis aids planning
How to justify large equipment expenditures
Get to know your local SBA agent

If engineering managers could relive the past, which subjects would they most like to have had more training in before they became managers? In a survey of dozens of engineering managers conducted by *Electronic Design* magazine, some 80% specified "business and finance" as the area where they most wished they'd had more education. This section will help meet that need.

The first three chapters take up three major financial areas that every engineering manager must deal with. They are costs and cost accounting methods, budgeting, and finally profit/volume analysis.

A common financial problem in the engineering department involves the purchase of large capital equipment, instrumentation, computers, checkout systems, and so on. Engineering reasons are easy to give, but unfortunately approvals must usually be sought from financially oriented managers higher up on the corporate hierarchy. "Profit/volume analysis aids planning" shows how the return-on-investment method can be used to convince even the hard-headed financial executive that a large equipment purchase makes sense.

For the engineering manager in a small company, "Get to know your local SBA agent" shows just what sorts of benefits are available from the Small Business Administration. Their range of services may surprise you.

Profit by learning cost analysis

Any engineer can spur his advance to the ranks of management by knowing how to control business expenses.

You're a design engineer, and there's no reason why you should be concerned with costs and budgets. After all, that's the job of the controller's department. Right?

Wrong.

Regardless of your engineering responsibility, a working knowledge of costs and budgets is an asset.

As a design engineer, it will give you a better understanding of the total company structure and where you and your department fit into it. If you want to move into management, you will find a background in cost and budgets invaluable.

Even front-line or middle managers may need a refresher course to live successfully within their budgets and make the best use of allotted funds.

Fortunately, as an engineer you have a head start in learning about costs. Your engineering training has stressed rationality, analysis and decision-making based on facts. These same techniques are used in cost analysis.

Three kinds of costs

There are three types of costs: *fixed, variable* and *mixed*. All costs are classified on the basis of how they are affected by changes in volume.

Fixed costs are those that remain constant regardless of production or sales volume. Typical examples are depreciation, property taxes, rent, most insurance and salaries.

Variable costs vary directly with volume. The best example of a pure variable—one that varies directly with sales volume—is a commission. Two other examples are materials and direct labor.

A true variable cost has these characteristics:

- There is a direct relationship between the cost and the level of activity.
- The initial cost is incurred at the start of production or sale of the product and not when the plant is established.

In between these two are *mixed costs* which combine the characteristics of fixed and variable. Some mixed costs have a fixed base and then an additional increment that increases in a straight line as volume—usually production volume—increases.

Other costs are mixed in that they stay at a given level for a relatively narrow range of activity, then

step upward for the next higher range, such as indirect labor. For example, maintenance costs go up in steps as each man is added to the force.

If you examine costs closely, you'll soon realize that there are very few pure variable or absolutely fixed costs. Most fall somewhere between the two extremes.

These are the main reasons why:

- Fixed costs, in general, are not fixed ad infinitum. At some point, as volume increases or decreases substantially, corresponding increases or decreases can be expected. For example, if additional product lines are added, more engineers may be needed. Thus the fixed cost of salaries will rise.

■ Even the cost of materials is not always a pure variable. For example, you invariably have scrap. Therefore, some portion of the material—namely, the scrap—may have to be treated as an accepted and fixed cost. This scrap, then, is a portion of the material that is not a pure variable.

Why analyze costs?

The reason you are breaking down costs this way is that you are looking for a better basis for management to make decisions, such as setting up flexible operating budgets and determining into which products the marketing department should put its major effort, as well as looking for areas of potential cost improvement. For these reasons, you must analyze, identify and formulate your costs.

To illustrate, consider fixed costs. The examples previously cited are also called *burden costs* (or overhead), which gives a clue to what they mean in the over-all financial picture.

Your company has relatively little control over burden costs. Regardless of production volume, these costs will occur and must be paid. Before your company can show a profit, it must first meet this overhead.

Therefore, assuming things don't become so bad that workers must be discharged and a smaller plant leased, you must look to variable and mixed costs for cost improvement. Both have one thing in common: variable increments. Both rise in relation to volume. Thus, they are termed *controllable costs*.

To control these costs, you must first analyze

them and calculate the size of the variable increments of each over a period of time. It is from these increments that you usually will find areas to control costs.

Also, determine the variable cost for each product. A total of all variable costs will not give a true picture of any individual product.

How to analyze costs

Now that you know what types of costs there are and why you should analyze them, start the analysis:

1. Select a measure that is representative of departmental activity over, say, the most recent 12 months. The measure selected will depend upon the department being analyzed, and it may be the number of pieces produced, the direct labor hours involved, tons, yards or gallons produced.

2. For the given cost being analyzed, match the actual dollars spent in each of the 12 months against the activity measure for each month. Thus, dollars of cost in January is matched against January's activity as expressed by the selected measure.

3. It is helpful next to plot the dollars of cost versus the activity on graph paper. The resulting data are then studied in the light of the manager's experience to determine the realistic formula or tabulation that can be used to predict how this cost will or should act in the future.

To illustrate this procedure, plots for the two most common types of mixed costs, *linear* and *step*, will be worked out.

Assume that at a given plant, cost data are being compiled to be used in product cost estimating to set up flexible operating budgets. The two particular costs to be analyzed are "electrical power" and "receiving and shipping labor." It has been determined that the total direct labor hours in the plant are a realistic measure of total plant activity. This activity measure is the base against which variations in this and other costs will be gauged in your cost analysis.

(The costs to be analyzed in this situation happen to involve the total plant operation. The same procedure can be followed for a specific department, division or product. Also, in this instance "total plant direct labor hours" is used as the measure; "total direct labor wages," "total materials used" or some other measure could have been chosen.)

The data to be analyzed are:

Month	Activity measure direct labor hrs.	Power cost	Rec., Ship. labor cost
Jan.	5900	$2900	$2900
Feb.	6000	3400	2800
Mar.	6600	3500	3200
Apr.	6500	3100	3000
May	5200	3000	2600
June	3400	2100	1700
July	3200	1800	1850
Aug.	3600	2400	2000
Sept.	3900	2100	1800
Oct.	4400	2600	2200
Nov.	5000	2500	2300
Dec.	4600	2200	2400

Before you plot the costs, ask yourself why these two costs, electrical power and receiving and shipping labor, are mixed—that is, why both fixed and variable costs are combined.

Now, plot the two costs on separate graphs. Are they linear (straight line) or step costs?

Figure 1 shows what your graph for electrical power should look like. The activity measure (direct labor hours) is scaled along the x axis and electrical power costs along the y. Once the scattered points are plotted, they are best described by a straight line. It is preferable to determine this line by the Method of Least Squares (see box).

The manager's knowledge of how electrical power

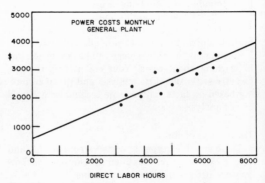

figure 1

is used and paid for, combined with the line describing the 12 plotted points, indicates that a linear relationship exists between this cost and activity. Thus, the power is a linear mixed cost.

Why? All evidence shows that it does not start from a base of zero dollars at zero activity. Instead the data show a fixed base and then a direct, linear increase as activity rises.

With the Method of Least Squares, the formula for this cost is:

Monthly power cost = $408 + 42¢
$\times$ direct labor hours

With this formula, you can predict what the cost will be for intermediate activity levels. At the end of a budget month, when the total direct labor hours are known, the formula can be applied to establish the budgeted allowances for electrical power costs. Similarly, it can be used in estimating product costs and in profit planning.

Now examine the data for receiving and shipping

Least Squares Method yields best fit

The Method of Least Squares is widely used to draw a straight line of best fit through a set of experimentally obtained points. It consists of determining all deviations of observed points from such a line, squaring them, and then minimizing this sum of squares.

Here is the essence of the method:

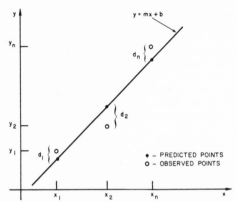

A straight line that comes closest to fitting a set of experimentally observed points is determined by finding all deviations of this line from the observed values of y, squaring and adding them, and then minimizing this sum.

Consider a set of experimentally observed points (above) such as $(x_1, y_1), (x_2, y_2), \ldots, (x_n, y_n)$. The problem is to find a straight line

$$y = mx + b \qquad (1)$$

that best fits all these points.

Corresponding to each value of x are two values of y—namely, the observed value, y_{obs}, and the value predicted by the straight line $mx_{obs} + b$. This difference

$$y_{obs} - (mx_{obs} + b) \qquad (2)$$

will be called a deviation, d. Each deviation measures the amount by which the predicted value of y falls short of the observed value. The set of all the deviations

$$d_1 = y_1 - (mx_1 + b), \ldots, d_n = y_n - (mx_n + b) \qquad (3)$$

is indicative of how closely the predicted line, Eq. 1, coincides with the observed data. If you can minimize these deviations, you will obtain the line of best fit.

Obviously some of the deviations will be positive, some negative. Their squares, however, will be all positive, and the equation

$$f(m,b) = (y_1 - mx_1 - b)^2 + (y_2 - mx_2 - b)^2 + \ldots + (y_n - mx_n - b)^2 \qquad (4)$$

counts both positive and negative deviations equally. Note that in this expression the desired constants m and b are treated as variables for the time being. This sum of squares of deviations depends on the choice of m and b; it is never negative, and it can be zero only if m and b have values that produce a straight line of perfect fit. Another way of saying this is: "Take as the line $y = mx + b$ of best fit that one for which the sum of squares of the deviations

$$f(m, b) = d_1^2 + d_2^2 + \ldots + d_n^2 \qquad (5)$$

is a minimum."

To determine such a minimum, we apply the standard minimization procedure—that is, that of taking derivatives of this sum with respect to m and b, setting the results equal to zero and solving the two equations with two unknowns for m and b.

Here is an example: Suppose we have a set of observed points (0, 1), (1, 3), (2, 2). The first numbers in each parentheses are the observed values of x, and the second numbers are the observed values of y.

We must first form the deviations and their squares. Let's do this in this table:

x_{obs}	y_{obs}	dev. = $y_{obs} - mx_{obs} - b$	dev.^{2}
0	1	$1 - b$	$1 - 2b + b^2$
1	3	$3 - m - b$	$9 - 6b + b^2 - 6m + 2mb + m^2$
2	2	$2 - 2m - b$	$4 - 4b + b^2 - 8m + 4mb + 4m^2$

Adding all expressions in the last column, we get the sum of deviations:

$$f(m, b) = 14 - 12b + 3b^2 - 14m + 6mb + 5m^2. \qquad (6)$$

Now we differentiate this expression with respect to m and set it equal to zero:

$$\partial f(m, b)/\partial m = -14 + 6b + 10m = 0. \qquad (7)$$

Then we do the same for b:

$$\partial f(m, b)/\partial b = -12 + 6b + 6m = 0. \qquad (8)$$

Rearranging Eqs. 7 and 8, we get

$$6b + 10m = 14, \qquad (9)$$

$$6b + 6m = 12. \qquad (10)$$

Subtracting Eq. 10 from 9, we get

$$4m = 2,$$

$$\therefore m = 1/2.$$

Substituting this value of m into Eq. 9 or 10, we get

$$b = 1.5$$

Consequently the best equations for the best straight line for the set of points of this example is

$$y = (x/2) + 1.5$$

labor (see Fig. 2). Again, activity data are scaled along the *x* axis and dollars of cost along the *y*.

Monthly cost of receiving & shipping labor

Direct Labor Hours		$ of Cost
3000 to 4000	=	1800
4001 to 5000	=	2250
5001 to 6000	=	2700
6001 to 7000	=	3150

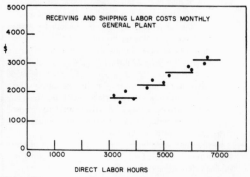

figure 2

If you consider only the plotted points, you might conclude that a linear relationship exists between this cost and activity, as in the previous analysis. However, if you are familiar with the operations of individual departments, you know that this would be an incorrect conclusion.

Often in indirect labor use, which this is, a given crew size is sufficient only up to a certain level of activity. Above that activity, additional manpower must be added. Thus the cost literally rises in steps.

This analysis illustrates why the cost analyst must be familiar with company operations. Often cost figures alone don't give a true picture. Subjective evaluations are also necessary at times.

The step mixed cost is usually expressed in table form. The tabulation in this case would be:

You may think it is illogical to say that when direct labor hours rise from 4000 to 4001, an additional $450 monthly cost will result. But some arbitrary break between step levels must be selected, and the evidence supports this selection.

Here's one final point on plotting mixed costs:

You may logically expect that certain items of cost will vary directly with volume at a decreasing or increasing incremental value, rather than at a constant increment. However, in practice, such parabolic curves are a rare phenomenon in cost analysis, budgeting and estimating work.

Practical hints in cost analysis

Now you have the basic tools of cost analysis. To complete the picture here are some additional tips to make your analysis results more meaningful:

■ Your first duty in cost analysis is to know the

company operation. Some wrong conclusions can be drawn if formulations are developed solely from the data or their plots. One example has already been given in the case of the step mixed cost (Fig. 2).

■ Your analytical results will depend on the quality of the cost data. Good cost analysis requires good cost gathering and reporting. For example, you should segregate large, continuing items of costs, so that they can be analyzed separately. To lump welding rods and gasses under operating supplies, for example, may result in inadequate control of both.

■ Within practical limits, charge costs as close to the time of use as possible. When a three months' supply of an item is charged to a department at one time, the costs are distorted for all three months. They are overstated in the month charged and understated for the two other months. This is particularly important on high-cost items.

■ The very act of plotting your cost data against activity can yield clues to recent cost performance. If the plot shows a wide deviation and you are satisfied with the quality of the cost reporting, chances are the cost is relatively uncontrolled. As a result, you have a good area for potential cost savings.

■ When one or more plotted points fall well above the line, further and detailed study of those months can uncover poor operating practices that warrant correction. Conversely, points well below the line reveal a temporary method or practice that should become standard.

Profits don't grow on trees: The successful company doesn't leave cost control to chance. Cost analysis is the first step in preparing a budget. The entire budgeting process is the single most effective method for a company to control costs and then attain or increase its profits.

■ If you plot cost versus activity monthly and end up with too diverse a pattern to make a meaningful decision, then try plotting for two-month periods. The 6 points may reveal a pattern and relationship not apparent with 12 points.

■ The relationship between cost and activity often forms a pattern only when one month's cost is plotted against the previous month's activity. This is because your company will usually charge off the bill a month after the service or material is used.

■ The cost analyst often has to use the data available to him without being able to make a detailed, intensive investigation of them. In these cases, when working in an area of relatively uncontrolled costs, he should base his cost formulations on lower levels than those experienced in the past.

■ Whenever possible and practical, use the Method of Least Squares and avoid eyeballing the line to describe the plotted points. When a mixed cost is erroneously formulated as a pure variable, it is understated or under-allowed at the lower levels of activity and overstated or over-allowed at the higher levels of activity.

■ Be realistic in analyzing and formulating costs. Utilize the available data. You are predicting costs for levels of activity that are actually going to be experienced, not for some unrealistic theoretical minimum. ■ ■

Glossary of terms

Activity measure—This is the specific yardstick that is felt accurately reflects or measures the level of activity of a cost center. It is against this activity measure that costs in the center will be matched, to predict how the costs may act in the future.

Cost center—A segment of the enterprise under the direction of a specified member of management who is responsible for the effective operation of that segment. A typical example of a cost center in a capacitor plant would be electrolytic capacitor winding, which is under a specific foreman. When a given cost center is very large or involves great amounts of money, subdivisions of the center, called subcenters, may be used.

Bibliography:
Maynard, H. B. *Handbook of Business Administration.* New York: McGraw-Hill Book Co., 1967 ($29.95).
Moroney, M.J. *Facts from Figures.* Baltimore, Md.: Penguin Books, 1951 ($1.95).

Good budgeting can boost profits

Learn the fiscal fundamentals and you'll know how management plans profits by controlling costs.

Lawrence M. Matthews, Vice President, Stevenson, Jordan & Harrison Management Consultants, Inc., New York.

Budgets are two-faced!

But, unlike the colloquial two-faced person, each face of the budget complements the other.

One face is a *control*. A budget provides the mechanism for predicting income and costs, and then comparing them against ensuing actual company performance to achieve control over that performance.

The other face is a *profit plan*. Laying down a projection of income goals and cost restraints is an act of management that is clearly also a plan for the company's future.

Put the two faces together and a budget is seen to be a realistic statement of objectives, a plan, against which actual performance is matched so that control can be achieved.

Experience shows that budgeting is the single most effective way to control costs and so make profits.

What type is best?

There are two types of budgets, *fixed* and *flexible*.

When sales are relatively stable month by month, it is often entirely practical to project a budget month by month. Then in the course of that fiscal year, actual sales and expenses are simply compared with the budget. The comparisons made are:

Budgeted sales   vs   Actual sales
                     and
Budgeted expenses   vs   Actual expenses
at budgeted sales   at actual sales

This is called fixed budgeting and has these advantages:

■ It is simple and relatively easy to understand.

■ It involves a minimum amount of effort and expense, because there is no need to analyze costs to determine their variable element for such interim periods as a month.

■ It is easier to apply because budgeted allowances are calculated once a year and are not adjusted to actual month-by-month activity.

In reality, however, actual sales almost never equal budgeted sales, so you should want to compare actual costs with budgeted costs.

Fixed budgeting does not allow for this comparison because it does not show the budgeted expense of the actual activity. As a result there is no standard against which to compare actual expenses, and thus no controls.

A more meaningful control is the flexible operating budget, under which variable expenses are identified, and budgeted allowances can be revised to a more realistic allowance based on actual activity.

Under flexible operating budgets, the sales comparison is still the same as under fixed budgets:

Budgeted sales   vs   Actual sales

The comparison for expenses, however, is now:

Budgeted expenses   vs   Actual expenses
at *actual* sales   at actual sales

Now what was actually spent can be compared with what you believe should have been spent at the given actual volume. And with these data, operating costs can be controlled.

Budgets should be both a control and a plan. Only flexible budgets meet both these requirements. Fixed budgets fall short in the control category.

Start with the basics

If budgets are to be effective, three basics, which comprise the foundation of a budget, must first be established:

1. *Cost centers*—sometimes called work and/or profit centers—must be established to reflect how the operation is actually set up, so that responsibility for budget performance can be pinpointed. In an electronics firm, cost centers might be manufacturing, sales, research and development, administration, etc. It is often advisable to subdivide these centers. In manufacturing, for example, such subdivisions might be individual production departments, shipping, stock room, etc.

2. A *chart of accounts* must be drawn. It should

be complete and well-defined and fit the needs of both accounting and operating departments. Budgets are operating controls and must reflect actual operating conditions, not artificial accounting classifications. The accounting classifications (chart of accounts) must therefore reflect the operating requirements of the plant and its cost centers.

3. *Cost charging (or distribution) procedures* that are well-understood and disciplined must be used in day-to-day operations, so that all operating costs (labor, supplies, etc.) are properly identified and charged to the cost center or centers that use them.

Develop your budget

A flexible operating budget passes through three phases:

Predictive—a forecast of future performance (that is, the actual preparation of the budget).

Comparison—actual performance related to the budget's predicted performance.

Followup—constructive action on the findings of the comparison between predicted and actual, rewarding good performances and correcting bad.

With the basics established, the actual budget can be prepared:

1. Begin with a sales projection—an estimate of income for the budget year. Sales forecasting usually is the function of the sales or marketing department, which should provide this information.

2. Break down the sales forecast into product lines and quantities of units; then into activity measures for each cost center involved in making the products. If this type of detailed breakdown is impossible, then the budgeting department must translate the dollars of forecasted sales into some form of activity measures for individual cost centers. Such measures could be direct labor hours, engineer's salaries, materials used, machine hours, units produced, etc. It is important that the activity measure chosen charts and reflects changes in production activity and production costs during the budget year.

3. Determine the following for each cost center:

■ What specific items of cost must be budgeted for the cost center?

■ How much has been spent in the past for these items of cost?

■ How are these costs identified? Are they fixed, variable or mixed? The previous chapter on cost analysis will help in determining this.

■ How much should be allowed or budgeted for each cost at various levels of predicted activity? This is the actual establishment of budgeted costs which will be based on past history, personal judgment or both.)

Don't hesitate to use historical costs as the basis for developing budget allowances. They have the following advantages:

- They provide the needed starting point.

- The data are needed to help identify the nature of each cost (fixed, variable or mixed) as it actually reacts to volume changes.

- They are the data most readily available.

- They provide standards that will be beaten if your budgets are effective.

4. Establish a complete record for each cost item in each cost center by using a budget data sheet (Fig. 1). Once these are included in a budget data book, you have a record of how you reach your specific budget decision, as well as a starting point for next year's budget.

5. Summarize, on one sheet for each cost center and subcenter, the budget allowances at normal or average activity for all costs incurred in that cost center. These summary sheets (Fig. 2) can be tied into the profit plan calculations.

6. Review in detail with each department head or foreman all the budget allowances for each cost item' in his department. If possible, have him work with you in the development of his allowances. He must have the opportunity to make a complete review and express his views on each item.

Be alert in the course of the budget review to whether unrealistic goals have been established. Oddly enough, the most common fault in preparing budgets is to set budget goals that are too high to be realistic and cannot be met. In such circumstances, the experienced budget man advocates looser or lower standards. They may be higher than yet attained, but still are reachable.

BUDGET DATA SHEET

DATE	COMPILED	ACCT. CLASS	COST CENTER NAME		COST CENTER NO.		
DATE	ACCEPTED	PERIOD	ACCOUNT NAME		ACCOUNT NO.		
DATE	APPROVED	UNIT			UNITS IN PERIOD		
DATE	REASON FOR REVISION OF BUDGET			AMOUNT	TOTAL REVISION		
				$	$		
				$	$		
				$	$		
				$	$		
THIS ACCOUNT IS CHARGED WITH:							
BUDGET WAS DETERMINED AS FOLLOWS:					TOTAL	CONSTANT	VARIABLE

Figure 1

BUDGET SUMMARY SHEET

COST CENTER NO.	COST CENTER NAME					COMPILED	DATE
						ACCEPTED	DATE
UNITS IN PERIOD	PERIOD	UNIT				APPROVED	DATE
ACCOUNTS		TYPE OF COST	STANDARD BUDGET			RATE PER UNIT		
NO.	NAME		TOTAL	VARIABLE	CONSTANT			VARIABLE

Figure 2

MANUFACTURING COST AND VARIANCE STATEMENT

DEPARTMENT _____

MONTH OF: YEAR TO DATE:

			EXPENSE ANALYSIS			
VARIANCE (BAD IN RED)	ACTUAL	STANDARD OR BUDGET	ACCOUNT		ACTUAL	VARIANCE
			NO.	TITLE		

Figure 3

Follow up your budget

The followup is most important because it is the payoff of all the budget effort.

The first step in budget followup is periodic reporting, usually monthly, of actual performance to budget. These reports are commonly called cost and variance statements (Fig. 3). One such report is issued for each cost center and subcenter with summary reports for major departmental groupings and for the business as a whole. The cost and variance report for any cost center shows the following for each item of cost:

- What dollar amount was budgeted at the actual activity level.
- What was actually spent.
- What the difference or variance between the two was.

Again note that in flexible budgets the budgeted amount listed on the cost and variance statement is for the actual activity for the budget period, not the

Glossary of terms

Activity measure—This is the specific yardstick that is felt accurately reflects or measures the level of activity of a cost center. It is against this activity measure that costs in the center will be matched, to predict how these same costs may act in the future months.

Actual expense—The dollars actually spent by the cost center in a budget period for a given cost item.

Budget allowance—The dollars allowed by the budget for a budget period for a given cost item in a specific cost center.

Budget period—The segment of a full year for which budget and actual expenses are compared and variances developed, usually monthly.

Budget year—The twelve months of the fiscal year, which may or may not coincide with the calendar year.

Chart of accounts—A list by name and code number of cost, asset, liability and capital money items, needed to apply standard accounting practice to the financial and operating affairs of an enterprise and to produce meaningful statements in both financial and operating departments.

Cost and variance statement—The enumeration for a budget period of all the budget allowances, actual expenses, and variances for a given cost center.

Cost center—A segment of the enterprise under the direction of a specified member of management who is responsible for the effective operation of that segment. A typical example of a cost center in a capacitor plant would be electrolytic capacitor winding, which is under a specific foreman. When a given cost center is very large or involves great amounts of money, sub-divisions of the center, called subcenters, may be used.

Variance—The difference between the budget allowance and the actual expense for a given cost item in a specific cost center for a particular budget period. Where actual expenses are less than the budget allowance, the variance is called "favorable" and is most commonly printed in black. Where actual expenses exceed the budget allowance, the variance is called "unfavorable" and is most commonly printed in red or within brackets.

R&D budgeting is a greater challenge

Developing a budget for research and development is a greater challenge than other budgeting. It is less susceptible to close prediction: it is difficult to measure progress in clearcut and objective terms. As a result, it can be difficult to measure performance at specific intervals within the budget year.

R&D budgeting must include the following steps:

1. Top management must determine what percentage of forecast income will be allocated to R&D.

2. Once the R&D allocation is roughed out, the available funds must be spread among the research functions or projects. How the monies will specifically be budgeted depends on how the R&D effort is organized—that is, by functions, by projects or by a combination of the two. This step of dividing the total R&D allocation requires the efforts of three management areas:

- Research—to propose specific areas of promise worthy of effort and expenditure of company funds.

- Marketing—to propose specific product developments needed to maintain and increase the company's share of the market.

- Top management—to weigh alternatives and reconcile differences.

This step implies the existence of company policies and long-range plans that will provide the basis for decisions on the potential of each R&D program. Without such long-range plans, decisions can only be made in the light of current conditions. Such decisions are more prone to change than those based on long-term plans. This in turn increases the danger and frequency of misallocations of R&D funds.

Long range plans become particularly important when a total program, or programs, require more funds than are allocated. Then it will be necessary to evaluate and compare programs and select those that offer the greatest potential from available funds.

3. Budgets or planned cost estimates are then laid out to control the flow of money to specific programs.

4. Finally there must be periodic progress reviews to decide whether to continue programs, rechannel funds or terminate programs.

Though this final step implies the ability to measure objectively the progress of R&D programs and to establish and define stages of progress, there are times when progress can only be stated in subjective terms. Regardless, the important point is that an attempt to measure progress in the best available terms should be made.

---

activity originally forecast for the period.

These reports should be issued within 10 days after the budget period ends.

To ensure meaningful reporting, make sure of the following:

- That accounting clerks, receiving clerks, storeroom men, purchasing people, and others involved understand what cost items are charged to what account. Put the account definitions in writing.

- That too many diverse items of cost are not lumped into one account. Each major item of expense should have its own account. When several such items are lumped in one account, gains in one item may disguise over-budget costs in others.

- That purchasing and the storeroom are not charging several months of costs to one operating period. If a number of months' needs are purchased for delivery at one time, the item should be doled out in monthly quantities and not charged in its entirety in the month received. The latter practice distorts all the months affected, overcharging the month received and undercharging subsequent months.

At the start of a new budget or budget revitalization program, large variances are frequently encountered. The cause of these variances must be investigated at once. If they are caused by procedural or clerical errors, correct them immediately. If

poor operating performance is the cause, the variances obviously cannot easily be changed immediately. Further performance analysis or supervisory correction will be needed.

The final followup step is the establishment of a fairly rigid program of checking with cost center supervisors on their performance to budget. This step is vital because it provides supervisors with the opportunity to ask questions and obtain answers, and it affords budgeting personnel the chance to detect areas of potential cost reduction.

There are three other follow-up guidelines:

1. Do not depend solely on the cost and variance statements for all cost control. Recognize that there are certain costs that involve so much money that they warrant weekly and even daily reports. Direct labor and direct material are two examples of costs that commonly need more than monthly control.

2. Alert top management to the fact that department managers can go only so far in improvement efforts, because of time, experience and training limitations. After that they need staff assistance from industrial engineering, product engineering, plant engineering, etc.

3. Keep a continuing critical eye on the budgeting program:

- Set up quantitative measures of budget results

Measure the results

by, for example, continuing comparisons between current and past actual costs.

▪ Set up qualitative measures such as the way department heads and foremen react to their budgets, how actively they follow them up and, most important, what action they take as the result of their budgets.

If the budget installation and followup actions are effective, costs will be reduced and favorable variances generated. In subsequent budget years, the allowances will be reduced to reflect the improved performance. However, you must be realistic when raising budget standards so that the new standards can be attained.

Effective budgets always yield a dollar return that is many times their cost. A common and readily understood measure is a comparison of the most important costs for three months before budget versus three months after budget, with production activity equalized for both periods. Another measure is the tracing of cost improvements directly into the monthly profit and loss statement.

This measure leads us into the subject of the next chapter in this section covering profit/volume analysis—a technique for evaluating and measuring the effects of improvement in fixed and variable costs, which is one of the chief aims of budgeting.

Profit/volume analysis aids planning

There are three indicators to sound income planning and wise managers know how to manipulate them.

Lawrence M. Matthews, Vice President, Stevenson, Jordan & Harrison Management Consultants, Inc., New York.

Listen to an inexperienced businessman:

"I don't need any financial expert to tell me how to increase profits. It's just common sense. The more you sell, the more money you make. Any fool knows that."

He's right. Any *fool* knows that. But a wise profit planner knows that it isn't necessarily true. Increased sales do not automatically guarantee that profits will rise, too. Increased sales could result in decreased profits, or even a loss.

Wise businessmen—including good engineering managers—use three barometers to plan profits. They are the profit/volume ratio, the breakeven point and the margin of safety.

The *profit/volume ratio* tells you how much of each sales dollar is available after direct or variable costs are paid to help absorb overhead—the fixed costs. Once the overhead is absorbed, the balance of the sales dollar contributes to profits. Ideally, you want the P/V ratio to be as high as possible, thus absorbing overhead costs as quickly as possible.

One formula* for determining the P/V ratio is this one:

$$\text{P/V ratio} = \frac{\text{Profit} + \text{Fixed Costs}}{\text{Sales}}.$$

The *breakeven point* tells you the minimum sales volume (income) needed to absorb the overhead. Ideally, you want this amount to be as low as possible.

A formula for determining the breakeven point is:

$$\text{Breakeven Point} = \frac{\text{Fixed Costs}}{\text{Profit/Volume Ratio}}$$

The *margin of safety*, which can be expressed in either dollars or a percentage, is the difference between the breakeven·point and your present average sales volume. It is the dollar amount or the percentage that sales can drop before the breakeven point is reached and losses begin. Ideally, you want this margin to be as great as possible. If a company is losing money, it is the amount of dollars or percentage that sales must increase before a breakeven operation is achieved.

---

*Another method of determining the P/V ratio is:

$$\text{P/V Ratio} = \frac{\text{Sales Income} - \text{Variable Costs}}{\text{Sales Income}}$$

In this article, however, all calculations will follow the formula cited in the text.

Table 1. Monthly profit and loss statement

Sales

70,000 units @ $10 apiece				$700,000

Expenses	Fixed	Variable	Total	
Material		$200,000	$200,000	
Direct labor		230,000	230,000	
Indirect labor	$ 20,000		20,000	
Instruments	25,000	25,000	50,000	
Operating supplies	15,000	15,000	30,000	
Depreciation, taxes, insurances, etc.	60,000		60,000	
Selling expenses	40,000	10,000	50,000	
Administrative expenses	40,000		40,000	
	$200,000	$480,000	$680,000	
Total expenses				680,000
Profit				$ 20,000

Table 2. Monthly profit and loss statement

A. Action taken:

    (a) Applied ratio-delay study findings and reduced crew by 2 men.
    (b) Started small instrument requisition system, improved test set-up design, obtained certain purchase price reductions.
    (c) Installed monthly flexible budget, installed a supply requisition system.
    (d) Reviewed insurance coverage and costs, reduced monthly expenses.
    (e) Tightened up on entertainment and travel costs, combined two territories.
    (f) Through a secretary-typist pool, saved one girl, reduced certain miscellaneous expenses.

B. Results of the action:

Income – sales				$700,000
Expenses	Fixed	Variable	Total	
Material		$200,000	$200,000	
Direct labor		230,000	230,000	
Indirect labor	$ 11,000(a)		11,000	
Instruments	22,500(b)	25,000	47,500	
Supplies	13,500(c)	15,000	28,500	
Deprec., insur., taxes, etc.	56,000(d)		56,000	
Selling expense	37,000(e)	10,000	47,000	
Administrative expense	35,000(f)		35,000	
	$175,000	$480,000	$655,000	
Total expenses				655,000
Pre-tax profit				$ 45,000

Table 3. Monthly profit and loss statement

A. Action taken:

    (a) Purchasing action and value-analysis studies reduced material cost by 10%.

    (b) Overtime reduction drive, work measurement and budgets reduced labor by 11%.
    (c) Instrument requisition system, purchasing action and better design reduced test equipment costs.
    (d) Monthly budgets and supply requisition system reduced supply costs.

B. Results of the action:

Income – sales				$700,000
Expenses	Fixed	Variable	Total	
Material		$180,000(a)	$180,000	
Labor		205,000(b)	205,000	
Indirect labor	$ 20,000		20,000	
Instruments	25,000	20,000(c)	45,000	
Supplies	15,000	12,000(d)	27,000	
Deprec., insur., taxes, etc.	60,000		60,000	
Selling expenses	40,000	8,000(e)	48,000	
Administrative expenses	40,000		40,000	
	$200,000	$425,000	$625,000	
Total expenses				625,000
Pre-tax profit				$ 75,000

The formulas for determining the margin of safety dollars and percentage are:

$$\text{Margin of Safety \$} = \text{Sales} - \text{Breakeven Point}$$

$$\text{Margin of Safety \%} = \frac{\text{Sales} - \text{Breakeven Point}}{\text{Sales}}$$

Let's calculate the P/V ratio, breakeven point and margin of safety for a hypothetical company called DEF Electronics and interpret our findings.

Table 1 shows its monthly profit and loss statement.

This company makes one product selling at $10 a unit. With 70,000 units sold in the average month, sales income is $700,000. Analyzing its costs, we determine that at that sales volume, its variable costs are $480,000 and its fixed costs $200,000 more. Subtracting $680,000 in costs from $700,000 of income, we have a $20,000 profit.

From these three knowns—monthly sales volume, monthly fixed costs and monthly profit—we can develop the P/V ratio, breakeven point and margin of safety.

The profit/volume chart (Fig. 1) shows sales income scaled along the x axis. The y axis, however, is bisected with a zero intercept. Above this intercept on the y axis are scaled dollars of profit. Below the zero intercept are scaled both dollars of loss and dollars of fixed costs.

We know the company has $20,000 profit at the current monthly sales income of $700,000. Therefore above the $700,000 sales point on the x ordinate, we go past the zero intercept to $20,000 on the profit scale of the y axis. Thus we have one point.

From our analysis, we determine that fixed costs total $200,000 a month. Therefore at zero sales income we go below the zero intercept to $200,000 on the fixed cost scale of the *y* axis. We now have a second point.

We can now draw a straight line connecting the fixed cost point on the *y* axis that is below the zero intercept with the point of profit above both the zero intercept line and the average monthly sales income. This is our *profit/volume line*. Where this line crosses the zero intercept is our breakeven point. The linear distance along the *x* axis between the breakeven point and the average monthly volume is our margin of safety.

Though you can read these three items off the chart, you obtain more precise answers by doing the actual calculation.

First, get the P/V ratio

You start the calculation by determining the P/V ratio. Using the previously mentioned formula:

$$P/V \text{ Ratio} = \frac{\text{Profit} + \text{Fixed Costs}}{\text{Sales}}$$

and using the data for DEF Electronics, we calculate:

$$P/V \text{ Ratio} = \frac{\$20,000 + \$200,000}{\$700,000}$$
$$= 31.4\%.$$

Thus $31.40 of every $100 of sales is available for the absorption of overhead and, once overhead is absorbed, for additions to profit.

Next, find breakeven point

Knowing the P/V ratio, we can calculate the breakeven point, which is reached when the overhead or fixed costs are totally absorbed. With the formula:

$$\text{Breakeven Point} = \frac{\text{Fixed Costs}}{\text{Profit/Volume Ratio}},$$

we calculate:

$$\text{Breakeven Point} = \frac{\$200,000}{0.314}$$
$$= \$637,000.$$

Finally, determine margin of safety

With the breakeven point, it is a simple deduction to obtain the margin of safety for DEF Electronics:

$$\text{Margin of Safety \$} = \text{Sales} - \text{Breakeven Point}$$
$$= \$700,00 - \$637,000$$
$$= \$63,000$$

$$\text{Margin of Safety \%} = \frac{\text{Sales} - \text{Breakeven Point}}{\text{Sales}}$$
$$= \frac{\$700,000 - \$637,000}{\$700,000}$$
$$= 9\%.$$

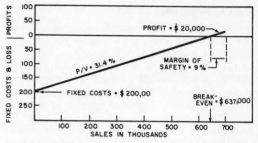

1. The monthly profit/volume chart of DEF Electronics Co., before reducing any costs.

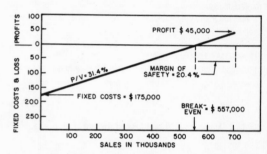

2. The P/V chart of DEF Electronics after fixed costs have been reduced.

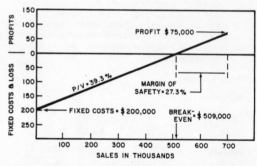

3. The P/V chart of DEF Electronics after restoring fixed costs and reducing variable costs.

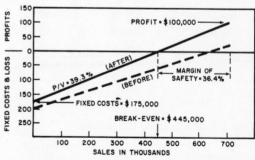

4. The P/V chart, as it looked initially (broken diagonal line) and after cost reductions were made.

Planning improvements

Obviously DEF Electronics is not doing too well. In a month when sales are 9% below the monthly average, a loss is likely. Its margin of safety is dangerously thin. Also, DEF is making only $20,000 on $700,000 sales volume, a profit margin of slightly less than 3% before taxes.

So we institute a course of action that will improve this situation. We will first take action to reduce fixed costs and see what effect these reductions have on the P/V ratio, breakeven point and margin of safety. Note that we will do nothing to increase or decrease sales; the only change will be in reducing fixed costs.

Table 2 shows the revised profit and loss statement after making cost improvements.

Comparing this with the first profit and loss statement, we see that costs have been reduced from $200,000 to $175,000. As a result, our profits increase from $20,000 to $45,000.

We now revise the P/V chart (Fig. 2).

The new P/V ratio calculation is:

$$P/V \text{ Ratio} = \frac{\$45,000 + \$175,000}{\$700,000}$$
$$= 31.4\%.$$

Thus reductions in fixed costs have no effect on the P/V ratio. They did, however, affect both the breakeven point and the margin of safety:

$$\text{Breakeven Point} = \frac{\$175,000}{0.314}$$
$$= \$557,000.$$

$$\text{Margin of Safety \$} = \$700,000 - \$557,000$$
$$= \$143,000.$$

$$\text{Margin of Safety \%} = \frac{\$700,000 - \$557,000}{\$700,000}$$
$$= 20.4\%.$$

Thus the breakeven point has been improved — lowered by $80,000. The margin-of-safety dollar figure has been increased from $63,000 to $143,000, while the margin of safety percentage jumped from 9 to 20.4%.

Reducing variable costs

Suppose we return the fixed costs to their pre-reduction level of $200,000 and initiate a series of actions to reduce variable costs. What effect will this have on the P/V ratio, breakeven point and margin of safety? Again, we neither increase nor decrease sales; the only change is the reduction in variable costs.

Table 3 shows the revised profit and loss statement after reducing the variable costs and returning the fixed costs to their original levels.

At the same $700,000 monthly sales volume, we have reduced variable costs by $55,000 to $425,000. As a result, our profits rose from $20,000 to $75,000. Thus we have a revised P/V chart for DEF Electronics (Fig. 3).

The P/V ratio calculation now is:

$$P/V \text{ Ratio} = \frac{\$75,000 + \$200,000}{\$700,000}$$
$$= 39.3\%.$$

Reductions in variable costs have increased the P/V ratio, which means that the contribution to overhead absorption and to profits has been increased. In this instance, we now have $39.30 instead of $31.40 of every $100 of sales available to cover overhead and eventually to add to profit, once all overhead is covered.

These reductions in variable costs also improve the breakeven point and the margin of safety:

$$\text{Breakeven Point} = \frac{\$200,000}{0.393}$$
$$= \$509,000.$$

$$\text{Margin of Safety \$} = \$700,000 - \$509,000$$
$$= \$191,000.$$

$$\text{Margin of Safety \%} = \frac{\$700,000 - \$509,000}{\$700,000}$$
$$= 27.3\%.$$

The breakeven point has been reduced by $128,000. The margin of safety dollars and percentage go up threefold.

Combining all reductions

Now, we shall combine the reductions in both fixed and variable costs.

Table 4 shows the new profit and loss statement for DEF Electronics.

For the same average monthly sales volume of $700,000, we have increased profits to $100,000— a rise of $80,000—by reducing costs by $80,000.

The "before" and "after" P/V chart is shown in Fig. 4.

And here are our new calculations:

Table 4. Monthly profit and loss statement

Income – sales				$700,000
Expenses	Fixed	Variable	Total	
Material		$180,000	$180,000	
Labor		205,000	205,000	
Indirect labor	$ 11,000		11,000	
Instruments	22,500	20,000	42,500	
Supplies	13,500	12,000	25,500	
Deprec., insur., taxes, etc.	56,000		56,000	
Selling expense	37,000	8,000	45,000	
Administrative expense	35,000		35,000	
	$175,000	$425,000	$600,000	
Total expenses				600,000
Pre-tax profit				$100,000

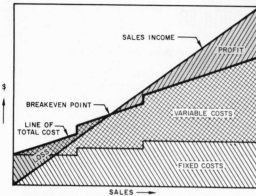

5. A standard breakeven chart. Note that the fixed costs are not fixed ad infinitum, while the variable cost line is both linear and step.

$$\text{P/V Ratio} = \frac{\$100,000 + \$175,000}{\$700,000}$$
$$= 39.3\%.$$
$$\text{Breakeven Point} = \frac{\$175,000}{0.393}$$
$$= \$445,000.$$
$$\text{Margin of Safety } \$ = \$700,000 - \$445,000$$
$$= \$255,000.$$
$$\text{Margin of Safety } \% = \frac{\$700,000 - \$445,000}{\$700,000}$$
$$= 36.4\%.$$

By reducing the fixed and variable costs of DEF Electronics, we have effected these improvements:

- The P/V ratio has increased from 31.4% to 39.3%.
- The breakeven point has been reduced from $637,000 to $445,000.
- The margin of safety dollars has risen from $63,000 to $255,000.
- The margin of safety percentage has increased from 9 to 36.4%.

By effectively controlling costs, we have greatly improved the company's profit picture.

From this experience we can draw some rules.
When fixed costs are reduced:
1. Profits are increased.
2. The breakeven point is reduced.
3. The margin of safety is increased.
4. The profit/volume ratio is unaffected.
When variable costs are reduced:
1. Profits are increased.
2. The breakeven point is reduced.
3. The margin of safety is increased.
4. The profit/volume ratio is increased.

Using the P/V ratio

The P/V ratio is a measure and control that has a great many applications for management. It may, for example, be used to evaluate the following:

- The relative effectiveness of two plants making similar products.
- The relative performance of divisions within a corporation.
- The company's performance versus the competition's.
- Current operating performance compared with past periods.
- The effect of cost changes. If, for instance, a new labor contract has been negotiated, P/V analysis can show the effect of the increases upon the company.
- What sales volume increase, what cost improvement action or what combination of the two will be needed to maintain the past company profit position in the face of increased costs.
- The net effect of proposed capital-investment projects that will increase fixed costs but reduce variable costs.
- The net effect of proposed marketing actions, such as:
1. Price reductions that will reduce income per unit but yield a greater unit sale. ("How many more units must we sell if we reduce prices 10%?")
2. Advertising and sales campaigns calculated to increase volume. ("What increase in sales will we need to cover an advertising campaign costing $100,000 or to pay for four additional salesmen?")
- The relative contributions to overhead absorption and profit of products, territories and/or customers.

Applying breakeven knowledge

A company may feel itself comfortably past the breakeven point. "Of what importance is it to know the breakeven point?" the neophyte may ask.

The reply: Every management should know the effects of its decisions and actions upon the corporate breakeven point. Management should establish its own desired margin of safety and then make a concerted effort to assure that the company maintains that margin.

More than one engineering manager has been caught unawares when the company's breakeven point and margin of safety deteriorated. Disaster often resulted. ■ ■

How to justify large equipment expenditures

Return-on-investment methods can help sell your purchase plans to top management.

Price D. Wickersham, Vice President, Engineering, Brooks Research & Manufacturing, Inc., Kansas City, Mo.

"Okay, Jones, you want this piece of equipment? Fine, as long as you can justify it in dollars and cents."

Engineer Jones is stymied, puzzled and perhaps angered. "How come I have to do it?" he asks. "I'm an engineer, not an accountant."

But Jones doesn't have to be an accountant to be able to show that the capital equipment is a worthwhile buy for the company. And his boss *is* being fair in asking for this justification.

An engineer who proposes a capital purchase often finds his request in competition with capital demands from other sources. It is management's task to decide where best to place the stockholder's money. Often management must make a choice between a number of alternatives.

There are practical ways in which the "payoff" can be shown in a quantitative manner—methods that will get the proposer's argument across effectively.

One approach you can use is the return-on-investment method.

Will it lead to profits?

The basic object of any investment is to obtain a profitable return. Thus a meaningful comparison of the relative merit of two or more proposed capital expenditures would be based on a comparison of their expected rate of return.

If you consider an investment over a fixed period of years, it may be represented by a cash flow time series over that period. For a simple example, Fig. 1 depicts the cash flow from the lender's, or investor's, stand-point for a $100,000 bond having a stated rate of return of 5 per cent over a 10-year period. The investor puts out $100,000 at time-zero, receives $5000 interest at the end of each year as a cash inflow. At the end of the 10th year he receives the last year's interest plus the return of his original capital.

The flow of dollars related to an item of capital equipment may also be considered in this way, although since we are engaged in a prediction process, many of the factors affecting the cash flow (positive and negative) for any given year are

estimates and cannot be reduced to the exactness of the bond transaction of Fig. 1.

As an example, consider the proposed procurement of a fairly large automatic circuit analyzer system. In proposing to purchase the analyzer, you have estimated a schedule of cost savings per year over an eight-year period, in comparison with present manual methods of testing complex circuitry. This savings estimate has taken into account the expected volume increase in production over the next five years, based on a five-year plan published by company management. Although the estimated life of the circuit analyzer is 10 to 12 years, you are aware of a management objective to realize payoff on equipment of this type in no longer than eight years. It is further assumed that at the end of eight years this analyzer will still have two to four useful years left, and, if necessary, it could be sold at a salvage value price of 15 per cent of the original cost.

Cost savings in the sixth through the eighth years will be based on a production volume the same as the fifth year, as no growth projections are available beyond that time.

You know that an area in the plant must be set aside for the analyzer and its auxiliary equipment. Therefore you obtain from the accounting department the company's standard facility-usage charge, on a dollar-per-square-foot basis, for equipment of this type. Further, you find out that about three weeks' start-up expenses will be incurred in the training of programmers, operators and maintenance personnel. You generate a dollar estimate of these costs, knowing burdened hourly rates for all personnel that would be involved.

A summary of these costs is given in Table 1, with the estimated cash flows on the bottom line of the table. These in turn are plotted in Fig. 2. The figures are rounded-off values, chosen to illustrate one method for generating the cash flow data. Notice that the equivalent rate of return is not readily derived by inspection of Fig. 2, whereas a glance at Fig. 1 reveals a 5 per cent return without any calculations required. In an actual case you might find a series of plus and minus cash flows of varying magnitude over the period. Negative cash

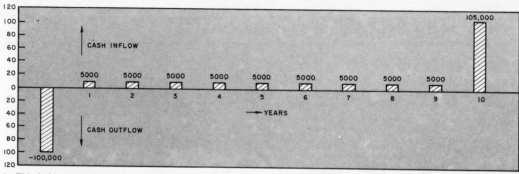

1. This is how cash flow looks from the investor's stand-point for a $100,000 bond having a stated rate of return of 5% over a 10-year period. He puts out $100,000 at time-zero, receives $5000 interest at the end of each year as a cash inflow, and then receives at the end of the 10th year $100,000 plus the final year's interest.

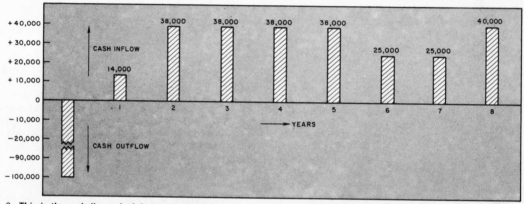

2. This is the cash flow schedule based on figures computed in the table for a $100,000 automatic circuit analyzer.

flows after the initial purchase may represent periods in which the equipment will not be used, or where some major overhaul operation is contemplated.

Determining equivalent rate-of-return

Given the cash flow time series, how can the equivalent return-on-investment be calculated?

First of all, the time value of money must be recognized. This is, of course, basic to all calculations dealing with interest rates. A lump sum, P_o, invested now at an annual interest rate, i, will have the increased value of P_n at the end of n years:

$$P_n = P_o (1 + i)^n \qquad (1)$$

The concept of "present value" implies the reverse of this process—that is, a payment at some future date is considered to have a present value of less value than the future payment. Thus the present value of future payment, P_n, is P_o:

$$P_o = P_n/(1 + i)^n \qquad (2)$$

The reason that such an approach must be taken is that your new equipment will be considered as an investment of company funds by management. You need a way to relate your cash flow estimates to some rate of interest.

In the cash flow time series example of Fig. 2, involving varying disbursements and receipts associated with this analyzer, each year's cash flow has a present value at some unknown interest rate, i. This may be found by determining a value of i that will satisfy this equation:

$$\sum_{o}^{N} F_n/(1 + i)^n = 0, \qquad (3)$$

where F_n is the cash flow at time n, expressed in years. N is the total number of years involved. Equation 3 simply says that the return-on-investment rate is that value that will cause the present value of all cash flows to algebraically sum to zero.

You may wish to check this approach by trying it out on the known-answer case of Fig. 1 for the $100,000, 10-year, 5 per cent bond.

Calculation of analyzer purchase

Finding i involves the solution of a high-order

Table. Analyzer installation cost factors

1. Purchase price: $100,000

2. Mandatory pay-off period: 8 years

3. Estimated crash-sale salvage value at end of 8th year: $15,000

4. Installation—training—start-up cost: $5000

5. Facility—usage cost allocation: 500 ft^2 @ $2/ft^2/yr or $1000/yr

6. Maintenance labor and spares:

	1st year	$0 (warranty)
	2nd thru 5th	$1000/yr
	6th thru 8th	$2000/yr

7. Operational cost savings schedule:

	Year	Savings
50% Operational efficiency estimated	1	$20,000
	2	40,000
	3	40,000
	4	40,000
	5	40,000
	6	28,000
70% Operational efficiency estimated due to increased downtime on machine {	7	28,000
	8	28,000

Estimated cash flow schedule (in thousands of dollars)

	Time – Years								
	0	1	2	3	4	5	6	7	8
Initial cost	-100	–	–	–	–	–	–	–	–
Start-up cost	–	-5	–	–	–	–	–	–	–
Facility usage	–	-1	-1	-1	-1	-1	-1	-1	-1
Maintenance	–	–	-1	-1	-1	-1	-2	-2	-2
Salvage value	–	–	–	–	–	–	–	–	+15
Opn. savings	–	+20	+40	+40	+40	+40	+28	+28	+28
Net cash flow	-100	+14	+38	+38	+38	+38	+25	+25	+40

equation. For the example of Fig. 2 and Table 1, we have an eighth-order equation in i, but since relatively low precision is required, there is no need for a computer. The solution can be obtained very quickly to a close approximation with a log-log slide rule or a table of present values.

Taking the values from the cash flow schedule of the table for the automatic analyzer example, and substituting in Eq. 3, we have:

$$0 = [-100/(1 + i)^0] + [14/(1 + i)^1] + [38/(1 + i)^2]$$
$$+ [38/(1 + i)^3] + [38/(1 + i)^4] + [38/(1 + i)^5]$$
$$+ [25/(1 + i)^6] + [25/(1 + i)^7] + [40/(1 + i)^8] \quad (4)$$

At this point we must make a trial estimate of i. Inspection of Eq. 4 indicates a pretty good return, so we will make a first estimate of $i = 20$ per cent or the present value factor $(1+i)^n$ equal to $(1.2)^n$. Values of $(1.2)^n$ are quickly found on a slide rule to be:

$$0 = -100 + 14/1.2 + 38/1.44 + 38/1.73 +$$
$$38/2.07 + 38/2.49 + 25/2.98 + 25/3.58 + 40/4.30,$$

which reduces to:
$$0 \neq -100 + 118.4.$$

This indicates that our first-trial estimate for i was a little low. A second trial will be made for $i = 25$ per cent or $(1 + i) = 1.25$. Again, substituting in Eq. 4:

$$0 = -100 + 14/1.25 = 38/1.56 + 38/1.95 +$$
$$38/2.44 + 38/3.04 + 25/3.82 + 25/4.76 + 40/5.95,$$

which reduces to:
$$0 \neq -100 + 101.7.$$

This inequality indicates that the second trial of 25 per cent is very close, but slightly low, with 25.5 per cent probably a more correct value. However, in practical cases, one recognizes the basic estimation inaccuracies involved and will round off the estimated rate of return on investment to 25 per cent.

Depreciation and tax considerations

It may be argued that return on stockholders' invested capital should be carried to the point of determining net return after taxes, with depreciation included for fixed assets. These factors were not included in the foregoing because they vary so widely between companies with their particular financial situations and policies. Also, the man-

agers for whom this evaluation tool is suggested are usually not in a position to get such data easily. The method presented, however, does provide a meaningful comparative tool between alternatives, and tax and depreciation factors may be applied by management as a second-order refinement.

Here's how the calculation would be modified to include tax and depreciation factors: Eq. 3 is changed to:

$$(1 - t) \sum_1^N [F_n/(1 + i)^n] + t \sum_1^N [D_n/(1 + i)^n] +$$
$$[S/(1 + i)^N] = 0,$$

where F_n, i, n and N are as defined in Eq. 3 and $t =$ tax rate, fractional.
$D_n =$ depreciation allowed at year n, and
$S =$ equipment salvage value.

Depreciation should be included if the engineering manager knows his own proposal might have to be judged against alternate capital equipment purchases. It is possible that a proposition providing a high depreciation will be preferred over another with a higher rate-of-return but having a lower depreciation schedule.

Method has many applications

This rate-of-return method can be applied to other problems or situations facing the engineer and engineering manager. For example, it could serve as a tool for comparative evaluation of various proposed product developments. Say the engineering department proposes several new proprietary products, and the company manpower or dollar resources will allow pursuit of only one or a restricted number of the proposed objectives. A decision must be made from among the alternatives.

For each proposal, the following can be estimated by engineering, manufacturing and marketing personnel:

- Projected market life of the item.
- Development costs over one or more years.
- Projected sales volume over the life of the product.
- Production and marketing expenses.

These figures can be used to generate a cash flow time series like the one shown and Eq. 3 can be applied to derive an equivalent rate of return for each venture. ■ ■

Get to know your local SBA agent

If you qualify, he can help you obtain loans, management assistance, and government contracts.

In an industry that has a built-in capacity for rendering itself obsolete before its latest innovation can be comprehended, it's essential that electronics entrepreneurs and company managers learn of the government assistance that's available to them. Large numbers of companies have gone either public in search of funds or to a consultant in search of organization, when they might have gone to an independent government agency called the Small Business Administration.

How large is small business?

There's nothing small about the Small Business Administration or the segment of the business community it serves. Created by an act of Congress in 1953 to encourage, assist, and protect small business, and particularly to aid in getting government contracts, SBA is a big business operation with 4,000 salaried employees and over 3,000 voluntary counselors. They serve 73 field offices in the principal cities of every state, as well as Guam, Puerto Rico, and the Virgin Islands. They assist small companies that make up more than 95% of the business population, account for more than 40% of the business activity and provide employment for 35-million people.

Although, according to an SBA spokesman, the main thrust of agency activity recently has been toward helping low-income, disadvantaged businessmen belonging to minority groups, the agency has also assisted major companies when they're considered to be the smallest company in their industry in competition for a particular market.

Financial assistance varies in kind

The size standards of a small business vary widely from industry to industry, and from one type of assistance to another. Each standard is covered in the following descriptions of the four prime areas of assistance offered by SBA. They are: financial; lease guarantee plan; management; and procurement.

SBA loans are available to small companies that want to construct, expand or convert facilities; purchase buildings, equipment and materials; or obtain working capital. They are available for such disparate reasons as natural disasters and displacement caused by urban renewal or other government construction.

By law, the agency may not make a loan if a business can obtain funds from a bank or other private sources. And for purposes of making loans, SBA defines a small business as follows:

- Wholesale—annual sales of not more than $5-million.
- Retail or Service—annual sales or receipts of not more than $1-million.
- Manufacturing—not more than 250 employees.

The agency will consider either participating in, or guaranteeing up to, 90% of a bank loan. If the bank cannot provide the funds, SBA will consider lending the entire amount as a direct government loan. Two-thirds of SBA's loans are now made in participation with banks.

Limits for SBA loan participation are:

1. Guarantee of up to 90% or $350,000 of a bank loan, whichever is less, up to 10 years at 5-1/2% interest, and up to 15 years if the loan is for construction.

2. $150,000 as the SBA share of a participation loan with a bank.

3. $100,000 on a direct SBA loan.

SBA looks to past records and future prospects of a small businessman to decide whether he has the ability to repay a loan and any other debts out of company profits.

Three other loans made by SBA include:

- Pool Loans, whereby the agency lends money to corporations formed and capitalized by groups of small business companies for purchasing raw materials, equipment, inventory or supplies for the use of their individual businesses. Such loans may also be used to obtain the benefits of research and development or to establish facilities for these purposes;
- Economic Opportunity Loans, whereby the agency assists low-income or disadvantaged persons, who own businesses or want to go into

business but are generally unable to obtain financing;

▪ Economic Development Loans, whereby the agency helps small firms to acquire or build facilities, expand or modernize through loans to state and local development companies formed to finance small businesses.

Another service offered by SBA in the area of financial assistance is Small Business Investment Companies (SBICs).

Such companies are privately owned and privately operated, and have been licensed by the Small Business Administration to provide equity capital and long-term loans to small firms that often have difficulty obtaining long-term capital to finance their growth.

Many SBICs are owned by relatively small groups of local investors. However, the stock of over 40 SBICs is publicly traded; more than 80 SBICs are partially or wholly owned by commercial banks; and some SBICs are subsidiaries of other corporations.

The size standards for a firm eligible for SBIC financing are:

1. Assets do not exceed $5-million.
2. Net worth does not exceed $2.5-million.
3. Average net income after taxes for each of the preceding two years was not more than $250,000.

SBA will often guarantee your rent

To help small businessmen obtain leases in choice business locations, such as new shopping centers or industrial parks, SBA will often back an insurance policy guaranteeing to the landlord that rent payments will be made. The guarantee extends for a minimum of five years up to a maximum of 20 years on a participating basis. Where private policies are not available, SBA will guarantee the leases directly for a period of 15 to 20 years.

For lease-guarantee purposes, SBA defines a small business as one that is independently owned and operated, is not dominant in its field, and meets employment or sales standards developed by the agency.

Premiums, based on insurance-industry standards, are payable in advance with no refunds. The small businessman is required to pay three months' rent in advance (held in escrow), to pay rent defaults, but this will be returned to him at the end of his lease with 4% interest if no defaults occur.

Applicants for lease-guarantee policies are evaluated under a risk rating system that analyzes the applicant's management skills, his financial position, the location he wishes to rent, and his business.

Management aid—a spectrum of services

To strengthen small business, SBA offers a diversified program of training and management assistance.

Specialists in SBA field offices advise small businessmen on problems of marketing, accounting, product analysis, production methods, research and development. They also advise and assist prospective small businessmen who want management assistance or information on specific types of business enterprises.

To implement this management service, SBA provides the following programs:

CALL (Counseling At the Local Level). This program provides individual counseling and information services at locations where the public ordinarily has no easy access to a regional office.

SCORE (Service Corps of Retired Executives): This corps is composed of more than 3000 retired business executives in more than 190 chapters throughout the nation. A SCORE volunteer will visit the small businessman in his operation, and through careful observation make a detailed analysis of the business and its problems.

A businessman doesn't need to be in trouble to get such aid. Perhaps he thinks that his business should be doing better or that the record-keeping system is a little out of date. Perhaps he's not even in business yet, but needs some expert advice to help him plan one soundly.

The SCORE service is free—except for direct expenses—to all businessmen who might otherwise not be able to hire experts to help them with their business difficulties.

Management Courses. Administrative management courses, co-sponsored by SBA, public and private educational institutions, and business associations are offered to help increase management skills. These are generally evening courses and are designed for owners and managers of small firms. They deal with planning, organizing, directing, co-ordinating, and controlling a business, as distinguished from day-to-day operating activities.

AIMS (Association and Industry Management Services): This program encourages large firms and trade associations to serve as co-sponsors for training programs for their small-business customers, suppliers, or members.

ACE (Active Corps of Executives): These are usually middle-aged mid to top-level executives who find time during the work week to advise small businessmen.

Conferences, Workshops, Clinics: Conferences, usually running one day, cover such subjects as working capital, business forecasting and diversification of markets.

Workshops generally cover subjects related to starting new businesses, including capital requirements and sources of financing, forms of business, organization, and choice of location.

Clinics cover specific problems of small businessmen within a particular industry.

Getting a piece of the government action

The SBA helps small businessmen to obtain a share of the billions of dollars' worth of business the Federal Government does with private companies each year. SBA specialists counsel small businessmen on prime contracting and subcontracting by:

1. Advising them on which government agencies buy the products or services they supply. The SBA publishes "The U.S. Government Purchasing and Sales Director," which lists the principal goods and services bought by military and civilian agencies and the purchasing offices that buy them.

2. Guiding them to have their names placed on bidders' lists so they will be notified of opportunities to bid on purchases.

3. Helping them to obtain drawings and specifications for proposed purchases.

4. Providing information about scheduled meetings where government contracting agencies and prime contractors present their needs and requirements and discuss bidding opportunities.

5. Watching out for purchases on which few small firms have bid in the past.

Two additional assists

The major government purchasing agencies voluntarily set aside contracts or portions of contracts for small business. To increase this unilateral action, SBA has its own representatives stationed in major military and civilian procurement installations. They recommend additional "set-asides," provide small-business sources to contract officers, assist small concerns with contracting problems, and recommended relaxation of unduly restrictive specifications.

As an additional assist to the small company, which is the low bidder on a federal contract

SBA Field Offices

Agana, Guam	Fresno, Calif.*	Newark, N.J.
Albuquerque, N.M.		New Orleans, La.
Anchorage, Alaska	Harlingen, Tex.	New York, N.Y.
Atlanta, Ga.	Hartford, Conn.	
Augusta, Me.	Hato Rey, P.R.	Oklahoma City, Okla.
	Helena, Mont.	Omaha, Neb.
Baltimore, Md.	Honolulu, Hawaii	
Birmingham, Ala.	Houston, Tex.	Philadelphia, Pa.
Boise, Idaho		Phoenix, Ariz.
Boston, Mass.	Indianapolis, Ind.	Pittsburgh, Pa.
Buffalo, N.Y.		Portland, Ore.
	Jackson, Miss.	Providence, R.I.
Casper, Wyo.	Jacksonville, Fla.	
Charleston, W. Va.		Richmond, Va.
Charlotte, N.C.	Kansas City, Mo.	
Chicago, Ill.	Knoxville, Tenn.	St. Louis, Mo.
Cincinnati, Ohio		Salt Lake City, Utah
Clarksburg, W. Va.	Las Vegas, Nev.	San Antonio, Tex.
Cleveland, Ohio	Little Rock, Ark.	San Diego, Calif.
Columbia, S.C.	Los Angeles, Calif.	San Francisco, Calif.
Columbus, Ohio	Louisville, Ky.	Seattle, Wash.
Concord, N.H.	Lubbock, Tex.	Sioux Falls, S.D.
		Spokane, Wash.
Dallas, Tex.	Madison, Wis.	Syracuse, N.Y.
Denver, Colo.	Marquette, Mich.	
Des Moines, Iowa	Marshall, Tex.	Tampa, Fla.*
Detroit, Mich.	Miami, Fla.	Toledo, Ohio
Dover, Del.	Milwaukee, Wis.	Tucson, Ariz.*
	Minneapolis, Minn.	
Fairbanks, Alaska	Montpelier, Vt.	Washington, D.C.
Fargo, N.D.		Wichita, Kan.
	Nashville, Tenn.	* Post-of-duty Office

and whose ability to perform the contract is questioned by the contracting officer, SBA specialists make an on-site study of the company's facilities, management, performance record, and financial status. If it concludes that the company can perform the contract, it issues a Certificate of Competence to this effect.

Assistance for electronics companies

The following are examples of electronics companies that asked for assistance at one SBA field office. They had the usual business problems: no capital; no work in the house; too small a staff.

One of the firms produced signal breakers, radio telephones and depth gauges for marine electronics. The company head requested SBA specialists to assist him in the management areas of setting up a procedure for marketing and for records and control. He also requested financial assistance for expansion and received it.

Another company hadn't been able to generate business in burglar alarms. The staff was small and limited the amount of business that could be handled. The firm got a contract and requested—and obtained—a small SBA loan so that a larger staff could be hired.

Another company is operated by a small busi-

nessman of a minority group. He worked for a large company before he gained enough confidence to start his own operation. SBA gave him a loan to finance equipment, facilities, and a payroll. He got a government contract, and then another to assemble and test megaphone and telephone sets. He requested an SBA loan for expansion. In eight months his company expanded its payroll from nine to 30 people. With SBA's assistance, this electronics entrepreneur was able to increase his contracts from $60,000 to $3-million in three years.

Congress has directed SBA to ensure free competition as the essence of the American economic system of private enterprise, and to strengthen the over-all economy of the nation. One enthusiastic advocate of the agency wrote a letter saying that the free classes, services and other programs, arranged through SBA by retired and salaried consultant personnel, "have saved many a small business from collapse." ■■

Bibliography:
"Lease Guarantee," *Small Business Administration*, October, 1968.
"SBA Business Loans," *Small Business Administration*, October, 1969.
"SBIC Financing for Small Business," *Small Business Administration*, March, 1968.
"Small Business Administration—What It Is, What It Does," *Small Business Administration*, March, 1968.
"SCORE," *Small Business Administration*, 1968.

6 MANAGING COMMUNICATIONS

Make your next proposal sell
Put that new product idea across
Defend your proposal effectively
Here's how to get word to the top
Plan a communications workshop
Listen! Don't just hear
Turn arguments into discussions
For sales/EE interface: Sell—don't tell
Good slides are keys to good technical talks
Join the 'experts'—publish

Successful engineering management requires successful communications. The engineering manager will often be required to "sell" some product or proposal ideas either to outside contractors or within his own company. He will also find that as a supervisor, and as engineer moving up within his organization and his profession, that he must communicate "himself" to others.

Making engineering proposals and presenting new product ideas and new engineering methods are the communications problems covered in the first four articles of the section. "Make your next proposal sell" tells how a proposal can be tailored to sell by meeting the customer's information needs. The next two articles explain how to get a new product idea across, and how to successfully defend some new proposal against common objections raised by those favoring the status quo. Finally, the problem of getting important information all the way to the top in the organization

is discussed in "Here's how to get word to the top."

The engineering manager should be skilled at communicating himself as well as his ideas. Because of the neglect of this area by otherwise excellent managers, six articles are devoted to it here. First, a plan for a communications workshop is presented by a man who ran one. Then some tips on effective listening and ways to turn arguments into discussions are covered. The next article, "For sales/TE interface: Sell—don't tell!," probes the difficulties in communication between engineers and the salesmen in the company. Then, for the manager who plans to prepare a presentation on his project, some handy tips on slides are given in "Good slides are keys to good technical talks." Finally, the last article advises the engineer who wants to make a mark in his profession on the possibilities of becoming a published author.

Make your next proposal sell

Answer every point requested by the customer and follow these rules for clear presentation.

"We have the lowest price, the fastest delivery, a good technical proposal and look what happened —that fly-by-night outfit ran away with the award!"

Sound familiar? Relax. Don't start howling about payola and customer ignorance until you see the other company's proposal.

Your own proposal may not have been as good as you thought. Clearly, if your price was rock-bottom, your delivery the speediest, you were well on your way to landing the job. Now ask yourself what went wrong. Did you explain your proposal satisfactorily?

Provided that the proposal's technical approach was sound, it's likely that your trouble lay in the explanation—you failed to get your point across. It didn't sell. The customer may even have had trouble understanding it.

Let's face it at the outset of this discussion: the object of any technical proposal is to sell. As in any selling campaign, you must display your product in its most favorable light.

Before you begin, be sure you can answer yes to the following questions:

- Do you know your customer?
- Are you certain you understand the customer's needs?
- Have you made sure that all people associated with the contract award can appreciate the details in it, even details that do not directly concern them?
- Is the proposal responsive to the customer's request?

Know your customer

Your customer may be a government agency, another company or, sometimes, a division of your own corporation. Always try to gather as much information about the customer as possible. Such information may include the following:

- The customer's past experience with bidders on the program, with particular stress on pitfalls to avoid. What past technical approaches have left him high and dry, for example?
- The points that are most important to the customer—on-time delivery, cost, technical in-

genuity, or whatever.

Remember, after the job is lost, it is too late to blame your marketing people for not supplying you with the information. If you write the technical proposal, it is up to you to obtain information from the marketing staff, salesmen and others who have dealt with the customer.

Understand the customer's needs

More often than not, a request for a proposal contains a mixture of specifications, some of which are important, some superfluous, some even contradictory. Whenever time permits, draw up a set of working specifications by meeting with the

Know your customer

customer and resolving all gray areas. In most cases, agreement can be reached by pointing out that a better product at a lower cost may result from a thorough understanding of the specifications. Depending on the nature of the contract—CPFF (cost plus fixed fee), CPIF (cost plus incentive fee), FP (fixed price) or any other — get together with your contract administrators and ask for advice before talking to the customer. Whenever possible, ask the administrator to come along when you meet with the customer. Under all circumstances, make sure that you understand every request of the customer.

Write for the proposal evaluators

A contract award usually depends on several evaluations. In the case of government agencies, a proposal is read by contract personnel, program managers, efficiency experts and technical specialists. If you have fulfilled the first basic requirement (know your customer), you should know who will evaluate your proposal. The next basic step is to summarize all your data in tidy sections, so that every reader will find exactly what he needs to know in one place.

There are eight main sections to the average technical proposal, ranging from "Introduction" and "Statement of the Problem" to "Experience" and "Facilities." The contract administrator, for example, who may well not be an engineer, is interested in your program organization and how you propose to meet schedules and costs. Don't bore him in these sections of your proposal with flowery descriptions of the company's technical prowess. Technical qualifications and methods are stated in the engineering section.

In preparing your proposal, make sure that all points raised by the customer are answered. Ask yourself how you would react if someone ignored your questions. Simple or complex, pertinent or irrelevant, all customer's questions must be conclusively answered. To facilitate reading by the customer, the answers to such questions may even appear as headings or subheadings in the outline of your technical section. In any case, don't substitute your own jargon for the customer's definitions. For example, if the customer asks for a "flat frequency response to 100 kHz," make sure that there is a title exactly like this. Don't hide it someplace in reams of pages entitled "Improved Amplifier Performance."

Remember, the customer had certain reasons for asking specific questions. They must all be answered.

In preparing the proposal, start with an outline, such as the one below:

1. Introduction to the Company.
2. Statement of the Problem.
3. Program Summary.
4. Program Organization.
5. Technical Approach.
6. Key Personnel.
7. Company Experience.
8. Company Facilities.

This general form will cover a wide variety of proposals.

Bear in mind that the written proposal will represent you, your colleagues and your company to the customer; it will be the only way a customer can judge whether or not to give you the award. The place to begin, then, is by introducing yourself to the customer.

Introduce your company

In preparing this first section, think how you introduce yourself at a business visit: "My name is so-and-so, I represent Awfully Big Laboratories (call me ABL, for short). We are making such-and-such, and the reason for my call is as follows."

These, in a nutshell, are the essentials of an introduction section. Try this approach:

"Awfully Big Laboratories, hereinafter referred to as ABL, is pleased to submit this pro-

Don't sing praises to your company

posal in response to the request for proposal XYZ. ABL proposes to furnish personnel, equipment, facilities (with the exception of _____) required to carry out the development of new molecular mousetraps.

"In the last several years ABL has gained considerable experience in this field. Our personnel have been involved in all phases of design and production of a variety of mousetraps.

"The deliverable items are listed in Section 3, 'Program Summary,' and organization of the program is outlined in Section 4, 'Program Organization.' Section 5 details our technical approach to the problem.

"To demonstrate that ABL possesses suitable talent for successful performance of the contract, we list the key personnel in Section 6.

"Our pertinent experience is summarized in Section 7, 'Company Experience.'

"Section 8, 'Company Facilities,' lists our specialized facilities. which will be available for the project."

That is all there is to it; there is no more to the introduction. Don't start singing praises to yourself and your company. Just tell the customer who you are, why you should get the job, and where to look for various details.

State the problem

Next, you want to be sure that you and the customer see eye to eye on the object of the program. This is done in the section called "Statement of the Problem."

In defining the problem, state it as clearly and concisely as you can, without any technical detail. For our mousetrap problem, for example, the statement should read:

"The problem is to design, develop and produce X prototypes of a molecular mousetrap."

This is the problem. How you are going to lure the mice, or how you are going to catch them, is not a problem. These are design details that will be treated in the section called "Technical Approach." State the problem in one sentence!

Let's review briefly at this point. After reading only two sections of your proposal, your customer should know:

- Who you are.
- Why you feel you should get the job.
- Where to look for detailed information.
- The object of the program.

Summarize your proposal

"Program Summary," the next section, tells the customer in easily understood language exactly what he gets for what he pays. Tell him that the program will culminate in delivery of X proto-

types, drawings, reports and manuals. Tell him, for example, that the mousetraps will be small (if this is important). light, reliable and inexpensive. Once again, don't bore him with details. If your device is really outstanding, one page of tentative specifications (alongside the customer's specifications) may be included.

Organization of the program

The section on "Program Organization" is one of the most important. Be sure to state all details that affect the success of the program. Your proposed organization, with all its key personnel, must be shown. Include details on program management (a staff with suitable technical backgrounds), documentation, cost control, reporting, production control, purchasing. Enclose easy-to-follow milestone schedules.

PERT charts can also be included, but for easy understanding by nonengineers, simpler charts should be prepared. List the assignments for personnel responsible for various phases of the program. In short, convey to the customer that if you get the job, you are ready to "jump in and grind with both feet." He is dealing with a responsible, business-like organization that knows very well how to produce.

Present the technical meat

You have now summarized fairly well most of the key points except your company's technical excellence. The reader, at this point, knows all about the job, except the details of various systems that are needed to produce what is promised. In fact, the presentation, being largely nontechnical, may even stir the interest of nonengineers. An elated customer contract man may wonder: "So far I understand everything about this highly complex technical program. Maybe these fellows will keep it this way in their technical section."

Try not to disappoint him. Do your best in the "Technical Approach" section to state your method in a simple, understandable way. If the Special Theory of Relativity can be explained to high-school students, you can explain your system to a contract man. No one will be taken in if you lard your proposal with incomprehensible jargon. If you want to say, "The building is very high," don't say, "The vertical extension of the edifice is considerable." Naturally there will be highly technical aspects that will leave a nontechnical reader gasping. But he is prepared for this, to a certain extent. Just keep in mind that if he succeeds in understanding the broad concept clearly, you have won another vote on the proposal evaluation board.

Roughly, the style of the technical section

should be that practiced by the news reporter. Begin with a general description of the system. (A set of preliminary specs should appear at this point, and the most important parameters should be emphasized.) Follow with a detailed, block-by-block system description, down to the circuit schematics.

Use simple examples: "Previously this was done with 100 components. Our approach will use only 10 with equal or better results." The illustrations will show your ingenuity, creativeness and knowledge of the field.

Write the 'boiler plate'

Now that you have told how you will do the job, both in general and in detail, provide more back-up information. Thus, in the section on "Program Organization," you listed the persons who will be responsible for the program. The customer, however, does not know these people. So provide a section entitled "Key Personnel." This states broadly the skills, education, and experience of those assigned to the program and demonstrates that they are technically competent.

Next, to demonstrate your readiness to start, list various facilities that will be needed to carry out the job. These facilities must be pertinent. Don't submit pages and pages of descriptions of electron microscopes, mass spectrographs and complex instrumentation just to impress the customer; he isn't apt to be misled. Give him a clear listing of facilities that relate directly to the job. If you want to show the general prominence of your company in other fields, make two facilities sections—one called "Specialized Facilities" and the other "General Facilities."

The experience section should be treated in identical fashion. Don't list your participation in a Mars landing program if you are bidding on a mousetrap development.

Make one final check

And now that you have finished drafting your proposal, check it. Remember these cardinal rules:

- Make sure that each section is complete and deals with one topic at a time.
- Be certain that every proposal evaluator finds the facts he needs in one place and that they are not obscured by irrelevant statements and references.
- Answer all questions raised by the customer.
- Use simple, everyday language in place of specialized jargon.

Good luck. At least you have a fighting chance now. ▪ ▪

Put that new product idea across

Sell your proposals with clear reports that focus on profit-making potential.

"I came up with a million dollar idea, turned it over to our management, and you know what happened? They sat on it for a year and a half, and now our competition has come out with an almost identical product!"

Chances are this person has only himself to blame. He failed to get his idea across. The best idea is useless unless you can communicate it in the right way to the right people—the people who can turn your idea into reality.

How do you get an idea accepted? By writing a lucid, selling engineering report.

Practically every new idea has to be presented in formal fashion. Before your immediate supervisors can recommend action on your idea, they must have written facts to back them up.

Written presentations fall into two categories:

1. Proposals—attempts to sell your company's services or products to an outside customer.

2. Reports—attempts to sell your own idea to your own company.

In writing a technical report, keep your reader in mind. Clearly understand this point: the management view of the value of any technical idea *focuses on its profit-making potential.*

Constantly remember that your reader probably does not have the technical background you have. So make certain that you do not get wrapped up in technical jargon that may be clear to you but meaningless to your reader.

Writing the engineering report may call for breaking some old habits. Let's examine, first, how not to write the report.

Do not organize it this way:

- Introduction.
- Technical discussion.
- Summary.

This format—widely used by engineers in writing technical papers—is the best way to assure that few, if any, people in management will read it. Usually the technical section will be read only after you have convinced the reader that you have something to offer.

If you present the technical section early in the report, the reader will get bogged down in its details and will put it aside to read "later." Nothing will happen "later." Instead, after a lapse of some time, it is probable you will get the report back with a polite explanation: "It's a good idea, but I don't think our company is ready to get into it. Maybe at some later time we can rehash it."

This is just another way of saying, "I couldn't wade through your report." Because of its poor organization, you failed to get your idea across.

Use the right format

For a far better chance of securing management approval of your technical idea, *do follow* this format:

- Purpose.
- Conclusions.
- Recommendations.
- Market and cost.
- Technical discussion.

Note that in this format you sell the reader first and then conclude the report by substantiating the soundness of your "sell" in the technical discussion. Let's consider each of these in detail.

Open your presentation by stating the purpose of the report. Avoid jargon. Use simple language, be concise. Don't include superfluous information.

Don't write it this way:

"**The purpose of this report is to describe a new, unique, all-solid-state, all-purpose, fully automated, versatile fly catcher. It is superior to all fly catchers now on the market because it has a wide-band amplifier with a gain of over 160 dB. Using integrated organizational flexibility coupled with systematized management options, it will result in a parallel reciprocal capability.**"

After reading such verbiage, the reader still doesn't know: Is this a paper to be presented at

a technical conference? Are we going to sell the device? Is there a profit to be made?

The flashy talk will get you nowhere. In fact, after reading it, your supervisor, who most likely is a practical man, may yawn, put the report aside and reflect: "Maybe our public relations people will want to schedule it at a conference."

Here is the *correct way* to write the same opening statement:

"**The purpose of this report is to present conclusions, recommendations and technical discussion that show the feasibility of developing and marketing a new automatic fly catcher.**"

This example is concise and to the point. It answers the key questions and is devoid of superfluous information.

Give your conclusions

Your conclusions constitute the key section. Here you tell management what the prospects are for successful marketing on the basis of the data you will describe later in the technical discussion. Again, simple, concise language must be used.

Don't do it this way:

"**At this time, it may be concluded that more studies are required in order to explore fully the unique promise of the fly catcher. In particular, we want to develop a more accurate mathematical model, so that the calculus of variations, a powerful method, can be applied. More specifically, an approximate solution for the integral (see page 37) must be checked, using a new Liapunov function. It may result in a new approach to the stability of nonlinear systems of the fifth order.**"

There are at least two fatal flaws in this approach: Not only does it contain technical mumbo-jumbo, but the conclusion reflects a negative, uncertain attitude—"more studies are required," "an approximate solution . . . must be checked."

Even if the reader is not bored, he is certain to react negatively: "If it needs more study, why present it now? Come back when you have something more concrete to propose."

Now, consider the *correct way* to put the point across:

"**On the basis of the data in Section 4, Market and Cost, and Section 5, Technical Discussion, the following conclusions can be made:**

"**There is a growing market for fly catchers.**

"**Present manual fly catchers retail for X.**

"**The proposed automatic fly catcher can be retailed for half that price.**

"**The production of automatic fly catchers does not involve new technology.**

"**We can manufacture the product with existing equipment, thus minimizing capital outlay.**"

Anything beyond what is said here will only obscure your point. Your reader can see that you have approached the problem in a business-like fashion: you looked at the market place, you discovered a demand for the product, you solved the technical problem of supplying an improved product for the existing market, and you indicated that the company's initial outlay would be small.

Recommend the approach

Having convinced your reader that you have a money-making proposition, tell him how you feel it should be achieved. This is Section 3, "Recommendations."

Don't write it this way:

"On the basis of this report, we recommend that our unique fly catcher be mass-produced at any and all costs. We'll make it all back in a jiffy, and the market will be saturated before the competition comes into the play."

All you have told your reader is: "Let's do it on my say so." You haven't told them how or why your report should be accepted and how it can be carried out.

Do write this section of your report so that it contains all the necessary comments:

"On the basis of the above conclusions and other facts in the remainder of this report, the following recommendations can be made:

"A program to convert the laboratory model into a production prototype should be started.

"A detailed marketing survey should be conducted to prepare a specific marketing plan.

With this, the "sell" part of the report is finished. Whether or not the rest of it will be read depends on how well you succeed in convincing your reader that you have something realistic.

Note that thus far there has been no attempt to sing the praises of technical excellence, ingenuity, etc. Neither were there lengthy discussions of the frequency responses of the fly catcher, its bandwidth and the size of the flies it is intended to catch.

Present market and cost facts

Now that you have sold the reader (your supervisor) you must give him the ammunition to push your idea and win the support of his supervisors. You do this in the body of the report. Note once again that since the ultimate goal of any program is to turn a profit, you place the market survey ahead of the technical discussion.

It may be difficult to prepare this part of the report yourself. You may have to enlist the aid of your company's sales and marketing people to compile all the data. Find the best way possible to assemble all the facts on the number of existing devices sold annually, the dollar volume and past trends. If you are proposing an entirely new product, cite the need (again in terms of possible demand and sales dollars).

Present the complete picture of what it will

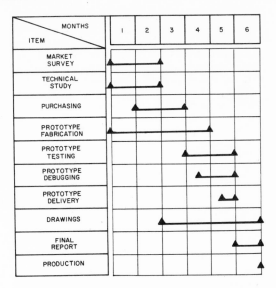

A **detailed milestone** chart illustrates your businesslike approach to introducing a new product. It demonstrates your understanding of the total company operation, as well as the functions of each department.

cost your company to enter the market. These costs, by necessity, will cover only the technical side of the story—that is, how many engineering and supporting personnel hours will be needed to develop the product and how many weeks or months the development project will take to complete. As an engineer, you are not expected to include promotion and advertising costs.

Give a full description of the production facilities that will be required to produce the anticipated number of units. In particular, pay attention to the capital equipment outlays.

Here is the place to include development, preproduction and production schedules. Use simple milestone charts (see accompanying chart).

Besides providing useful information, this method also serves to indicate that you have approached the whole problem in a sound, businesslike fashion.

Present the technical meat

Now that the reader is interested and convinced that your idea will result in a profit-making product, explain it to him technically. Once again, use simple language and avoid double-talk and jargon. The whole intent is to explain your idea without confusing or impressing the reader with high-sounding, meaningless phrases. Your supervisors will not back up something they don't understand.

A good way to open a technical section is to explain (qualitatively) how the over-all system operates. A table of preliminary specifications should be included here. A functional block diagram of the system should also appear here.

Once the system is defined and explained in the functional block diagram, describe each block. This is the place for detailed schematics and detailed descriptions of how each circuit operates. Explain all operations in a simple, straightforward fashion. Again, this reminder: Even if management is technically oriented, don't expect it to be as knowledgeable about the specific subject as you are.

Throughout this discussion, pinpoint areas where some difficulties may be experienced in production, tight component tolerances or special testing requirement. In fact, include a section entitled "Anticipated Difficulties," where a list of all troublesome areas is spelled out.

A general format of the technical section could

be as follows:
- Technical discussion.
- System description.
- Subsystems.
- Testing requirements.
- Incoming inspection requirements.
- Anticipated difficulties.

This completes the presentation. What you have done boils down to this:

1. You have told the reader why he should follow your advice.

2. You have told him how to implement your approach.

3. You have given your immediate supervisor enough ammunition to secure higher management approvals.

In short, you have sold your idea. ▪▪

Defend your proposal effectively

Prepare in advance to meet the familiar objections when you submit your ideas to management.

Don Fuller, Director, Engineering Div., Industrial Education Institute, New York.

"Your idea has merit, but there isn't any money in the budget for it."

"We've tried it before. It just won't work."

"Too much of a departure for us—we've never done it."

"Why bother changing our line? We're doing all right with this."

These statements and others like them have shot down thousands of good proposals submitted by engineers. And often the ideas were rejected simply because the engineer didn't have all his answers ready.

These engineers forgot one fact: When anyone submits an engineering proposal, he becomes a target. No matter how logical he believes his

position is, his safest course is to assume that, naturally, there will be opposition. It may not be inevitable, but an engineer is wise to expect it—and he had best marshal his arguments against the expected objections.

But how do you know what objections will be raised? You don't know for certain, but you still need not be unprepared or caught off balance. Certain objections are advanced so frequently that they may always be assumed to be in the mind of the opposition. Cover these, and usually there will be little else to defend. As a matter of fact, you would be very wise to subject each proposal as you prepare it to the "torture test" of all the 15 following objections:

1. 'It's not in the budget.'

This comment usually comes from the watchdog of the company treasury who, as part of his approach to the job, may start with the premise that money not spent is money saved. And he will probably ask: "What do we have budgets for if we're not going to stick to them?"

We have budgets for two reasons, you can tell him: to forecast the company's financial needs and to control its expenditures. You must ask yourself to what degree your proposal is outside the forecast and control, or whether it is within both.

As for the forecast: If the proposed expenditure is one that you should have been able to foresee but didn't, this may condemn your operations as inefficient or inadequate, but it does not, by itself, justify the withholding of necessary funds. If you forgot it, admit it. Explain the oversight if you can, but don't waste everyone's time by trying to excuse it. Instead, take the position that the oversight, having been discovered, must now be corrected.

If your proposal is something new, it could not have been put into the budget, since the budget represents yesterday's thinking. Thus take the position that the budgeter provides for what he can to the extent that the information at hand permits. Beyond that he can only hope for the best. But no company can afford to let the present remain captive to the past.

As for the control aspect: The budget, as it stands, is often the best argument in your favor. Be prepared to argue that although the item as such is not in the budget, the money for it is. "We can get money from here, here and here, by effecting savings." Show familiarity with and respect for the budget.

2. 'It won't work in our department.'

If this objection has any validity at all, you have wasted your time in preparing the proposal and are wasting the time of others in presenting it.

No thinking man is going to submit unworkable proposals to his superiors, unless he has been misled. Therefore, if you are convinced that your sources of information are dependable, and if you or your subordinates have the necessary knowledge and experience to interpret your data correctly, the facts must be on your side and the objection represents no more than the misguided opinion of the objector. All that is needed to change that opinion is a convincing demonstration of feasibility, and certainly you should be prepared to mount such a demonstration, if required to do so.

Also, try to secure an endorsement of your ideas from those who have put them into practice. To be able to say that experience shows the proposal is workable should be a sufficient refutation of the objection.

3. 'We've tried this before'

This is the once-bitten-twice-shy attitude of the person who has seen or been the victim of failure. If you have not consulted with him, it may well be that he is right and you have something to learn from his experience. On the other hand, it is possible that what was tried before is not what you now propose, but something that has only a resemblance to it. Perhaps the circumstances surrounding the earlier experience differ materially from the present situation. It is possible that the earlier action was premature, for example?

When this objection is raised, tread lightly and be sure of your ground. To compound failure after being warned would be dangerous. But, on the other hand, do not regard this objection as equivalent to defeat.

4. 'The change is too radical.'

Perhaps to the conservative, it may seem so. Obviously, to gain this man's support, you must try to convince him that you are not a wild-eyed radical. If possible, have him concede that your goal is a desirable one that he might be able to support, if it did not, in his opinion, call for such a radical change or approach, right now. Then wonder if it might not be possible to effect this "radical" change through a conservative approach—setting less disruptive minor goals or steps that ultimately will lead to the final goal.

Don't improvise such a step-by-step program. Have it prepared and available to meet the conservative's objection.

5. 'We don't have the time.'

Meet this objection, if you can, by showing that what you propose will develop time, and in so doing will give rise to further improvement.

6. 'The price is too high for us.'

Unless a price tag carries a figure so patently outrageous as to be unquestionably beyond the company's means, you should be able to meet this objection. Persuade the objector to forget price, as such, for the moment and think of costs and values. If you can demonstrate that the values derived will be greater than the costs involved, the values defray the costs, and price need not be of concern. If, on the other hand, the values returned are less than the costs, the price is too high, no matter how low it may be; you might as well forget about your proposal.

7. 'It's impractical for the operating people.'

This objection implies that you are one of those

If other departments are involved in carrying out your proposal, you should already have scouted their opinions on feasibility and gained their support before you submitted the proposal.

vague "theory" fellows with your head in the clouds. It is an objection that cannot be met unless it has been previously forestalled. If operating people are involved, you should already have scouted their opinions on feasibility. A wise engineer will gain the support of the operating people by having them participate in the planning and assist in the preparation of his proposal.

8. 'It will make our present system obsolete.'

If the idea is good, then the idea will not make the company's system obsolete—it already has! The only question is how long the concern can get along with an obsolete system before circumstances force a change upon it.

9. 'We've never done it before.'

So what? Every progressive step ever taken was a company "first." Isn't it possible that your proposal is long overdue?

This objection might be followed by the statement, "We're not ready for it yet."

You can fire back: "When will we be ready? Shouldn't we be preparing for that time when we will be ready, so we won't be caught flatfooted?"

The objection is likely to come from the man who will usually suggest "further study" rather than getting down to work.

10. 'You're a couple of years ahead of your time.'

First, you might consider whether this is another way of saying: "The answer is 'no,' but I don't want to hurt your feelings.

If the objector is sincere, you must consider the price of following where others lead. Two years from now, will the company find itself desparately trying to catch up? You, as the proponent of the advanced idea, should be in a position to list the penalties of procrastination.

11. 'That's not our problem.'

If it affects the company, it is the problem of everyone in the company; if it affects the industry, it is the problem of everyone in the industry. The "I'm all right, Jack" attitude is not a worthy one.

Such selfish isolation is not good sense, much less good management. Of course, the unwarranted interference of one department head in the affairs of another is never justified, but a company climate that labels every interdepartmental interest as interference and considers all interference as unwarranted is not conducive to cooperative effort. Every department in a company performs a staff function for every other department to the degree that it supports and advises in the areas of its special competence.

12. 'Why change? What we have is okay.'

Complacency is probably the greatest enemy to progress. The serenity of a smooth operation can lull one into accepting it as perfect. That is has worked well in the past, and is working well in the present, is no guarantee for the future.

Another thought: To what degree is the company being compelled to adjust peripheral operations rather than disturb the status quo?

Or, you might hear: "But we've done all right without it."

Do our potential customers feel that way about our product? We hope not.

13. 'The . . . . . . will never go for it.'

This is prejudgement. How does he know it will not be received with open arms? Does he have a private pipeline into another's mind?

On the other hand, the speaker may indeed have special knowledge of the prejudices of the person he says "will never go for it." The answer to this objection is probably: "Why do you say that?" You invite the speaker to share his special knowledge with you, so that you, too, will know where the possibilities of veto exist.

14. 'It's against our policy.'

Policy is not sacrosanct. If a good idea is barred by a bad policy, consider changing the policy.

15. 'Has anyone else tried it?'

This is a good question when it is asked by someone looking for information, a bad question when asked by someone looking for an "out." If you know the experiences of other companies, present them. If you don't, try to find them out.

If you put your proposal through the 15 objections, one of two things will happen: Either you'll strengthen it, thus gaining greater assurance of its acceptance, or you'll find that it wasn't so good after all. ▪▪

Here's how to get word to the top

If you have information important to top management you may need a plan to see that it gets there.

Roger D'Aprix, Manager of Advertising and Public Relations, Bendix Vacuum Division, Rochester, N.Y.

Your latest brainstorm, or the news you stumbled on at the X-Y-Z conference last week, may be the very information needed by top management in your company to make a crucial decision! For such decisions *are* made at the top and effective decision making requires information—all the information available.

In spite of their position, the people on top are not omniscient; nor do they have the only vantage point. Many of the facts and much of the creativity they depend on come from a variety of individuals in various capacities down the line. The design engineer, the manufacturing engineer, the accountant, the market research man, the salesman—all of these hold bits and pieces of the puzzle that top management is involved in putting together.

But though the critical information-need exists at the top, it's simply not possible in most organizations to knock on the president's door in person and repeat the news of a technical breakthrough by a competitor or to present your brainstorm.

The usual course is to discuss the information with your boss. If the reception is good, there is no problem. He will probably take over from there. At least you feel that the message is on the way up.

But what if nothing happens? This can be a

pretty frustrating situation if you are convinced that your news, or your ideas, could make a substantial profit for the company or affect the success of the project.

The concern of this article is to suggest some things you can do if this first course fails.

The trouble with many of us in such a situation is that we give up, primarily because we assume the effort required to be passive. We offer our information once and then wait for a decision. And if the message meets any resistance at all, this approach will probably fail because it totally ignores the relevant facts of business and even of human nature.

Positive effort is required, based on an awareness of the company's organization, its problems, and what management is really interested in. And getting the response you desire may well require a good deal of strategy on your part.

What if the news is bad?

Let us first take a look at the "intelligence" you have uncovered. Good news is welcome. No problem here. But the situation can become pretty sticky if the news is "bad"—that is, if it brings to light some problem that must be solved.

One immediate question is: Why make the effort to get such information through at all?

Admittedly, it would keep life much simpler if we didn't persist in trying to warn the ship's captain of impending dangers. The broadest answer is that we are passengers on that ship and if it goes down because of our neglect, it's possible that we will be among the casualties. In addition to this general, self-evident truth, there are more specific reasons to recommend your making the effort. If you are successful in your communication and your judgment about the value of the information is sound, you may

- Gain professional recognition
- Be rewarded by salary increases, advancement, or both
- Contribute to your company's competitive position.

On the other hand there are risks—your idea may not work out, or your information may not be completely accurate—and if you want to "play it cozy," you had best refrain from the kind of activity that will be discussed here.

Whatever the nature of the intelligence, the facts must finally be evaluated by management and a decision made as to whether any action is required. You are in a position only to recommend, and of course your recommendation must be weighed against all the other information that management has. Sometimes these other circumstances will dictate a course of action different than the one you advise, or quite modified.

With this knowledge in mind, you can present your news in one of two ways. You can say what amounts to "Here is some interesting information, for whatever it is worth," or, "This information seems to be important to us for the following reasons (enumerate) and, as a result I propose the following action."

The first can hardly be considered a presenta-

tion. It is the kind of communication that is likely to occur daily at the water cooler or in the normal course of business with people both in and out of your own department. It finds its way into the "grapevine" and is a good way of spreading some kinds of news.

The second way is obviously the stronger one if you want some response or feel that some action is required. But it will require some thought about who to approach with your proposal and how to present it in the most effective manner.

Where do you take an idea?

Assuming you have already approached your immediate supervisor without success, what do you do now? How do you go about getting your idea or information to the top?

Before you can answer these questions you must understand the framework in which important decisions are made in your company. Does one man at the top make all the key decisions or is it management by committee? Who are the real decision makers and what does it take to convince them?

The protocol in most companies is patterned after the army's chain of command and the intent is to protect the top man from intrusions on his time and energy. But it can also shelter him from vital information.

Some chief executives object to this isolation and play fast and loose with the chain of command. They may actually go out of their way to cultivate an informal atmosphere. The professional in this circumstance might be asked for his opinions and so have opportunities to express them.

Other executives pay strict attention to protocol and will listen only through the highly formalized channels they have established. Communication with the top in these situations is by invitation only, or else through the prescribed layers of management—and this inaccessibility of management is one of the greatest barriers to upward communication.

In all companies certain business "facts of life" exist. One is that protocol must be respected. Going directly "to the top" is fraught with peril. Another is that the lower down on the totem pole you are, the greater is the tendency to muzzle you. In general, the lowest echelons of management seem to be the most intimidated by the sanctity of the organization.

Since you have no influence over these factors you must be prepared to tailor your strategy to the situation!

In addition, you must know your immediate supervisor—what his needs are, his desires, and his prejudices. How much authority does he really have? How much time can he devote to your

problem? What is your relationship with him?

Customize your proposal

Each situation is different and must be explored in depth. Then you must fit your proposal to the realities of the situation.

Take the following example: Joe is a design engineer for an aerospace electronics company. He has been selected to head up a proposal team for a new guidance computer. The "request for proposal" calls for integrated circuits but doesn't specify what type. Though his company has an expensive new thick film facility, Joe wants to use thin film circuits. What's more, he wants to make custom circuits in house, requiring a fairly sizable expenditure for new capital equipment. He feels the improved reliability of thin film circuits will more than justify the additional cost. He is also prepared to argue for the need for a good thin-film capability within his company over and above the extensive requirements of this one job.

When Joe approaches Fred, his group leader, the first reaction he gets is negative. Several reasons are given Joe as to why such an approach is not feasible. But instead of knuckling under, Joe is well prepared. He knows that Fred is tremendously cost conscious. He also knows that Fred's boss, the chief engineer, wants both thin and thick film production capabilities to better suit customer needs. In fact, Joe himself heard him express this desire just recently at an internal engineering meeting.

The problem has thus become how to overcome Fred's negative reflex action to any suggestion that costs money and to reach the chief engineer at an opportune time with a suggestion that Joe knows he is already receptive to. Sizing up the situation properly, he contacts a number of reliable vendors and has them give him ballpark estimates on the equipment that would be needed for a reasonable facility. He also lets them give him substantial ammunition to counter cost objections he knows Fred will offer. For the vendor this is a simple matter since countering cost arguments is a routine part of his selling job.

Next Joe takes his carefully prepared quotes and goes to work to convince Fred that he should recommend such a facility to the chief engineer. Note that Joe *doesn't* go directly to Fred's boss himself. If he did, he might win the battle but lose the war!

In selling Fred, Joe shows him exactly how such a recommendation can benefit him personally. In short Joe lets Fred "invent" the idea and take the credit in the eyes of the chief engineer. Fred is a hero; Joe gets the thin film capability he believes will enhance his own contribution

and thereby earn him personal recognition. Everybody benefits including the chief engineer who has the needed justification for something he has wanted for some time.

The idea is accepted first because Joe knows who he must reach. Second, he does his homework carefully to supply Fred with the necessary ammunition to carry the proposal to the next layer of management. And finally, he has displayed a keen sense of timing, turning an immediate need into a long-range benefit. Those are the key ingredients—knowing the audience, careful preparation and timing.

Of course, the job isn't always that easy. In fact, some ideas, regardless of how good they are, simply can't be sold. Resistance may be met at any level and unless your supervisor is willing to pass your suggestion up the line, you had best drop the matter.

Success is much more likely if you give due attention to the practical question of how best to present your idea.

A common fault of many presentations is that they are too complex to understand. You don't have to be an orator to make a convincing speech. What you do have to do is explain your scheme in clear terms and in a framework that the listener can follow. Instead of trying to dazzle your audience with your expertise:

- Ask yourself what major points you want to communicate.
- Find appropriate and convincing evidence.
- Anticipate the opposing arguments and be prepared to counter them.

Then, if you customize the whole presentation to fit your audience's needs, aspirations, and preconceived ideas, you are halfway home.

What does all this mean to you, the individual engineer? One very clear message is that you must know what problems management is really interested in and what it's worried about. Then you must learn to make your contribution fit these needs and responsibilities. And, since you and top management must ultimately have common goals, it is essential to stay well informed about your company, its organization, its plans for the future and how it will get there.

Some companies make it a point to communicate such information to their employees through orientation sessions, house organs, organization charts, staff meetings, etc. In other companies, the engineer may need to seek it out by asking questions and expressing his interest wherever possible.

Remember, it may seem safer in your organization not to "rock the boat"; but when job opportunities open up above you, it will be the man who has shown he has a good sense of the competitive situation, has ideas, knows how to present his case and is interested in management's aims and problems, who will stand out. ▪▪

Plan a communications workshop

Here's how your organization can set up a program to improve technical writing and speaking skills

Charles J. Higgins, PR Associates, Inc., New York.

Gone are the days when an engineer worked exclusively in a vacuum—in a world unto himself. Today's engineer must relate to and communicate with the outside world . . . and the outside world must relate to and communicate with him. But how do the twain meet?

One of the most practical methods is for a company itself to offer communications workshops for engineers (and other employes, too).

Examine the benefits to the company that performs this internally:

▪ A company knows its own people better than any outsider; therefore, such workshops can be expected to satisfy more fully specific company and individual needs.

▪ The cost is relatively low, especially when compared with sending a number of employes to an outside program.

▪ It's more convenient for the employes and, usually, more practical for the company.

▪ If the course is offered to employes in more than one department, the company will reap an important side benefit—the engineer, the salesman and all the participants will learn about each other's section or department. For example, in the communications workshop described, the members transmitted to others—in writing and speaking assignments—many new details about the work of each.

What is a communications workshop?

The course is designed to cover the broad spectrum of oral and written communications in which engineers (and others) become involved—from writing short memos to preparing detailed reports and proposals, from handling a simple telephone call to delivering a formal speech. Thus, the communications workshop is an overall exercise in the use of language in all business areas.

Participants improve their skills in communicating technical and business information more accurately and clearly, and they have fun while learning in a relaxed, professional atmosphere.

The communications workshop described here is a model for a 10-week program, in which participants meet once a week, after working hours, for 2-1/2 hours. (Two 1-hour sessions are sandwiched around a half-hour hot buffet supper provided by the company.)

A communications workshop, however, is not restricted to this structure. Each company can—and should—embellish, expand, shorten, elaborate on, adapt and/or extract ideas to suit the needs of the company and the course participants.

First the sales pitch

The opening night of the session can be pretty deadly for both the instructor and the students, particularly during the first few minutes. It is quite probable, especially in a large company, that most of the attendees know few, if any, of their fellow classmates. Perhaps they are attending because their bosses "suggested" they attend—or maybe they came for the free meal. They really don't expect to get too much out of the course.

So they sit there in neat rows in the company auditorium challenging the instructor to teach them something!

A wise instructor will throw the challenge right back at them. He will consider this first night class a sales pitch for the entire course.

The first thing he does is to answer the question (even before it is actually posed by anyone): "What's in it for me?"

And the blunt answer is, "Money—both from the short-term and long-range points of view. The more immediate economic benefit is that the technical article which the participant will write during the course might be published and he will be paid for his efforts.

The more important financial benefit, however, is long-range. More often than not, the more articulate—in both speech and writing—is the person who will advance professionally. And advancement means money!

A further inducement could be monetary prizes given by the company at the conclusion of the entire program—awards for the best article, the best speech, and the like.

Once the initial sales pitch is out of the way, the instructor outlines the 10-week course (or whatever length may be set up).

For those who cannot spare the time, a simple acronym—the first of many acronyms used in the course—is introduced as a sort of 10-second short course in communications:

KISS ME, AIDA

What does it stand for?
Keep It Simple, Stupid.
Methodize, Elucidate.
Attention, Interest, Desire, Action.
The meaning is simple:
If you write the way you talk, you have to *keep it simple.*
Organize what you're writing, using some *method* you find comfortable. *Elucidate* by using the words and phrases you need.

Use the easy plan that gets results: get the guy's *attention;* offer him something that *interests* him; create a *desire* in him in order to get the *action* you want. (Without that action you want, you are not communicating!)

By the end of the first evening, the participants start organizing material to begin writing a technical article for publication. This technical article will be the skeleton for the entire course. (The first night's assignment is shown below.) Each participant is assigned to write an article about a subject in his own work area. During the 10 weeks, he will be talking and writing only about his own work.

The second evening will tell

The end of the sales pitch coincides with the end of the first evening's program. How successful the instructor was in selling the program will be evident by the number that return for the second evening.

Starting with the second session, the sterile auditorium atmosphere is eliminated. Instead of a teacher-pupil setup, with rows of students lined up facing the instructor, the participants are arranged four to a card table—facing each other.

For this second session, participants are "allowed" to sit where they choose. Most likely, they will sit with their colleagues—engineers with engineers, marketing men with marketing men, and so on. This is natural—individuals tend to drift to their own work group, their own peers. Face-to-face, these men are almost forced to talk to each other. The communications process has begun. Each evening thereafter, a different seating arrangement affords maximum communication among all participants.

So, when card tables are arranged for the subsequent meetings, there are place cards at each seat; thus each table has a mixed group.

In this way, each participant first discusses his technical article with his associates. Then, when the article has been polished off a bit, it is discussed with people from other work areas a week later (the third evening of the program).

This arrangement also produces a significant added benefit by the end of the course: Each participant has direct contact with more people and so learns further details about other departments and areas; each makes friendly, personal

---

Assignment #1

1. Choose a subject related to your own work activity which you will use as the topic of your own technical article. (You're really going to write one!)
2. Start to assemble in rough form the data which you will use in the article.
3. In your own manner, start your preliminary preparation.

At the next meeting of the class, we will start working on preparing your article for publication!

(Publication of an article *is not* a requirement for "satisfactory course completion." However the work involved *is* required.)

contacts with representatives of other departments—that until now were impersonal—perhaps even hostile, entities.

By the time the second session arrives, the "students" have already chosen their subjects and started preliminary work on the technical article each will write.

With their first writing efforts in front of them, the students learn two communications guidelines:

- Determine what you're trying to do and organize your material to do it.
- Think positively and talk and write only about what you know.

The first guideline merely means, "Prepare an outline of the potential article." The standard methods of preparing an outline are reviewed.

The second guideline backs up the technical writing assignment given out at the end of the first session. (Remember that the assignment reads, "Choose a subject relating to your own work activity . . .")

The participants are told that most technical publications prefer an outline of a proposed article before actually soliciting the article itself.

The second session is a good time to acquaint or reacquaint the students with the company library, and the professional help and reference materials available. Therefore the class moves for the second hour into the library where the company librarian becomes the course's first "company resource" offered to the class. He (or she) covers practically everything, from how to find a book through where to search when you don't know where to look.

Who is your audience?

The first 20 minutes or so of the third session are spent in identifying the potential readers (or listeners) of each article (or talk). This audience profile will include their needs, desires, backgrounds, requirements and the like so the author can put the article into meaningful language for his audience.

Now it's about time to introduce another acronym: SHAD—"Keep your writing Simple, Human And Direct." Know your audience; don't overestimate their knowledge; you are writing the article because you know more about something, not merely as much as they do. Beware of technical and/or company jargon.

The dull subject of grammar, punctuation and so forth, is brought up, discussed briefly and then quickly dropped. The surest way to lose a class is to become an English teacher and bore an adult, professional audience with a public school grammar review.

Instead, the instructor should simply recommend that each purchase a copy of a reputable writing guide or a good dictionary which includes a condensed section on common word use, grammar and punctuation.

By the fourth evening, the technical papers should be "good enough" to show to some professionals. If the company is fortunate enough to be reasonably near a technical publishing house, it should take advantage of the situation. Who can give a better and more meaningful evaluation to a technical paper than the editor who may be getting the final product?

If there are no outside editors available, then the obvious place to look is within the company—its technical writers and editors, or representatives from the public relations department.

This can be the most meaningful evening of all for the participants, especially if professional editors are available.

By the end of this fourth session, the articles should be in fairly good shape, or the potential authors have learned some good guidelines for putting them in shape.

Next, the graphic arts

With the manuscripts in reasonably good shape, the instructor—in sessions five and six—begins the discussion of the "window dressing;" specifically, the graphic arts to accompany the article or speech.

Obviously, the first place to look for professional advice is within the company art department. Its representatives can elaborate on the methods available to illustrate an article or talk, pointing out such facts as the type of art element which best illustrates a certain point.

The participants should be given practical advice on how to take 35-mm slides and overhead transparencies. Eastman Kodak in Rochester, N.Y., publishes a wealth of practical material on preparing and selecting all types of audio-visuals.

Visuals for a talk

In the sixth session, emphasis is switched to visual aids for an oral presentation. The basic forms of visual communication—blackboards, flip charts, table-top charts, slides and so on—are discussed.

A search should be made within the company to find the best and most experienced speakers who could lend the class the value of their experience. Outside aid might come from a local radio personality or a representative from a local Toastmasters or Toastmistresses International organization.

On both evenings of the graphic arts presentations, the lecturers should not delve too deeply or technically into the mechanics of art preparation, but rather should concentrate on what the writer or speaker must know about using these materials. Most magazines will redo the original art work to meet their particular style requirements. So, even if the art work is professional in every detail, the magazine will probably redo it.

At the end of the fifth evening, the class should be divided into four or five groups (by plant location or department, if possible). Each group is given the assignment of preparing a 10-minute talk on "What my plant [or department, section, etc.] does, and how this contributes to the company profit objectives."

This will shake them up initially, but prior to the sixth session, they will get together and come up with some fine presentations the following session.

Each 10-minute group talk in the sixth session is followed by a critique, not only by the instructor, but by the other participants in the class as well.

How to speak effectively

Sessions seven, eight and nine are devoted to formal instruction in the total area of technical and business talks and other less formalized oral communications.

By the time these sessions come, however, the participants have literally completed most of the work involved in making a speech. After six weeks of concentrated work on writing a technical article, each needs to do very little to prepare a speech on the same subject. Material organization for a speech varies little from that of organizing for writing.

The first thing the instructor tells the group is, "We are not trying to become the world's greatest public speakers. Instead, we are trying to learn the basic needs of engineers communicating in the business world."

The more equipment available, the better this part of the course will be for the participants. Video tape recorders, microphones, audio tape recorders—all are valuable assets to use. In fact, the use of video tape playback can be the most effective technique of the entire course.

The less formal type of speech is emphasized; written speeches are avoided. One key point is stressed: "This is a course in business communication, not in public speaking."

Finally, the graduation

A full-scale graduation exercise is planned for the tenth (and final) session—guest speakers, awards, invited guests, diplomas and an exhibition of the technical articles and graphics produced during the course.

And that's a communications workshop.

Now, how is such a workshop initiated in a company and who conducts it?

The obvious place to plant the communications workshop seed is in the company training department. (This function is handled by the personnel department in many companies.)

The course instructor, coordinator and/or supervisor are likely to come from either the public relations or training department, or both. A competent PR department includes qualified writers and talkers. They also have the contacts and knowledge to supplement the instruction with meaningful "training aids."

Further, a PR department should be able to give the course participants a good feel for what kind of material various technical publications are looking for. ▪▪

Listen! Don't just hear

*You might modify your own ideas if you'd only listen better to others.**

Lydia Strong, former editor, American Management Association.

A movie critic for a newspaper writes: "What a stupendous waste of fine actors and a great story that could otherwise have made this one of the year's outstanding films!"

The ad quotes the critic: "Stupendous . . . fine actors . . . great story . . . one of the year's outstanding films!"

Cutting a few crucial words has turned the criticism into praise.

We're all familiar with this sort of distortion. Not all of us will admit, however, that we're adept at it, too. We tend to do the same thing while listening to people. It's an example of biased listening.

Here's another illustration of how not to listen to someone: A colleague has button-holed you, and you find yourself trapped by an essentially boring, meaningless oration. You try to fool the speaker by nodding and grunting from time to time, but you can never fool yourself. What should you really do?

Accomplished listeners know that it doesn't pay to pretend to listen to someone. If you have no reason at all for listening, make an excuse and leave. Don't waste the speaker's time and yours.

Good listening is an art that can pay high dividends in productivity and personal satisfaction on the job. *Listening can be learned.*

A company once looked into the reasons why some of its foremen were successful and others weren't. Workers said of the successful foremen in interview after interview: "He listens," or "I can talk to him." A disgusted worker summed up his feelings of an unsuccessful foreman this way: "He knows it all. And he don't know nothing! He always says, 'Why don't you tell me?' But if I try to, he won't let me tell him."

If your company asked its technicians what they thought of you as an engineer, would you pass or flunk the listening test? Or suppose you're a manager and engineers were asked to evaluate you? Let's examine some rules for good listening that can help you to job success.

Learn the right ways

Listening is an active process. You can't, if you want to be successful, just lean back dreamily and listen. That may work well for music, but you must

Adapted from Effective Communications on the Job, the American Management Association.

be alert and attentive when you're trying to take part in communication. As a good listener, you show it: your face and posture reflect the fact that your mind is alert. You show your interest further by questions and comments that encourage the speaker to express his ideas fully. If you've ever tried to talk with a poker-faced, bored, silent listener, you can readily appreciate the difference.

There are four stages to effective listening:
1. Actually hearing the speaker's words.
2. Understanding what the words mean.
3. Evaluating what the speaker is saying.
4. Understanding the speaker's point of view.

The first two stages are not quite as simple as they appear. The same word may have quite different meanings to different hearers. This is not surprising when you realize that the 500 most commonly used words in English have 14,070 dictionary meanings.

In his book *The Second World War,* Sir Winston Churchill told of a long argument that developed in a meeting of the British and American Chiefs of Staff Committee. The British brought in a memo on an important point and proposed to "table" it, which to them meant to discuss it right away. The Americans protested that the matter must not be tabled, and the debate grew quite hot before the participants realized they all wanted the same thing.

Connotations can shade a word's original meaning. To a manager the word "efficiency" probably connotes increased results from the same expenditure of energy. To a worker it may mean pay increase or pay cut, layoff or promotion, depending on his own, his family's and his friend's experiences.

Evaluating what the speaker is saying and understanding his point of view are the real tests of whether you are really listening. In evaluating what he is saying, you are judging the worth, relevance, strengths and weaknesses of his remarks. In understanding his viewpoint, you are doing what psychologists call "listening with empathy"—that is, with imaginative understanding It takes courage to listen with empathy. One psychologist, Carl R. Rogers, once explained: "If you really understand another person . . . you run the risk of being changed yourself. You might see it his way; you might find yourself influenced in

Recall the "active listening" idea in PET.

your attitudes or your personality."

Many people—engineers, managers and others —erect barriers to communication and understanding. There are ways to overcome some of the more common barriers.

Some 'don'ts' to avoid

Don't listen intellectually to the words alone. If the words were all that mattered, why hold interviews or conferences? Why travel across the country to see a sales prospect? Why not do all the work with memos? The answer is, of course, that face-to-face communication adds something that words alone can't convey. The speaker's tone, gesture, posture and facial expression may reinforce, amplify or even contradict his oral statement. Listening without observing is like getting the words of a song without the music.

Don't be a biased listener. You may decide just from looking at a speaker or listening to his voice that he has nothing to contribute. This could be true, of course, but it could be far wide of the mark most of the time. External features, such as the shape of the speaker's nose, the curl of his lip or the pitch of his voice, may be quite beyond his control. They're not likely to tell you much about the worth of what he has to say.

Or some word, phrase, or idea may similarly cut across your prejudices, and you just stop listening. The speaker says: "We've got to stop making widgets . . ." This is a sore point with you, this widget fight. So you consider him an enemy, and you either interrupt him or stop listening. As a result, you don't hear the end of his sentence, which is, ". . . until Tuesday, because this shipment of raw materials was delayed."

A more subtle, harder-to-spot form of prejudice is to distort the speaker's presentation, to hear only those parts of it that seem to support your point of view. This is the deception that movie and theater producers sometimes employ to counteract a bad review. They choose only those words of the critic that flatter the film or play; they ignore the condemnation.

Nobody can free himself completely from all forms of prejudice. The best you can do is expose yourself to facts and try to allow in advance for subjective kinks in your point of view.

Don't let boredom overcome you. It has been calculated that you can think four or five times faster than you can usually speak. If you're not deeply interested, if the subject matter seems too simple, or if the speaker is on the dull side, you tend to go off on your own private mental tangents.

You can stay on the same track as the speaker without slowing down to his pace if you use your spare time to get clear in your mind what you hope to learn, and listen especially for this. Try to anticipate the speaker's next point; review the points he has made already; weigh his evidence. Watch his expression and movements to get the fullest possible understanding of his point of view.

Apathy sets in also when the subject matter is too difficult or when the speaker is incomprehensible. If circumstances permit, you can help yourself and other listeners who may be present by asking the speaker to clarify his point.

Don't pretend to listen. You may fool the speaker, but it's better for all concerned if you face the fact squarely: You either have or you don't have a reason for listening. If you do—even if your reason is only inescapable social pressure —listen. If you don't, find the excuse to break away.

Practice listening exercises

Certain procedures can help you improve your listening. One is to practice by listening to a speaker on television or radio. Try to sort out the speaker's main theme from his digressions, irrelevancies and supporting subject matter. Try to evaluate his argument. Notice any words or statements that touch off your antagonism or sympathy. Note also any propaganda techniques: appeals to prejudice, the use of stereotyped symbols, state-

Self-listening: Even if interested in someone else's comments, we concentrate more on what we are going to say.

Going, going, gone: Boredom is a block to good listening. Having empathy with the speaker can avert this.

How's your listening?

Here's a listener's checklist which will help you gauge your own listening habits. Try to answer each question objectively. Then, in a month or two from now, take the test again and see if you have improved your listening skills.

When taking part in an interview or group conference, do you:

	Usually	Sometimes	Seldom
1. Prepare yourself physically by sitting facing the speaker, and making sure that you can hear?	√		
2. Watch the speaker as well as listen to him?	√		
3. Decide from the speaker's appearance and delivery whether or not what he has to say is worthwhile?	√		
4. Listen primarily for ideas and underlying feelings?	√		
5. Determine your own bias, if any, and try to allow for it?		√	
6. Keep your mind on what the speaker is saying?		√	
7. Interrupt immediately if you hear a statement you feel is wrong?			√
8. Make sure before answering that you've taken in the other person's point of view?	√		
9. Try to have the last word?			√
10. Make a conscious effort to evaluate the logic and credibility of what you hear?	√		

Score yourself as follows:

Questions 1, 2, 4, 5, 6, 8, 10: 10 points for "usually," 5 for "sometimes," 0 for "seldom." Questions 3, 7, 9: 0 for "usually," 5 points for "sometimes," 10 for "seldom."

If your score is below 70, you have developed some bad listening habits; if it is 70-85, you listen well, but it could improve; if it is 90 or above, you're an excellent listener.

ments that are cleverly worded to sound logical, even though they're not.

When the speaker has finished, write a single paragraph giving his main idea and supporting evidence and stating why he has or has not made out a convincing case. If you do this in a group, the group members can compare reactions. This practice, incidentally, will make you a more skillful speaker as well as a better listener.

Suppose there is to be a company meeting, and the arrangements are up to you. One thing that helps is to provide the best possible physical conditions. Arrange the seats so they are close enough for people to hear without straining: face to face for an interview, in a circle or square for a conference. Try to exclude distracting noises and interruptions. If notes must be taken, have pencil and paper ready. It pays to prepare yourself mentally and emotionally for listening. Give some thought to the subject of the meeting. If it's controversial, try to recognize your own prejudices and your possible private goals.

Once the meeting starts, your newly acquired listening skills come into play. You listen for the main points and supporting evidence, identify bias and propaganda appeals. *But use your skills with, not against, the other person.* Chances are you'll be working with him in the future.

Taking notes may be unavoidable, but you'll do well to keep them as brief as possible. Your time is better spent in concentrating on the speaker.

Put listening skills to work

Suppose you're to interview a subordinate on a proposed change in design which will require his full cooperation. You're for the change—in fact, it's your idea—and you already know that he's opposed.

If you decide that you really will listen, then you start by admitting to yourself from the start that the other person may just have good reasons for his opposition; also, you can't know these reasons fully until he has explained them fully, no matter what you've heard on the grapevine.

As he speaks, you listen closely and sympathetically. Your attention warms him, puts him at ease, lessens his (and your) aggressiveness. Because we all perform better when we feel at ease, he opens up, explains himself more ably than he could to a hostile listener. Instead of concentrating on your rebuttal, you take in his objections and try to judge their relevance.

After speaking his mind, he feels freer to listen to your point of view which in turn may have been modified by his statement. Sooner than you expect, you may find yourselves reaching a cordial consensus instead of a hard-fought compromise.

Will this happen every time? No, but it hap-

Don't fake it: Pretended listening is a damaging form of non-listening. It wastes his time and yours.

Split personality: Don't half-listen. The speaker deserves all of your attention, not just half of it.

pens often enough to make listening worthwhile.

Should you interrupt?

Let's say that a person whose point of view is opposed to yours makes a ridiculous, indefensible statement. On a debating team you'd pounce on the statement, make the man look foolish. But the usual purpose of a company meeting is cooperation, not competition. Should you interrupt him?

In a situation like this, the answer is yes. But do it in such a way as to ease any embarrassment for him. A timely question, for example, may help the speaker clarify a more obscure point, bring him back to the point if he has strayed. But remember: interruption and contradiction should be used sparingly. If you pounce on the speaker, he'll only get flustered or angry, and the result will be an even less effective presentation by the speaker.

Here are some interruption guidelines:

- If mentally you question a statement that is not actually erroneous, give the speaker a chance to complete his discussion of the item. If by that time he hasn't clarified the point to your satisfaction, interrupt then with a question intended to clarify what he means.

- If the speaker makes an obvious misstatement, interrupt as soon as is convenient, and tactfully ask him to repeat the statement in question or perhaps say, "Did you say . . . ?"

- Don't interrupt the speaker to agree with him. Let him finish what he has to say. Then it's your turn. Prolonged or continued interruptions only make it harder for the speaker to maintain his train of thought.

Develop listening empathy

Would you like a final test of good listening? Here's a suggestion: Next time an argument develops at a company meeting, stop the discussion and specify that each person may speak for himself only after he has first stated the ideas and feelings of the previous speaker. Any distortion may be corrected immediately by the original speaker.

This means, of course, that before presenting your own arguments you must place yourself in the other person's frame of reference; you must understand his ideas well enough to summarize them. You'll find this tough but rewarding. First of all, you'll open your ears as you never have before. Then, as you consider the other speaker's arguments carefully, you may find your own point of view changing. You will have achieved empathy.

There are benefits in this for the other person, too. He hears how his statement sounds to you. He may not have meant it just that way. He, too, may make changes. Quite suddenly, the heat goes out of the argument. The differences are easier to reconcile. In the end everyone feels he has gained some benefit. The conferees go out saying, "That was a good meeting." Not: "You can't win." ■ ■

Turn arguments into discussions

You may find that mutual conclusions may replace the poor compromises that come from heated debate.

Raymond E. Herzog, Electronics Engineer, Daytona Beach, Fla.

Communicating is a snap for you. You have no problem presenting your ideas to indifferent, even hostile listeners. They always grasp your logic. They always agree with you. Right?

If so, skip this article. If not, let's take a close look at a most common form of communication—the conversation. In this example, you are trying to explain an idea of yours to Mr. Smart. He thinks his idea is better. That's where you start.

But it may not be where you finish. Without your even being aware of it, a misunderstanding or a disagreement can easily turn this exchange into an argument. And nobody wins an argument.

no matter how good your points are, they may well be rejected if you cannot present them effectively.

Okay, you're talking to the group when Mr. Smart suddenly speaks up. He doesn't agree. Here you take the first step. You listen to him. Don't interrupt.

Get a clear picture of Mr. Smart's thoughts. For unless you really know his views, you can't comment intelligently on them. Most likely, the stronger he disagrees with you, the more he'll talk about it.

So the first step is quite simple: just listen. Carefully and politely. Don't break in on him,

When you argue, nobody wins.

Listen closely to the other man's views.

To make sure that your conversation remains an intelligent exchange and to bring Mr. Smart around to your way of thinking, take these four steps when you respond to his objections:

1. Understand Mr. Smart's views.
2. Comment on his views.
3. Present your own ideas.
4. Control interruptions.

To illustrate how to use these steps, let's assume Mr. Smart does not accept your idea the first time you offer it.

Start by listening

Here's the situation: You are telling a group how to follow a new policy. What you are telling them is not at issue now; *how* you do it is. For

except to agree with his thoughts. This will let him know you're paying attention.

Simple as it sounds, this first step serves a dual purpose. First, you get to know Mr. Smart's ideas. Thus, when you get to Step 3 (which is where you will present your own thoughts again), you can focus on what *he* has just said, not on what you *expected* him to say. Second, by courteously listening, you show Mr. Smart you respect him and are not trying to steamroll him. You've also probably earned his respect—and his silence—when you are ready to speak.

Tell him what you heard him say

After Mr. Smart has spoken his piece, you take the second step and say a few words your-

self. What words? Well, surprisingly, your first
remark should be a restatement of his objection.
But you recount it in your own words. Repeat:
his opinion, your words.

When Mr. Smart hears his objection coming
from you in your words, he'll know that you
understand him. This will allay his anxiety and
he should be ready to listen to your side.

When you repeat his thoughts, try to agree
with some point—any point, even a small one—
that he made. Your agreement again shows him
that you respect his reasoning. Also, by first
agreeing on a point, you will soften the impact
of your views, the third step. This creates a less
argumentative atmosphere and induces far more
cooperation.

Why pay so much attention to the atmosphere?
Remember that your purpose is to compare Mr.
Smart's thoughts with your own. The goal is
mutual understanding. To achieve it, you can't
merely present facts and force him to accept
them. Instead, you build a series of agreements
with him and let him come to his own decision.

Now offer your views

Up to now you've held Mr. Smart's attentive
ear while he listened to his thoughts as you
restated them. Your next move is to keep his
interest while you offer your views. Here is
where you need to watch your words carefully.

First, show that there is more to the matter
than just the views (his views) brought out so
far. Now it's time to approach the points of
disagreement. But present your comments and
thoughts cautiously. A good way to lead into
your views is:

"I see your viewpoint, but you also may want
to consider these additional thoughts." And then
you relate some ideas that will help him to see
your attitude more clearly.

Other approaches you might use are:

"Perhaps if you thought about it this way . . ."

"Let's think this matter through together."

"John Doe once thought the same way. Let me
tell you what he learned that changed his mind."

Do you see what these approaches are doing?
They're leading Mr. Smart to rethink his own
views, or to consider additional points. They're
suggesting that he form his own conclusion,
rather than be forced to accept yours.

Conversely, the incorrect way to lead into your
comments would be to tell Mr. Smart that he is
wrong. Instead, suggest that there might be another way to look at the matter. Tell him *what*
could be wrong. Then, he can decide for himself,
and remember that his own decision means more
to him than yours.

Comment on his views, present your own.

It's important that you take enough time over
each point you make. Pause after each one, so
that it will sink in. To check that Mr. Smart
understands you, try questions like:

"Is that point clear?"

"You agree with that, don't you?"

These questions will move the discussion back
and forth.

Another way to make a convincing presentation is to deliver it with plenty of action. For
example, when you are giving facts or descriptions about something, make them *move*. Don't
just show a chart or diagram—draw or sketch
it as you talk.

Handle the interruptions

So far, you've gained an understanding of Mr.
Smart's differing opinion, commented on it, and
then presented your own views. Most likely, Mr.
Smart will be almost fully sold by this time. One
possible problem yet remains. This is the matter
of interruptions which he is quite apt to make.
He may interrupt, unless he, too, is a good
listener.

But if he isn't, he may pop questions, or he
may throw out objections to what you say—
sometimes before the words are out of your
mouth. Whatever the interruptions, having to
stop in the middle of your presentation can weak-
en your case.

How can you avoid interruptions that side-
track the discussion? When Mr. Smart asks a
question that you can answer later, tell him so.
Let him know that you recognize his reasons for
asking, and say that he will be able to better
understand the matter after you've given him
more information in the discussion.

On the other hand, if you feel that Mr. Smart
is contradicting you just to be objectionable, try

Logic plus psychology often spell agreement.

this. Pause briefly, and then quickly give your reply in less than half a minute. When you pause, don't seem to be in a hurry. Know what you're going to say and when you do speak, speak quickly. Then go right on from where you left off before the interruption. The brief silence may well disconcert Mr. Smart.

Still another cooling-off technique is to take a deep breath, fix your eyes directly on him and say: "Mr. Smart, I don't think I fully understand what you're saying." As he recollects his thoughts and tells you once more, his answer may come in a softer tone than it did before.

People who use this technique have found that sometimes the pause will unnerve an aggressive person. To break the silence, he will say something and, quite often, will thereby answer his own objection.

When it looks like interruptions are imminent and will require immediate answers, here is one more technique. Use the familiar "yes, but" and "yes, and" answers. In these replies, you compare what Mr. Smart has just said with one of the selling points of the idea you're trying to get across.

A sharp contrast can be made with a "yes, but" statement. In it, you turn his reason for not accepting your idea into a reason why he shouldn't be without it. To illustrate: When the objection is, "I don't have time to do this," you can suggest: "*Yes*, it's possible that you may not have the time to do this, *but* do you have time to do. . . .?" Here you mention time-consuming chores that he could avoid by doing what you suggest. This type of question prompts Mr. Smart to reconsider.

There may be times, however, when the "yes, but" reply is too strong, since the word "but" can be quite explosive. So, another, softer approach might be the "yes, and" answer. Let's say that Mr. Smart's objection is: "It's not the usual responsibility of my group to do this." Your reply would be: "*Yes*, you're right. It isn't your responsibility, *and* for that reason your group should receive unique recognition for having done it." Then go on to tell about the benefits of performing this unusual task; in other words, you justify the undertaking. The subject thus changes from an excuse for not doing something to the advantage derived from doing it.

Looking back to the paragraph where we discussed handling interruptions, you'll recall that we talked about a person being "almost fully sold" on something. Let's take a closer look at that word "sold". For when the purpose of a discussion is to get an idea across without an argument, "selling" Mr. Smart on the idea really isn't quite the right technique.

Rather, you should tell him things that start him thinking—thinking that there might be more to a matter than just what he sees at first. Then, when he considers, understands, and finally accepts your views, he has really *sold himself* on your idea.

The point was made long ago by the English poet Samuel Butler:

"He that complies against his will
Is of the same opinion still." ■■

For sales/EE interface: Sell—don't tell

When designers and salesmen battle each other, they stand to lose not only the war, but the customer as well.

Frank J. Burge, Marketing Consultant, Ness Consultants Division, Ness Industries, Inc.

The telephone rings in an engineering department and this dialogue follows:

Salesman: This is Collins. Why didn't you return my call?

Engineer: Sorry, we got busy.

Salesman: I'm busy, too, trying to sell your damned product design to a hard-nosed customer!

Engineer: Okay, okay! What do you need this time?

Salesman: I still need what I asked you for two months ago—that product proposal.

Engineer: (Grimaces.) We haven't started on it yet.

Salesman: What! My customer is expecting your write-up on the special self-calibration feature—and you haven't even finished the proposal?

Engineer: You'll get it as soon as you give us the details on the application you promised us seven weeks ago.

Salesman: I got busy, too. Why didn't you remind me?

And so the conversation goes until the salesman or the engineer says something he's sorry for, or hangs up, which leaves the customer hung up as well.

In this particular case, the salesman was at fault. The factory was waiting for the details he promised, and he should have followed up on them. But there's another twist: had he sold the importance of time to his proposal, his support man might have reminded him that he was awaiting details.

Why is there friction between salesmen and engineers? What are the basic antagonisms between them, and what's behind them? Salesmen and factory support men alike complain about being let down, misled, or just plain lied to.

Factory troops claim that the salesmen know nothing about the products they're trying to sell and even less about how they'll be used. They say also that salesmen call in with impossible questions, demand solutions yesterday, and won't take "no" for an answer.

Salesmen, in turn, complain that the factory isn't giving them any support, because they're late on delivery, and they never return a call. Sales types also complain that designers talk like computers instead of people, emphasizing specifications instead of interpreting their meaning to the customer.

Although there's an element of truth in both sides of the story, both protagonists are to blame for the friction between them. On each side, the conflict arises out of a basic misunderstanding that results from a *breakdown in communications*.

For example: Perhaps the salesman hasn't asked the factory the right question. (There's a big difference between "When does that order get out of production?" and "When will it be shipped?" The real question is, "When will my customer have it?") Or the factory hasn't given the salesman useful information. Technical specifications may not communicate much to anyone outside the design team.

Getting to know your counterpart

One of the keys that will help to open a door to more effective communications is understanding the function of your counterpart. What are the needs of the salesman, and of the engineer? Let's examine the sales function first.

The salesman is much more than an order taker. Not only is he responsible for developing relationships with potential customers so that they will want to own his company's products, but he is also responsible for explaining new products or possible customization that may solve the customer's needs. To do this, he must have a thorough knowledge of the product and how its features relate to the specific application.

To help him carry out this function he needs cooperation—proposals, sales-promotion material and engineering support from the factory. In short, he must be able to do more than recite specifications if he is to gain the confidence of his customers.

If he's done his product homework he won't be guilty of bugging the factory with a lot of irrelevant questions. For he must convince the factory that his needs are important. If he treats every problem as a crisis, his inside contact will soon learn to ignore him.

Another function of the salesman is to provide the factory with feedback on product acceptance, changing needs, new product requirements, new markets, and the like. All too often, this function is overlooked, despite the fact that the salesman is in a much better position to supply these inputs than anyone else. He is out in the field, in constant contact with the customer. His observations are vital if the factory is to supply products that coincide with market demand.

The factory engineer, for his part, must be responsive to market needs in terms of product development, and the factory must provide the salesman with adequate product education in terms of customer benefits. The product must be explained to the salesman not in terms of technical specifications, but of what benefits it will bring to the customer's application.

The factory must also provide technical support so that the salesman can respond directly to customer needs. If the salesman has been adequately trained, he will not be asking for proposals that aren't needed.

Stringing the guidelines

Now that you have a better idea of what your opposite number is responsible for, you should have greater insight into his needs during your next conversation.

Four elementary guidelines in communications will also help to improve understanding. They are: listening; summarization; examination; and commitment.

Since most factory-sales communications come in from the field, we'll take the receiving end, the engineering end, for our analysis. But remember that communication is a two-way street, and the following guidelines apply equally to both parties.

- When the salesman calls make sure you *listen* to him, even though you think he's making an unreasonable request. If you listen carefully enough, you may find his request is not so unreasonable after all, because the idea behind it may be sound. Establish, by example, with each salesman that you are a good listener. He, in turn, will listen more carefully to what you have to say. All too often, we begin to plan our reply even before the other person has finished talking. The only way you'll ever learn what he wants to communicate is with your mouth shut and your mind focused on what he is saying. If the salesman is "windy," let him talk. Later, you can develop a strategy for making him get to the point.

- Then in your own words, *summarize* what you think you heard. The time to clear up any misunderstanding is while he is still on the phone. If you have misunderstood ask that the data be repeated and listen more attentively. Then, repeat again what you understand has been said. It is the author's belief that at least half of all communications problems between the factory and the field are a direct result of misunderstanding what was communicated.

- Now that you know the problem, *examine* why the customer wants a certain application. During this phase of the communications, you may learn the cause for what seemed like an unreasonable request from the salesman. You may find that what has been requested will not solve the customer's problem. The salesman may have suggested some options that are really not required, or you may find certain important measurements cannot be made unless the product is modified. Since the factory technical troops usually know much more about the product than the salesman, they are in the best position to evaluate and make suggestions on hardware configurations. On the other hand, the salesman is more familiar with his customer's needs. In any case, examine the application carefully.

A word of caution: The salesman may go on the defensive when questioned about the customer's application. If he does, it's because he doesn't know all the answers and feels threatened. Don't pin the poor devil to the wall. Simply explain what data you need and why. He will then realize that you are trying to help him close the sale, and will be more cooperative in finding out what you want to know.

Finally, make certain you both understand what investment the customer is prepared to make. A customer with $18,000 cannot afford a $60,000 solution to his problem, even if it is creative.

- Now, make a *commitment* to the salesman—one you can keep. You know how long it will take to get an answer, and how much time is required to write a proposal. Don't be pressured into making unrealistic promises. Normally, the salesman will allow some margin for slippage, but if you always let him down, he'll start demanding immediate answers even when he doesn't need them for a month. He wants to protect his relationship with his customer.

Sell it—don't tell it!

The important thing to remember is to sell the other person on what you're saying instead of just giving orders. The constant frictions generated by broken promises, delayed reports, and misinformation could, more often than not, be replaced by impressive results of cooperation based on selling instead of telling. ■■

Good slides are keys to good technical talks

Why lose your audience, when it's easy to keep it with meaningful and lively visual aids.

B. A. Aumuller, Photography Manager, and **H. E. Marrows,** Technical Information Manager, Western Electric Co., New York.

When was the last time you fidgeted in your seat during a technical talk or conference?

Chances are that the talk was poorly illustrated, or not illustrated at all.

The value of visual material is readily apparent to anyone who has tried to communicate with an audience or anyone who has tried to sit through a dull technical presentation. In most instances, words alone cannot get the total message across. A skillful blending of words and illustrations is a good way to guarantee success in presenting a technical paper.

The problem for most engineers is that they don't know how to prepare the slides, if their company doesn't have an art department to help them. Even some art departments, accustomed to turning out technical drawings or wiring diagrams may produce very poor slide copy. Many are accustomed to producing blueprints or fineline drawings, which may be 8-1/2 × 11 inches or even two or three feet wide, for reading at a distance of 10 to 18 inches. The requirements for slides differ markedly from these specifications.

It never hurts to learn to do it yourself.

There are five stages in producing effective slides for a technical talk:

1. Organize the presentation.
2. Select the method to be used.
3. Prepare the material.
4. Produce the slides.
5. Evaluate the results.

Organize the presentation

A good presentation with slides requires a careful analysis of the material to be communicated. It calls for selecting only the pertinent portions of the technical presentation for illustration. Keep these basic points in mind:

▪ All the the narrative and all of the slides must be functional. Every word, idea or point—everything that will be seen or heard—must blend with the whole.

▪ A visual aid is used because it helps get the point across better than words alone. The most beautiful, technically perfect slide is a time-waster unless it has a specific purpose in your talk.

It's a good idea to tape your talk and listen to it. Then ask yourself these two questions: What are the key points I want to get across? What points in my talk will benefit by illustration?

In planning your slides, use one 3 × 5 card for each slide as a planning guide. Clip out the illustration you want or make a rough drawing of what you want the slide to show and paste it on the card. Beside the drawing, list the instructions in preparing the slide. In the lower lefthand corner cite the page and paragraph in the manuscript to which the slide alludes.

At this stage of your planning, aim for the maximum. Pick out as many potential illustrations as possible, even if you are positive that you have selected more than your talk can possibly absorb without turning your technical talk into a slide show with accompanying text. Then review your text again and trim, if necessary.

In choosing material, remember that copyrights must be observed. Permission to use material, especially if it is an excerpt, is easy to obtain, provided credit is given. Allow yourself enough time to get this permission.

Select the method to be used

Now that you have decided *what* you want to illustrate, you are ready for the "how" of your preparations. How can you best illustrate the points? Photographs, diagrams, sketches, statistical displays, even words—all are potential slides.

Photographs lend a feeling of reality, even though it may be difficult to see the technical aspects of the subject matter under discussion.

Diagrams and sketches can be used to show the makeup of an item, or how it works. Often a diagram or sketch can demonstrate the functional aspects of items better than a photograph. With a sketch or diagram, for example, you can use different colors or varied shading to illustrate your points more clearly. Usually you cannot achieve this color breakdown in a photograph.

Statistical displays, which can take many

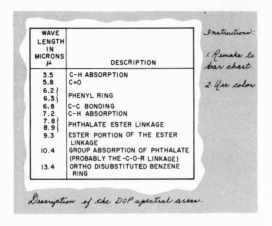

WAVE LENGTH IN MICRONS μ	DESCRIPTION
3.5	C–H ABSORPTION
5.8	C=O
6.2 } 6.3	PHENYL RING
6.8	C–C BONDING
7.2	C–H ABSORPTION
7.8 } 8.9	PHTHALATE ESTER LINKAGE
9.3	ESTER PORTION OF THE ESTER LINKAGE
10.4	GROUP ABSORPTION OF PHTHALATE (PROBABLY THE –C–O–R LINKAGE)
13.4	ORTHO DISUBSTITUTED BENZENE RING

Instructions:
1. Remake to bar chart.
2. Use color

Description of the DOP spectral areas.

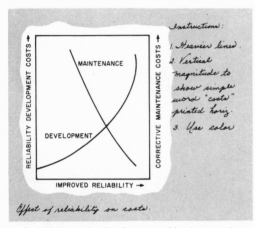

Instructions:
1. Heavier lines
2. Vertical magnitude to show simple word "costs" printed horiz.
3. Use color

Effect of reliability on costs.

1. **An initial step in planning** your slides is preparing a series of index cards listing what you want the slide to show. As shown in the two examples above, you clip out the illustration you want or make a rough drawing. Then list the instructions for preparing the slide and cite the page and paragraph in the lower left-hand corner.

pictorial forms, are useful in showing relative quantities, qualities, trends, peculiarities of cycle, etc. A comparison figure—a bar chart, a pie chart, etc.—often gets the point across more clearly and succinctly than a photograph, drawing or mere words.

Words on a slide can help emphasize a key point you are making. By showing just a word or phrase in big letters on a screen, the seed is planted firmly in your viewer's mind.

Prepare the material

If you are going to use photographs, select the subjects and get the photographic equipment ready. But keep one basic rule in mind: Don't over-estimate your ability or the capability of your camera. Taking color slides of the kids is

one thing; preparing professional-looking slides for a technical presentation is another.

For example, you cannot get a top-quality close-up of a small component without the proper camera attachments. Not even the possession of a telephoto lens will insure the desired results. Many telephoto lenses will not focus closer than several feet.

In this instance, it may be best for you to make a drawing or sketch. Or see a professional photographer.

Incidentally, here is where your company art department can be helpful to you. While it may not be expert in actually making the slides for you, it should be able to prepare the sketches, drawings and diagrams that will be made into slides.

Here are some guidelines in preparing material to be photographed:

- Crop the art work in proportion to the slide format. This will obviate the need for cropping later, which means more time and money in producing new slides from slides. Here are the sizes that scale to 35-mm dimensions:

3 x 2	10 x 6-3/4	15 x 10-1/8
4 x 2-3/4	11 x 7-1/2	16 x 10-7/8
6 x 4	12 x 8-1/8	18 x 12
8 x 5-3/8	13 x 8-3/4	20 x 13-1/2
9 x 6-1/8	14 x 9-1/2	24 x 16-1/4

- Avoid confusing the viewer's eye with repeated changes from vertical to horizontal slides. If you have a choice, prepare your material for horizontal slides.

- Try to make all your drawings, sketches and charts the same size. This will save considerable time when it comes to photographing them. You will be able to set up your camera equipment once and take all the photographs without having to move and readjust the equipment or subject each time.

- Trim or mask to exclude all extraneous materials. This not only avoids cluttering the slide, but it also saves the extra time of having to crop and then remake the slide.

- Include only the essential details. The simpler the slide, the better its effect. If you want to show one component or a piece of equipment, sketch just that one part, not the whole thing.

- Use glossy paper, mounted perfectly flat. Non-glossy surfaces tend to desaturate colors in the finished slides.

- Do not use paper with a watermark. It may reproduce on the slide.

- If your drawing is on paper, mount it smooth on cardboard, using rubber cement or dry mounting tissue. Do not use ordinary water soluble glue or library paste; they tend to cause wrinkles and bulges that will show up on the slides.

■ Restrict the use of words to basic titles or nomenclature where possible. A slide filled with words is difficult to read.

■ Type-set words—those set by a professional printer, that is—give good results. When you must use typewritten material, use an electric typewriter if possible. If the words are hand lettered, make the letters thick.

■ Words and messages should be centered on the paper within an area proportional to the slide format (see examples.)

■ Use brightly colored drawings for best results. Pastel shades often give the appearance of being washed out on a slide.

Produce the slides

If you have never done this type of photographic work before, don't start now. Unless you are extremely lucky, you will not get the desired results the first or second time; and you probably haven't got sufficient time to experiment.

For the engineer who plans to do his own photography, here are some guidelines:

■ Use color film. Not only are the results better, but the cost will be less than for black and white slides. Even if some of your material to be photographed is black and white, such as lettering, use color film anyway. This will obviate the need for changing film or for using more than one camera.

■ Stay with one type of film. You will get to know its capabilities faster, thus ensuring better slides. If you are not certain which type is best, a camera shop should be able to advise you.

■ A 35-mm single lens reflex camera, with interchangeable lenses, is by far the most suitable for making slides.

■ For copying indoors, use 3200K lamps for Type B color film and 3400K lamps for Type A; or you can use practically any color film with either light source by using the proper filters over the lights or over the camera lens.

■ Avoid any outdoor copying work, because you must have your camera at an exact angle to get good results. Otherwise, you will get glare on the photograph in direct sunlight. If you use daylight film and do not photograph in direct sunlight, the results will be too blue on a sunny day, because film is balanced for an average mixture of warm sunlight and blue sky light.

■ Once you get the reading from your light meter, take one shot at the prescribed setting and then take two more—one at 1/2 f-stop above and one at 1/2 f-stop below. Between the three, you should get just what you want in terms of exposure. Even the best photographer rarely takes just one shot of anything.

■ Keep a record of the camera settings, lighting conditions, etc., of each slide you take. It will save you considerable time later if you have to retake the slide.

■ If you want to photograph a piece of equipment, make certain the background doesn't compete with the item you want to show. A blank wall is probably best as a background. But make certain the color of the wall doesn't compete!

■ If you want to show just one component or section of a piece of equipment, photograph just the part and not the whole product. If the component is too small, it probably will be better to make a sketch rather than go through the frustration of not getting what you want.

Once your finished slides are at hand, try them out. Set up the slide projector, play the tape of your speech and flash each slide at the proper point. This will show if your slides are doing the intended job. ■■

Suggested reading:
The following are published by Eastman Kodak Co.:
1. *Producing Slides and Filmstrips*
2. *Effective Slide Lectures*
3. *More Here's How*
4. *Legibility Standards for Projected Material*
5. *Artwork Size Standards for Projected Visuals*
6. *Planning and Producing Visual Aids*
7. *Basic Copying*

Join the 'experts'—publish!

Overcome the obstacles to technical writing and learn how magazines work with authors

Roger M. D'Aprix, Manager, Management Communications, Xerox Corp., Rochester, N.Y.

One of the most direct roads to professional recognition is the one marked "Publication." The company man who has articles, or technical papers published on a regular basis becomes an "expert," whose opinions have been recognized. And this recognition is to management roughly equivalent to watching one's wife receive an appreciative glance from a stranger.

If publication does not affect attitudes very much where you are presently employed, watch a prospective employer take interest when you show him a collection of your printed work. The published article is usually acceptable evidence that one is dealing with an expect in technology.

The natural barriers to writing

If being published, then, is a promising route to fame, why haven't more engineers written technical articles? Perhaps they would if they weren't stymied by the natural barriers to writing.

Inertia and *procrastination* are two of the highest obstacles the unpublished author has to overcome. The man who wants recognition and promotion, however, must be willing to exact the price from his limited budget of time and physical capacity.

Another barrier for potential authors is the one they build for themselves when they decide that their ideas are *not worthy of publication.* This attitude is based on the notion that a technical magazine should communicate only specialized information from the frontiers of technical research. Alas, only so many people are capable of manning those frontiers. The rest of us must concern ourselves with the small piece of technology we have carved out for ourselves.

Too often, the prospective author decides that his offerings, which might not be sufficiently theoretical for the scientific journals, are "unworthy." How often have you been unimpressed with a feature article in a business publication simply because you felt that you could have written the same article yourself? And you probably could have, because someone with a background similar to yours did. We assume that what we know is common knowledge to everyone

working in our field, but an idea does not have to be new to be publishable, if it is given a special and different treatment.

The publication 'maze'

One of the most prevalent barriers to writing is unfamiliarity with the seeming "maze" of the publication process. But the steps are simpler than you think.

Assume that you have decided you want to publish an article. First, look for help within your company. If you work for a company progressive enough to recognize the enormous publicity potential of good articles and technical papers, search out the man responsible for that activity and follow his advice to the letter. If no such department exists, talk to the company's technical writers or advertising and public-relations specialists.

If you cannot get help from your company, you can help yourself providing that you:

- Determine the significance of your subject by asking yourself if you, as a technical man in your specialty, would be interested in reading about it. More important: Will this information be helpful to the reader in performing his job? (This, incidentally is a major criterion of business-magazine editors in judging manuscripts.) If you can honestly say that your idea is interesting, helpful, and as far as you know, not previously treated in just this way, then the subject is probably appropriate for publication.

- Determine if your potential subject lends itself to magazine treatment. To do this you must define the subject matter so that you can complete your article within a limit of about 2000 to 5000 words. That range is not rigid. Some magazines will serialize an important and interesting subject. And there is always space for the one-page or shorter feature items.

The next step to being published is to select a target publication and to dress up your idea for submission:

Zero in on your target

- Make a list of the business magazines you

PROOFREADERS' MARKS

Marks	Explanation	Marks	Errors Marked
ℰ	Take out letter, letters, or words indicated.	ℰ	He marked the proof.
#	Insert space where indicated.	#	He marked theproof.
9	Turn inverted letter indicated.	9	He marked the proof.
⋏	Insert letter as indicated.	⋏	He maked the proof.
lc	Set in lower-case type.	lc	He Marked the proof.
wf	Wrong font.	wf	He marked the proof.
X	Broken letter. Must be replaced.	X	He marked the proof.
ital	Reset in italic type the matter indicated.	ital	He marked the proof.
rom	Reset in roman (regular) type the matter indicated.	rom	He marked *the* proof.
bf	Reset in bold-face type word, or words, indicated.	bf	He marked the proof.
⊙	Insert period where indicated.	⊙	He marked the proof
tr	Transpose letters or words as indicated.	tr	He the proof marked.
stet	Let it stand as it is. Disregard all marks above the dots.	stet	He marked the proof.
/=/	Insert hyphen where indicated.	/=/	He made the proofmark.
eq.#	Equalize spacing.	eq.#	He marked the proof.
[or]	Move over to the point indicated. [if to the left; if to the right]	[	[He marked the proof.
⊔	Lower to the point indicated.	⊔	He marked the proof.
⊓	Raise to the point indicated.	⊓	He marked the proof.
⋏	Insert comma where indicated.		Yes he marked the proof.
⋎	Insert apostrophe where indicated.		He marked the boys proof.
⋎ ⋎	Enclose in quotation marks as indicated.		He marked it proof.
H	Replace with a capital the letter or letters indicated.	H	he marked the proof.
sc	Use small capitals instead of the type now used.	sc	He marked the proof.
⊥	Push down space which is showing up.	⊥	He marked the proof.
⌣	Draw the word together.	⌣	He marked the proof.
⋏	Insert inferior figure where indicated.	⋏	Sulphuric Acid is HSO.
⋎	Insert superior figure where indicated.	⋎	$a^2 + b^2 = c$
Out, see copy	Used when words left out are to be set from copy and inserted as indicated.	Out, see copy	He proof.
æ	The diphthong is to be used.	æ	Caesar marked the proof.
fi	The ligature of these two letters is to be used.	fi	He filed the proof.
spell out	Spell out all words marked with a circle.	spell out	He marked the 20 proof.
¶	Start a new paragraph as indicated.	¶	reading. The reader marked
No ¶	Should not be a separate paragraph. Run in.	no ¶	marked.
(?)	Query to author. (Encircled in red.)	(was ?)	The proof was read by / The proof read by
?	This is the symbol used when a question is to be set. Note that a query to author is encircled in red.	?	Who marked the proof
=	Out of alignment.	=	He marked the proof
/1-em/	1-em dash.	/1-em/	He marked the proof
/2-em/	2-em dash.	/2-em/	He marked the proof
/1-n/	En dash.	/1-n/	He marked the proof
▯	Indent 1 em.	▯	He marked the proof.
▯▯	Indent 2 ems.	▯▯	He marked the proof.

find particularly useful, and establish an order of preference for the submission of your idea.

- Determine the basic objective of the article, and make an outline. It will help you decide what information should be included or left out, and how to reach the most readers.

- Next, make a few very rough sketches of the material you feel must be presented visually and, if possible, include any relevant photographs.

- Get your outline typed and write a short abstract (150-200 words) of the article.

- Find out what your company's policy is on publication clearances. Even if there is no formal approval mechanism, you would be well advised to show the material to your immediate manager and get his approval in writing. Approval routines protect the author and the company against the release of proprietary or classified information or simply "sensitive" information.

- When all the company approvals are in, put the whole preliminary package together and send it to your first choice of publishers as an exclusive offering.

- Do not send the same article outline simultaneously to six or seven editors. What would you do if they all accepted it? An editor is much more inclined to look favorably on an article idea if it carries an "exclusive" tag.

Don't be discouraged

The elapsed time from the preparation of your outline to publication of the complete article can be anywhere from three months to more than a year. The two most common reasons for the delay is that either the magazine has a large backlog of manuscripts, or the editor has not yet made a decision about your material.

Some magazines normally acknowledge receipt of outlines and make decisions within a month or less. On the other hand, some publications do not acknowledge receipt of submitted material and may take as long as two or three months to decide if they want it.

If your outline is turned down, don't be discouraged until you've received a few rejections. You may simply be trying the wrong magazines.

Let the editor polish it

Once an editor expresses interest he will usually work with you, indicating where he feels you might improve your outline. He will also set a tentative date for submission of the manuscript. Follow his directions as carefully as you can and comply with the deadline that's set. Publication schedules are not very flexible, and you can put

your editor in an embarrassing position if you leave him with three or four pages of his magazine to fill at press time.

In preparing the manuscript, concentrate on the information you are communicating. Give the maximum amount of well organized information per page, and leave the polishing to the editor. You're the technical expert, he's the writer. If he does his job well, your manuscript will probably be edited rather heavily. You may not even recognize the style as yours when he finishes, but it will be concise and readable.

Assembling the package

When you submit your company-approved manuscript to the editor, send him an original copy typed double or triple-spaced on good white bond paper. Leave wide margins. The first page should include the title of the article, your name, and company affiliation. Keep at least one copy as insurance against loss.

Any photos submitted should preferably be 8 by 10 glossy prints for good reproduction. Drawings need be only penciled sketches, but be sure they are sharp and well labeled, and separate them from the manuscript. Include captions on a separate sheet keyed to the illustrations and the text.

In most cases the editor will give you an opportunity to review his version of your manuscript before publication. He wants you to check for technical accuracy to be sure he has not misunderstood and changed your idea. And this is exactly the way you should review the manuscript: Change only the misleading or inaccurate statements.

Don't hold out for your original style, or you may very well find a polite rejection letter returned to you with your manuscript.

Recognition is the payoff

When the final package is submitted, you have nothing to do but sit back and wait for the published article—and perhaps a modest check if the magazine pays its authors an honorarium. This payment, which is strictly a fringe benefit, usually runs anywhere from $75 to $150 for an average-length article. The fee is not intended to be payment for your time and effort; it is simply a token sum in appreciation for your contribution.

The payoff for you, personally and professionally, is the recognition you will receive from the magazine's readers and from your own company and colleagues. ▪▪